WARREN

The Golden Age of Quackery

BOOKS BY STEWART H. HOLBROOK

BURNING AN EMPIRE
The Story of American Forest Fires

ETHAN ALLEN

HOLY OLD MACKINAW
A Natural History of the American Lumberjack

IRON BREW
A Century of American Ore and Steel

LITTLE ANNIE OAKLEY AND OTHER RUGGED PEOPLE

LOST MEN OF AMERICAN HISTORY

MURDER OUT YONDER

NONE MORE COURAGEOUS

TALL TIMBER
(a Juvenile Book)

THE YANKEE EXODUS
An Account of Migration from New England

FAR CORNER
A Personal View of the Pacific Northwest

MACHINES OF PLENTY
Pioneering in American Agriculture

MR. OTIS

THE GOLDEN AGE OF QUACKERY

T·H·E G·O·L·D·E·N A·G·E
O·F Q·U·A·C·K·E·R·Y

BY

Stewart H. Holbrook

New York • **THE MACMILLAN COMPANY** • *1959*

First Printing

The Macmillan Company, New York
Brett-Macmillan Ltd., Galt, Ontario

Printed in the United States of America

Library of Congress catalog card number: 59–12338

FOR CECIL SCOTT

Friend and Editor

Contents

PART ONE

Panorama

1

High Noon: 1906

It was near the end of the horse-and-buggy era. To many of us who lived through them, those days now seem to have been a period of serenity, a magic time when the world was young, everything was possible, and the future stretched out illimitable and as filled with wonders as the recent great exposition to which all America had been invited by the lilting cadences of *Meet Me in St. Louis, Louis, Meet Me at the Fair.*

There is no emotion trickier than nostalgia; no matter how Webster defines it, it is at base a lament for lost youth. Looking back, Youth is seen as bright and cloudless as a June morning. The shadows have faded; so have the storms. The hard times are forgotten. Only serene happiness remains. Whittier set it down long ago, when the old man of the poem "closed his eyes on his garnished rooms to dream of meadows and clover-blooms."

Historians do not class 1906 as an extraordinary year in America. General Joseph Wheeler and Merchant Marshall Field died. High-button shoes for ladies were the rage. Harry Thaw shot Stanford White. There were earthquake and fire in San Francisco. And President Woodrow Wilson of Princeton University said publicly that nothing had spread socialistic feeling in the United States more than the increase of automobiles which, said he, had brought about "a picture of the arrogance of wealth."

Yet the nation was serene. No prophecy as to what 1914 held for the world was heard. It is doubtful that makers of harness and covered buggies paid any heed to the new and struggling Ford Motor Company; or that food processors gave much thought to Harvey W. Wiley, chief chemist in the United States Department of Agriculture, who claimed to be finding coal tars and formaldehyde and other oddities in canned meats and vegetables; or that the makers

3

of patent medicines were much worried because Samuel Hopkins Adams, a brilliantly competent reporter, was writing a series of shocking articles entitled "The Great American Fraud" for *Collier's Weekly*.

In 1906 the harness-and-buggy men had another three years before Ford's Model T would go into production. But the canners of foods and makers of patent medicines were to be given no grace at all. In June, 1906, President Theodore Roosevelt signed the Federal Pure Food and Drug Act that was to become law on January 1, 1907.

I am not concerned with either the automobile or the processing of food, but with the so-called patent medicines and other nostrums dating from colonial days to recent times. Their early morning began as early as 1692, and their great and gaudy noon reached meridian on the last day of 1906. After that, the manufacturers had something to deal with other than their individual consciences, which appear to have been grossly corroded in a business dominated by devout partisans of laissez faire. Up to then, and though it concerned the nation's health, the nostrum trade was subject to less control and reeked with more fraud and chicanery than even the more genteel con games operated under the generic name of Wall Street.

By 1906 the traffic in patent medicines was immense. In total volume it had reached $80 million a year. It did not reach this splendid mark by advertising its wares on fences, barns, and roadside boulders, or in the almanacs printed and distributed by the ton. These things helped, of course; but the rivers of compounds and avalanches of pills flowed and rolled thanks in overwhelming part to the daily and weekly press.

To turn the yellowing pages of the old files is startling. Was every other woman a victim of Female Weakness? Did every other man need a Truss? Were they both together suffering from Worn-Out Kidneys? Were they and their children falling swiftly into consumption? From page upon page, out of both classified and display columns, the sinister words leap black and threatening: CANCER . . . YELLOW FEVER . . . GOITER . . . PARALYSIS . . . PILES.

Yet you read on to learn that though these and other terrible afflictions were prevalent, if not epidemic, they were far from incurable. It said so in the advertisements which at the same time were both frightening and comforting.

There was no hedging about it, no qualification: Dr. King's New Discovery was the only Sure Cure for Consumption on earth; and for this reason "It Strikes Terror to the Doctors." There was Dr. Rupert Wells's Radiatized Fluid for Cancer. ("It will cure you at home without pain, plaster or operation.") Dr. Tucker had a specific for epilepsy. So did Dr. Kline and Dr. Grant. If the trouble had to do with kidney or liver, you need only to step into the nearest drugstore for a bottle of Dr. Kilmer's Swamp Root, which cured Bright's disease, Catarrh of the Bladder, Gravel, and trifles like Dropsy. And because Dr. Kilmer was not only a physician who had been "Graduated With Honors," but a good businessman too, he put his Swamp Root in a package so distinctive that patient and druggist had only to let their eye sweep the long shelves of patent medicines to stop at the tall pale-orange box. There it was, relief and cure for the afflicted, wrapped up in the identical shade that distinguished the austere *Atlantic Monthly* from all other magazines on newsstands. And lest the color blind be fooled by some shady druggist into buying a cheap substitute, there on the attractive box was the benign likeness of Dr. Kilmer himself.

Yet Dr. Kilmer did not stand alone for the renewal of the worn-out kidneys of America. James Doan, no doctor but "Formerly the well-known Druggist of Kingsville, Ontario," was already painting Doan's Kidney Pills on city billboards, and country fences, and using generous space in newspapers to tell how he had come by this remarkable remedy from "Aunty Mary Rogers of the Canadian Quaker Settlement," and was now "turning out millions of pills annually with the same care and precision that the Quakers used in olden times."

Until recent years the barns of rural America had served periodically as billboards for Barnum and Bailey, Buffalo Bill's Wild West, and lesser tent shows. Here and there, too, a barn might display a modest sign: "Sharples' Cream Separator Used Here," or perhaps it was De Laval's. But the far-seeing Dr. R. V. Pierce, of Buffalo, New York, author of *The People's Common Sense Medical Adviser in Plain English*, had been contemplating the uncounted millions of square feet of wasted space on the broad sides and roofs of barns in the United States. Soon enough they began to break out with messages of hope and cheer. Even the myopic could read them at one hundred yards: Dr. Pierce's Favorite Prescription on this barn, on another barn Dr. Pierce's Golden Medical Discovery. Dr. Pierce's

barn notices were supported by consistent advertising in the newspapers. His remedies were not wholly ignored in Dr. Pierce's enor-
mously successful book.

Throughout rural America, in 1906, medicine shows were troup-
ing, among them a score of companies under the hoary banner of
Healy and Bigelow, operating for the benefit of humanity with
Kickapoo Indian Sagwa. Other shows were on the road for the glory
of old Doc Hamlin, discoverer and proprietor of Hamlin's Wizard
Oil. There were lesser outfits, often posing as Quakers, like Hal the
Healer, Brother John and Brother Benjamin, all of whom used Thee
and Thou most of the time and never failed to open with a strong
pitch about the inherent honesty of the Friends and their remedies.

In 1906 rural America did not depend for its patent medicines on
the traveling shows, or on the drugstore at the county seat. The RFD
had brought the Post Office to the farm, along with the already fat
and growing catalogues of mail-order houses. The catalogue of Sears,
Roebuck and Company was then, as it is today, in complete harmony with the times. In 1906 it carried twenty full pages of patent
medicines and nostrums. But Sears did not plan to enrich the established manufacturers of such items. In its own laboratories it prepared its own brand of Female Pills; and from the same source came
Sears White Star Secret Liquor Cure. One cannot be certain about
the Female Pills, but here in the Secret Liquor Cure was something
that *worked*.

The Sears ad showed Mother furtively slipping the cure into
Daddy's coffee, and intimated that after a few doses Daddy would
cease helling around nights. The White Star nailed him home for
sure. Analysis showed it to contain sufficient narcotic to put him to
sleep almost as soon as he could reach the kitchen sofa right after
supper. If, as it could have turned out, Daddy became a confirmed
narcotic addict, in the same department of the catalogue was an advertisement for Sears Cure for the Opium and Morphine Habit.

It was a great and golden age, those latter years of the horse-and-
buggy times. Life might be strewn with dangers, yet for every threat
to health a good Samaritan stood by, ready to answer the cries of the
suffering, waiting to be of service.

Perhaps "waiting" is not the exact word: Dr. Hercules Sanche, inventor of the Oxydonor, The New Life-Saver for Self-Treatment, was actually *anxious* to help. He said so continuously and expensively in several of America's best monthly magazines which, for more than a decade already, had carried pictures of a typical American woman of the Gibson Girl type, who reclined on a stylish sofa reading a novel while absorbing God-given oxygen by way of the good doctor's God-inspired Oxydonor. Millions of Americans came to know her from the picture, but few could have appreciated the miracle they were looking at—that here for the first (and last) time in the history of applied physics, oxygen was being "forced through the myriad pores" of the lady's skin. Yet thousands of Americans, mostly female, were or had been patients, so to speak, of Dr. Sanche, who was not named Hercules for nothing; for at least two decades he successfully resisted the fraud orders of the Post Office Department.

Should oxygen fail, there were always the many brands of Sarsaparilla, the several brands of Celery compounds, the Bitters, Vermifuges, Alteratives; the Balms of Gilead, the Lung Balsams, the Pectorals; the Inhalants, the Asthma Powders, the Kidney Pads; the August Flowers, the Embrocations, the Anodyne Cordials; the Eye Salves, the Magnetic Plasters, the Soothing Syrups; the Black Draught, the Wine of Cardui, the Kings of Pain; the Expectorants, Family Drops, the Emulsions; the Nervines, the Liver Regulators, the Renovating Resolvents; there were a Kathairon, a Lithontriptic, a Buchu, a Cascarine. There were also Thayer's Slippery Elm Lozenges and Smith Brothers Cough Drops. There was also Peruna. One and all they were guaranteed to cure if the medication were continued regularly over a period which the labels usually failed to specify as to days, weeks, months, or years.

It was still a time when Temperance was a vogue of some militancy; "Whisky" had replaced "Rum" as the name of The Enemy. In spite of which, or just possibly because of it, Duffy's Pure Malt Whiskey Company was paying gratifying dividends from sale of its allegedly medicinal Pure Malt Whiskey. This remarkable remedy was made from "a formula worked out fifty years ago by one of the World's Greatest Chemists," and its protection from infringement "by low grade impure whiskey" was assured by "the Patented Bottle—Round, Amber Colored, and with Duffy blown into the glass"; and also by the trade-mark, which showed The Old Chemist's Head, doubtless the same savant of the formula, at work with retort and other scientific apparatus.

Duffy's crew were bold men. They knew that anything with "Whiskey" in its brand name must risk the real danger of antagonizing the Woman's Christian Temperance Union and allied groups. So Duffy's pitch asserted that the "Pure Malt" of the label meant "Medicinal," then brought in the claim that it was endorsed "by over 7,000 doctors and used exclusively in more than 2,000 hospitals." To quiet the protests of the Temperance people, Duffy's used half-page ads in daily newspapers, such as the *Sun* of New York City, announcing in large type that "Clergymen Endorse Duffy's Pure Malt Whiskey," beneath the photographs of three devoutly bearded types who were described as "Distinguished Divines and Temperance Workers."

The tendency of ministers of the gospel to speak a good word for patent medicines in the public prints had long been apparent, at least to the medical fraternity. Back in the 1840's the Connecticut Medical Society passed a sharply worded resolution calling attention to the fact that "the clergy, who have been recipients of free medical attention seem to be turning a penny by endorsing quack medicines," and applauded the action of three state medical groups which already had agreed "to discontinue free attention unless clergymen withdrew their endorsement of patent medicines."

The threat could not have been effective. Throughout the remainder of the nineteenth century, most religious journals and church periodicals swarmed with advertisements of all manner of nostrums and mail-order quacks; and well after the century's turn the American Medical Association made known that the *Baptist Record* was running an ad for the Interstate Remedy Company which said that "Here is a $3.50 Recipe that Cures Weak Men, Free." The ad was simultaneously appearing in the *National Police Gazette*, a nondenominational paper of varied interests.

In 1906, to say a word for Father John's Medicine, sold as a cure for tuberculosis, an imposing list of the names and parishes of Catholic priests was appearing in large advertisements in many big-city dailies. To a man the priests agreed that "We are pleased to indorse Father John's Medicine, knowing its merit and history." The priestly names made a happily comforting contrast to the single word CONSUMPTION in gigantic type across the top of the page.

The vast field of Men's Secret Diseases, in 1906, was being cared for in large part by individual quacks posing as specialists and operating either in offices or by mail, often both; and also by those havens of male therapy known as Medical Institutes. These relied chiefly on the walk-in trade attracted, and prepared, by the institutes' magnificent pitch, the Free Educational Museum of Anatomy.

There was nothing for women comparable to the Free Educational Museum of Anatomy, but one is not to think they were not well cared for by an immense faculty of Female Doctors, and Female Specialists of both sexes. All, of course, used the newspapers to advertise the cures that were to be had by mail or in stated offices. In 1906 one of the leading quackeries in this line was operated by a man-and-wife team, Dr. and Mrs. Dr. Chamlee, who cured cancer because they had "The Greatest Discovery and Wonder of the World —Without Knife or Pain, No Pay Until Cured." The Chamlee advertisements were particularly disquieting. "In any woman's breast," said Dr. and Mrs. Dr. Chamlee, "any lump is *Cancer*." They had many imitators.

By 1906 the chain-store idea had been adopted by dentists and opticians, and a few specialists in men's "secret diseases." It now began to appeal to quacks in other lines, among them specialists in diseases of women and at least one chain of fakers specializing in what was not yet advertised as proctology.

Yet neither individual quacks nor chains of quacks had made any noticeable inroads on the patent-medicine business. Free samples of the patents had been flooding the mails for many years. They were also to be had at drugstores, their natural outlet, along with the free almanacs and cookbooks put out by the larger concerns. The corner drugstore had only recently come into its own as a unique American institution. As a gathering place it was supplanting the slowly fading general store of the villages. In the big cities it had simply created a new place for trade and sociability. The increasingly elegant soda fountain played a part in this change, and so did the expanding variety of merchandise displayed.

Whereas the old chemist or apothecary, operating perhaps under style of The Sign of the Good Samaritan, with a swinging pictorial door sign of biblical aspect, sold drugs and medicinal herbs and little else, the American drugstore by the turn of the century was beginning to deal in almost everything except hay, grain and feed, and dry-goods. Some drugstores had even dropped the handsome and classic great vases of red and blue-green liquid which for decades had been to the drugstore what the red-and-white pole was to the barbershop.

Although the druggist had not yet entered the quick-lunch field, the threat was there in the soda fountain. He may have begun by selling bottled pop or tonic, and Moxie, the Healthful Nerve Food, but he soon moved to add fruit phosphate and a host of carbonated drinks, then ice-cream sodas, and so into banana splits and various combinations called sundaes.

The transformation of the apothecary shop into the drugstore did not go unchallenged. In the early nineties powerful sermons were being preached against "sucking soda" in drugstores which were open on the Sabbath because they were the source of medicine in case of accident or sudden illness. But the militant clergy were now hot after them, and in several Midwestern towns ordinances were passed against the abomination of dispensing soda on Sundays. Druggists responded by dispensing, on Sundays, ice cream with syrup added. This sodaless soda was called a Sunday Soda, and became popular on weekdays too. Out of respect for the cloth some cynical druggist changed the spelling to Sundae.

If the soda fountain provided a glittering social rendezvous for the drugstore, the Back Room supplied much of the marvelous aroma which pervaded the whole institution. It was in the Back Room that the pharmacist compounded the formidable drugs of the so-called allopathic physicians, and refilled the neat little bottles of the home-medicine chests left with their patients by the homeopath doctors. It was there that he composed many an esoteric compound formerly concocted on the kitchen stoves of customers who did not propose to pay fifty cents for an M.D.'s prescription.

It was in the Back Room, too, that the druggist in Temperance territory would fill a citizen's flask, with or without prescription, for a matter of twenty-five or fifty cents. These and lesser matters, carried on quietly in the room behind the frosted glass partition, all conspired to form the base of the drugstore smell. I know of nothing more conducive to remembrance of times past.

Many a patent medicine itself was born in the Back Room, notable among them the Cherry Pectoral and the Extract of Sarsaparilla, compounded in Jacob Robbins's Drug Store, Lowell, Massachusetts, by young James C. Ayer, which brought him a fortune; out of the Back Room in G. G. Green's store, Columbus, Ohio, came such marvels as Boschee's German Syrup and Green's August Flower.

The visible merchandise of the drugstore was displayed in three main divisions. One held the tremendous old wide-mouthed glass jars containing raw drugs, shelf upon shelf of them, each labeled in gold and black with the arcane Latin abbreviations of classic medicine. Another division held the packaged patent medicines. The third was given over to toiletries, perfumes, and the ever growing list of stationery, jewelry, sporting goods, hardware, and notions.

The patent-medicine department was an alluring study of packaging—and physiognomy. In a time when the facial hair of males was still a mark of solid worth, no business was better represented than that of proprietary remedies. The long shelves presented a stunning gallery of eminent or alleged physicians as imposing as a gathering of Civil War generals. In the great field of stomach bitters, leading the parade in popularity for decades, and always in whiskers, was the gorgeous full beard of Dr. David Hostetter, a man fit to sit with Moses in the biblical illustrations of Gustave Doré. His beaver was pure white, too, and so all-covering as to have made collar and necktie an affectation. From 1850, until well into the new century, Dr. Hostetter must have been the envy of all men, save perhaps the Smith Brothers of the cough drops and Mr. Beeman of the Pepsin Chewing Gum.

There was Dr. Kilmer, the Swamp Root man, with stand-up collar and lush, well ordered burnsides, who reminded his many admirers of the Honorable Chauncey Depew, Senator from New York, chairman of the board of the New York Central Railroad Company, and a public figure of the first importance. Doc Kilmer's whiskers took their name from General Ambrose Burnside who, although of an unfortunate military record, was noted for his "implacable integrity," which may well have influenced the myriad bankers who adopted burnsides for their façades, to say nothing of Dr. Kilmer and lesser therapists.

Another staunch and hairy worthy was R. V. Pierce, M.D., he of the Golden Medical Discovery, who operated from behind a mustache and a small beard that just missed being a Vandyke but was a bit outsize for the chin-piece made famous by Weber and Fields, the noted comedians.

Like the military, the patent-medicine men were not all bearded. Some preferred the mustache. In this category there may have been some argument as to which was champion, but none at all as to the two contenders for the honor. They were Dr. Sloan of the Liniment and Dr. Doan of the Kidney Pills. Here were astounding growths. The latter presented a frontage so sweeping as to indicate a background in the Austrian cavalry; Dr. Sloan's mustache was perhaps less elegant in grooming than Dr. Doan's, yet for sheer size and range nothing equaled it, anywhere. It pushed out from the face aggressively, then swept down in a curve to catch and hold the transfixed eye of the beholder. Little wonder if Dr. Sloan's fashion became known and much admired as the Over-Niagara type. It was, after all, a day of supreme effort in such matters.

Among all this patent-medicine hair on the packages, and often on the very labels, were two outstanding exceptions—Dr. Isaac Thomson of the Celebrated Eye Water, and Perry Davis, Esq., of the even more celebrated Pain Killer. Their faces were as innocent of hair as a babe's. Both were born in the eighteenth century, when Americans were wholly free of facial hair. (Try to find a Copley portrait, or a Ralph Earle, with a whisker in it.) And though both Thomson and Davis came of age in the 1810 period, both adhered throughout their lifetimes to the close-shaven style of the Founding Fathers.

From the label of his Celebrated Eye Water Dr. Thomson peers blandly forth through old-fashioned spectacles. His hair is long and white, almost like a wig. He wears a black stock tie.

Mr. Davis looks like sterner stuff, as was his Pain Killer. He displays a distinguished head and countenance, with large deep-set eyes remindful of Mr. Webster, more serene, perhaps, but somewhat austere, in a stylishly careless high stock, altogether the perfect Old School man of affairs.

In 1906, on the long shelves of the drugstore, the American patent-medicine business stood at the very peak of its untrammeled and imaginative golden age. Never again was it to reach the variety or the free-wheeling quackery of its claims to therapy as set down in the rich wild prose of the highest-paid talents in the advertising business.

There on the packages were the Moguls of Patent Medicine, their faces as well known as those of J. P. Morgan, Cy Young, and John L. Sullivan.

It was noon for the sarsaparillas, the celeries, the vegetable compounds; for assorted nostrums certified as cures for every recognized disease and for others that existed only in the fevered imaginations of writers of advertising copy. The chronology of their genesis and popularity extended full across the nineteenth century, and into the twentieth.

There in the drugstore you could stand in one spot and read that chronology in the pictures on the packages. It began with the eighteenth century's Dr. Isaac Thomson and Mr. Perry Davis, the whiskerless savants; and continued with the incredibly hairy faces of the middle period which late in the nineteenth century began to wane as the mustache advanced to take over the fashion of the American male. And then, somewhere around 1900, the mustache began to give way and men began to shave all over, as had been the custom of their great-grandfathers. You could see evidence of this final radical shift in 1906. In that year Dr. S. B. Hartman's Peruna was outselling every other patent medicine in the United States, yet there was Dr. Hartman on the label, as clean shaven and up to date as the leading man in a Broadway play. Facial hair had come full circle.

In this immense drugstore gallery of benefactors was the likeness of one woman, of course none other than Mrs. Pinkham of the Vegetable Compound and the college song. Alone, immaculate, unique, she stood immutable there on the shelf amid the great whiskered men of medicine, their peer in all things, their superior in the comforting assured pitch of her bedside manner.

Yet this was 1906, a year if not quite of apocalypse, then at least a time of locusts. Mrs. Pinkham, like all the rest of the drugstore galaxy, was about to change the text on the label, to modify it to conform to the restrictions about to be placed on the semantics of packaged and bottled therapy.

2

The Great American Fraud

The opening gun in the first over-all campaign against patent medicines in the United States was fired in *Collier's*, a weekly magazine,
on October 7, 1905, by Samuel Hopkins Adams, who called what he
was shooting at The Great American Fraud.

The thirty-four-year-old reporter was a graduate of the *Sun* of New
York City. On that distinguished daily he displayed such clarity and
aggressiveness as to catch the eye of S. S. McClure whose monthly
magazine was making a specialty of what President Theodore Roosevelt described as Muckraking. Adams went to the staff of *McClure's*,
leaving a little later to write for *Collier's* the historic series which
brought both that periodical and Adams himself to attention as of
major importance in forcing Federal legislation known as the Pure
Food and Drug Act. "Forcing" is the right word. The patent-medicine lobby in Congress turned out to be a potent enemy.

Reporter Adams was something of an oddity among newspapermen
of the time. He was a *college graduate*, class of 1891, Hamilton College, Clinton, New York. Varsity sports had contributed to his lean,
muscular figure, and academic exposure had left him with a fine background in classical literature, though it failed to make him stuffy
either in prose or in manner. The numerous patent-medicine kings
and quack doctors on whom he was to call saw a man of medium
height, smooth shaven in a day of beards and mustaches, quick but
soft spoken, whose penetrating blue eyes were perhaps the only
indication of the low boiling point that was a part of his equipment.

In October 1905, having completed his tour of the Nostrum Evil,
Adams sat down to write his shocking travelogue. Readers did not
finish the first article without knowing that carnage was to mark the
trail. Observing that gullible Americans were spending more than

seventy-five millions of dollars annually to purchase patent medicines, Adams was appalled to consider this sum as translated into the quantities of alcohol, the vast amount of opiates, and the wide assortment of varied drugs his countrymen were absorbing.

It was undiluted fraud, he said, fraud exploited by the most skillful of advertising bunco men. These fellows were the basis of the trade. Should the newspapers, he continued, and the magazines refuse their pages to this class of advertising, the patent-medicine business in five years would be as scandalously historic as the South Sea Bubble, and the nation would be richer not only in lives and money but also in drunkards and drug addicts saved. Having thus indicted, as an accessory after the fact, the very medium he was using, Mr. Adams started to call his shots.

To lead what he called the Bracers, Adams selected Dr. S. B. Hartman's Peruna, which he said was the most prominent proprietary nostrum in the country, having ousted the place formerly held in turn by Greene's Nervura and Paine's Celery Compound, and for the same reason that had made them popular—alcohol. Here he paused a moment to cite a recent statistical study, made by an inquisitive physician, which asserted that "more alcohol is consumed in this country in patent medicines than is dispensed in a legal way by licensed liquor vendors, barring the sales of ales and beer."

Peruna cost a dollar a bottle. Adams suggested that this was too great a margin of profit for a remedy which stood Dr. Hartman not more than eighteen cents a bottle. The reporter then provided readers who wished to manufacture Peruna for home consumption with a recipe: Mix half a pint of alcohol with one and one-half pints of water, add cubebs for flavor and a little burnt sugar for color. There it was, the absolute cure for catarrh which according to Dr. Hartman's advertising was the base of all disease.

In a personal interview with Dr. Hartman, Adams wrote, the doctor admitted that no drug or combination of drugs would cure disease, with the exception of quinine for malaria. But Hartman insisted that the belief in Peruna, fostered continuously by printed testimonials, "produced good results." Adams did not think so. On the contrary, a majority of tuberculosis cases showed that a history of the Peruna-type medicines, taken in the early stages, resulted in diminishing the patient's resistant powers, and that much of "the typhoid in the Middle West" was complicated by the victim's keeping up the stimulus of alcohol long after he should have been under a physician's care.

In respect to Hartman's claim that Peruna was not habit forming, and that "nobody could get drunk on the prescribed doses of Peruna," Adams admitted this might be true, yet he thought possibly that the Peruna prescription of three wineglassfuls in forty-five minutes "might temporarily alter a prohibitionist's outlook on life." To support his own skepticism that the Bracer-type of patent medicines was not habit forming, Adams quoted a letter from a well known authority on drug and alcohol addiction: "Physicians have called my attention to the use of Peruna both preceding and following alcohol and drug addictions. I have in the last two years met four persons who drank Peruna in large quantities. They were treated under my care as simple alcoholics."

Then Reporter Adams let go the blockbuster he had recently come by. It was an official document of the United States Department of the Interior, Office of Indian Affairs. Signed by Acting Commissioner C. F. Larrabee, it was directed "To Indian Agents and School Superintendents in charge of Agencies," and called attention to "proprietary medicines and other compounds . . . with special reference to the liability of their misuse by Indians on account of the alcohol they contain." Then the commissioner singled out Dr. Hartman's catarrh specific for honors. "The sale of Peruna," he ordered, "is hereby prohibited. As a medicine something else can be substituted; as an intoxicant it has been found too tempting and effective."

This brand-new order, until then unknown to the public, is one of the more celebrated documents of the Interior Department. Because it had to deal solely with "wards of the state," Mr. Adams felt it only fair to indicate the popularity of Peruna in the general trade too. He did so by citing druggists, physicians, and others in half a score of communities, including Chicago, to show that a new term had been added to the American vernacular. The term was a "Peruna drunk." Although Peruna drunks were particularly a product of no-license, or Temperance, towns, the inclusion of Chicago anticipated the appearance of the drinker later known as the "wino."

If Peruna drunks had come to be a generic as well as a specific term, such fame had already attracted imitators into "the stolen sunshine of Dr. Hartman's effective advertising," among them Pe-ru-vi-na, P-Ru-Na, Perina, and Anurep. And Adams wrote that several long-established compounds also were notoriously being used as alcoholic stimulants. He named them. They included Lydia Pinkham's, Paine's Celery, Kidney Specific, Hostetter's Bitters, Duffy's Pure Malt, and Dr. Kilmer's Swamp Root.

Possibly because he was never a Temperance man, Mr. Adams was particularly affronted by the 1906 advertising of Duffy's Pure Malt Whiskey. Privately Adams was against Duffy's for two reasons: he thought it inferior to most whiskies as a beverage; and he had a thorough distaste for men he called Temperance Drinkers, meaning hypocrites. Having digested one of Duffy's immense ads in, of all places, the *Sun*, he took off after the Three Distinguished Divines and Temperance Workers.

One was operating a get-married-quick matrimonial bureau; another was an Internal Revenue official among whose duties was the collection of Federal liquor taxes; the third had been called to trial by his presbytery for endorsing Duffy's Pure Malt, and was permitted "to resign from fellowship in his church."

Having clarified the "Temperance" testimony, the thorough Mr. Adams sent a photographer for proof that Duffy's liked to work both sides of the street: and *Collier's* ran the picture captioned "A Saloon Window Display at Auburn, New York." Pasted on the window was a large sign saying that Duffy's Pure Malt Whiskey Is for Sale Here, while beneath it were two dozen bottles of the product.

Though he was to return again and again to The Bracers, Adams closed his first article by suggesting that what the government should do was to carry out rigidly its promised policy no longer to permit liquors to disguise themselves as patent medicines, and thereby escape the tax which was put on other, and probably better, brands of intoxicants. Another thing: the government should demand that the nostrum vendors label every bottle with the percentage of alcohol it contained. "Then," said Mr. Adams, rubbing it in, "the innocent clergyman who writes testimonials for Duffy's, and the WCTU member who indorses Peruna, Lydia Pinkham and their compeers, will know when they imbibe their tonics, invigorators, swamp roots, bitters, nerve-builders and spring medicines, that they are sipping by the tablespoon or wineglassful what the town tippler takes across the license-paying bar." By the time Adams was through, these and many other demands aimed at The Great American Fraud were being made into laws.

Having paid his initial respects to The Bracers, Crusader Adams turned his attention to several of the more prominent individual quacks among whom, he was not astonished to learn, were a number of so-called Magnetic Healers. Dr. C. J. Thacher of Chicago appeared to be the biggest advertiser of these charlatans. He spoke to the world's afflicted in trumpet tones through the *New York American* and other large newspapers: "I want to say I can cure any disease that afflicts the human race. . . . I am as positive that I can cure them all with the famous Thacher Magnetic Shields as I am that the sun will rise in the morning."

This was a fairly positive statement. Adams went to call on Dr. Thacher at 161 State Street, Chicago, to find a big, gaunt old man, with a formidable head, a formidable voice, and a still more formidable manner. He was wearing a magnetic cap, a magnetic waistcoat, magnetic insoles, and his legs were swathed like a mummy's in magnetic wrappings. "It made one perspire," Mr. Adams remembered, "just to look at old Doc Thacher."

When Adams explained the reason for his call, the old man thundered eloquent denunciations of "the wholesale and unwarranted attacks" already put upon him by the American Medical Association. These were making it increasingly difficult, he complained, to get his advertisements into the *best* newspapers. He wanted his visitor to know that he was no quack. "My object," Adams heard him say, "is to spread the light, to rescue humanity. I can cure them of *anything*. In time I will compel the authorities to take notice of my methods. I will extend my Magnetic Shield treatment to the government. I will say 'Take it! Take it! and set the people free.'"

The old man was just warming up. "Insanity?" he shouted, whacking himself on his magnetic cap, "Insanity? Let the authorities turn over ten cases to me. I'll put my Magnetic Shields on 'em and restore the harmonious vibrations of the brain, and everything will be well!"

When the reporter got up to leave, Thacher followed him to the door. "Paralysis?" he cried, hammering his magnetic leg swathing,

"Paralysis? An easy problem. Had five cases. Couldn't wink or speak or move finger or toe. Cured 'em right off. Winked. Spoke. Got up and walked. Paralysis? Pish!"

If Doc Thacher's pitch sounded a little crude, one should know that it was probably just about the right pitch for urban disciples of magnetism who read the Hearst papers. Their country cousins were being exposed to similar appeals in the pages of the big mail-order house catalogues. Sears, Roebuck, for instance, was offering Electric Liniment, Magnetic Insoles (eighteen cents a pair), and Electric Battery Plasters. A special pitch was made for the Sears Electric Rings: "These," said the catalogue with a straight face, "are the first genuine electric rings introduced into the United States. All others are imitations." Sears added that the imitations were without curative properties. The implications were clear enough. So were the little flashes of lightning which the catalogue pictured as being discharged from the ring, the *genuine* ring.

Beginning to compete with the magic of therapy offered by devices styled variously as electric, galvanic, and magnetic was a new agent, radium, for the discovery of which the Nobel prize in physics had been awarded in 1903 to M. and Mme. Curie of France. Its workings were mysterious, but were believed to be effective in the treatment of cancer. By the time radium became a popular subject for the Sunday supplements or gee-whiz sections of American newspapers, quacks were already moving into the new field. One of these was a Mr. Isham who, in 1906, suddenly burst into the prominence that attends full-page advertisements in leading newspapers from coast to coast, to tell of the California Waters of Life, a cancer cure.

Mr. Adams read Mr. Isham's text with increasing interest, to learn that the chief reason for the advertisements was to "reply to the avalanche of anxious inquiries about Isham Spring, California." He also noticed that Mr. Isham already had acquired a number of signed testimonials of considerable horsepower. The *Collier's* man went to call at the Waters of Life Office, in New York City's famous Flatiron Building, an otherwise impeccable business address.

The investigator was met by Mr. Isham himself, a young man of the utmost assurance who, when asked if he really believed that from his spring, as advertised, there flowed the identical waters which gushed from the scriptural rock when Moses smote it, replied yes, that he did. He then went into an exposition which Adams found "too profound for me to grasp in detail." With some effort Adams managed to turn the conversation to the testimonials, but here he met with hesitancy and vagueness. Adams suggested that he would like to talk with a Professor Fogg, a testimonial giver by whom Isham seemed to set great store. Isham, however, could not say what kind of professor he was and knew only that he "lived somewhere in Long Island City." It was much the same with the other testimonials.

But when Isham was permitted to return to the Waters of Life he grew eloquent. Yes, the blessed spring was his own property. It was located in the San Miguel Mountains near San Diego; and its waters had proved so beneficent that he now guaranteed they would "cure rheumatism in seven days, and cancer in thirty days."

"*Cure?*" asked Mr. Adams.

"Yes, *cure*," replied young Mr. Isham, softly enough for so positive a statement. He went on to say the Waters of Life would cure Bright's Disease and diabetes in thirty days, and in three days would stop falling hair, while on the fourth day the first shoots would appear of "a luxuriant new crop of hair."

This was not quite all. The young man told Adams that any profits from Waters of Life would go toward a scheme to abolish poverty and suffering, a plan he himself had thought up but only after "consulting Deity." Whereupon Mr. Adams realized he was dealing with a characteristic wizard of southern California, and wrote in his article that Isham was "either of unsound mind or the most arrant and blasphemous faker before the public."

Government chemists soon analyzed samples of Isham Spring Water and found it to contain "no ingredients beyond those present in ordinary spring water." Federal agents laid hands on a large shipment of California Waters of Life and condemned it as misbranded because the label claimed for it "a miraculous power to destroy disease. . . ." The courts upheld the action.

Other waters were competing with Isham's biblical font. None were more potent than those put into jugs and sold by the Claremore Radium Wells Company, described uncharitably by Mr. Adams as an association of highly respected businessmen and bunco operators from Fort Smith, Arkansas. The reporter did not trouble to visit Radium Wells, but was content to publish an analysis of the product showing that it "contained absolutely no radium or radium-producing constituents."

Adams also went after other quacks he designated as Cancer Vampires, and became curious as to the source of the diplomas he saw on their office walls. A majority of them, he noted, were graduates of St. Luke's Hospital, Niles, Michigan.

The St. Luke's diploma was a beauty. Its handsome parchment was illuminated and had a great seal and a ribbon of rich silk. A fine vignette displayed a symbolic angel with banner held high. And the document bestowed the degree of Doctor of Medicine and Surgery with a flourish of Latin in black script and Old English. Most impressive, Mr. Adams thought. He was arranging to go to Niles when he learned that St. Luke's was no longer in existence, having been discouraged by the combined efforts of the Michigan Medical Society, the Michigan State Board of Health, and the American Medical Association. The latter group informed Adams that "the two founders of St. Luke's Hospital are at present fugitives from justice."

Yet other sainted names caught the reporter's attention—The St. James Society of New York City and the St. Paul Association of Chicago. Both advertised themselves, with what Adams wrote was a "pseudo-religious flavor in keeping with their corporate titles," as sure cures for the morphine habit; and their form letters, which were identically worded in several important particulars, suggested a community interest. Both insisted their treatment was *not* a "reduction cure," which meant a gradual lessening of the drug intake from week to week, a method which had long since been condemned by reputable physicians and hospitals.

Enrolling with both outfits under assumed names, Adams filled out the St. Paul blank to indicate his usual intake of morphine was twelve grains daily. When the medicine came, Adams wrote back to ask if it contained any morphine. In a reply signed by a Dr. I. W. Rogers, the St. Paul Association said that "we find your trial order is prepared. It contains a small amount of (　　) narcotic to each fluid dram." Noting the space left blank, Adams wrote demanding to know the figure of "the small amount" and the name of the narcotic. By return mail Dr. Rogers said it was "necessary to put $1\frac{1}{3}$ grains of morphia in each fluid dram" of the treatment.

Reflecting on the prescribed dosage of a dram six times a day, plus half a dram between times, Adams figured that the "treatment" would give the patient $11\frac{1}{3}$ grains daily, or only $\frac{2}{3}$ of a grain less than the twelve grains of his supposed habit. The St. Paul system was indeed less a reduction cure than a method of getting a continuous supply of narcotic. The St. James Society's system was identical. Describing these and other fake cures for drug addiction in an article entitled "The Scavengers," Adams felt need for other words and phrases than those he had been applying to patent-medicine vendors. These drug-cure fakers, he wrote, were men to do the work of Hell.

"At the very bottom of the noisome pit," he wrote, "crawl the drug habit specialists—scavengers delving amid the carrion of the fraudulent nostrum business. The human wrecks made by the opium and cocaine habits come to them for cure, and are wrung dry of the last drop of blood." It occurred to Adams, too, that no few addicts had unwittingly got their start with the "cocaine-laden secret patent medicines." Hence no single part of the pending Federal legislation was of greater importance than the clause requiring that the amount of habit-forming drugs in any medicine be stated on the label. In this and one other article in the series, Adams cited by name and address, and described the methods of, no less than nineteen so-called drug-cure outfits which he lumped together as Brothers in Villainy.

Looking for still more villains, the reporter began to investigate several patents which their promoters claimed would cure consumption, a disease then more publicized than cancer. Stating that consumption was "absolutely incurable by any medicine," though an increasing number of consumptives were saved by fresh air, diet, and methodical living, he declared that every man who traded in this market, whether he pocketed the profits of the maker, the purveyor, or the advertiser, "takes toll of blood." He could not deceive himself here, for "here the patent medicine faker is nakedest, most cold-hearted."

Consider Dr. King's New Discovery for Consumption. Proclaimed "the Only Sure Cure for Consumption in the World," the remedy naturally "Strikes Terror to the Doctors." You might have a trial bottle from Dr. King free of cost. The regular sized bottle cost one dollar. Adams had the nostrum analyzed, to find it was a morphine and chloroform mixture which, said he, was "a pretty diabolical concoction to give to anyone, particularly to a consumptive." The chloroform was calculated to allay the cough, thereby checking

Nature's effort to throw off the dead matter from the lungs; and the opium meanwhile drugged the patient into a deceptive cheerfulness. The combination, Adams concluded, was admirably designed to shorten the life of any consumptive who took it regularly. Then he bore down once more on the business of labels: There was nothing in Dr. King's label to warn the purchaser of the deadly stuff he was buying.

Another lavishly advertised specific in this field, Shiloh's Consumption Cure, had nothing in its label to show that among its ingredients were unhealthy doses of chloroform and prussic acid. Adams wrote to Shiloh's makers to know if the medicine really would "cure consumption." Back came a letter: "After you have taken the medicine for a while, if you are not firmly convinced that you are very much better, we want you to go to your druggist and get back all the money you have paid for Shiloh." Adams commented that "under our present lax system there is no warning on the bottle that this liquid contains one of the most deadly of poisons."

Adams, the pseudoinvalid, next wrote to A. C. Meyer & Company, makers of Dr. Bull's Cough Syrup, to know if it would cure an established case of consumption, as indicated on the bottle. The firm replied, "We do not claim it will cure such a case . . . but we can, however, say it has cured cases said to have been consumption in its earliest stages." Adams reread the label: "There is no case of hoarseness, cough, asthma, bronchitis . . . or consumption that cannot be cured speedily by the proper use of Dr. Bull's Cough Syrup."

Having quoted this letter, in an article entitled "Preying on the Incurables," Adams published a photostatic reproduction of a "Verdict In Inquest No. 821," signed by the coroner at Cincinnati on October 30, 1905, in regard to the death of Hilda Keck, two-year-old child, who came to her end "by the poisonous effects of opium, the result of drinking the contents of a bottle of Dr. Bull's Cough Syrup."

Adams then had something to say about Cincinnati newspapers. In reporting the death of little Hilda Keck they did not mention the name of the cough syrup, though it appeared in the coroner's official report. Adams wrote to the four dailies to ask why. "Two of them disclosed that they had no information on the point, which is contrary to the statement of the physician in the case." Adams dryly observed that this implied "a reportorial laxity difficult to credit." A third Cincinnati newspaper "ascribed the omission to a settled policy," while a fourth pleaded fear of libel.

The Dr. Bull Cough Syrup affair was a stunner, nationally, once Adams aired it. He was to use it again later when he turned to consider what he called "The Patent Medicine Conspiracy against the Freedom of the Press."

Early in his campaign Adams had paid his respects in passing to the Kilmer family of Binghamton, New York, proprietors of Swamp Root, which he characterized as one of the most blatant of patent-medicines swindles. The Swamp Root formula was the "discovery" of Dr. S. Andral Kilmer for the cure of many ailments, including all "diseases of the kidneys." But Dr. Kilmer had now, in 1906, left the business which was being carried on by his son, while he himself entered a new field.

As Adams put it: "Another quack family with a cancer branch are the Kilmers. Dr. S. Andral Kilmer is now proprietor of a CanCertorium and an itinerant charlatan. He itinerants through the large towns and small cities of New York state, advertising like Barnum's circus. Free consultation, remedies at $3 a week, and treatment at $2 a week, constitute his traveling plan." Doc Kilmer's billing on the road left not the least doubt as to who he was; he was Cancer's First Conqueror.

One of Doc Kilmer's gravest errors was to practice his cancer con game on a campus caretaker at Hamilton College, which happened to be the alma mater of Samuel Hopkins Adams. In *Collier's* for July 14, 1906, he described the case of the campus caretaker:

"He was afflicted with facial cancer, and went to Dr. Kilmer's CanCertorium on a fund raised for him among the undergraduates, who did not know the nature of the institution. He was there provided with all the liquor he could drink, evidently with a view of keeping him drugged, until Kilmer had extracted $800 from him, when the progress of his disease was so marked that he became frightened and left, going to a reputable surgeon, who at once operated. He is now back at work. This man kept track of seven of the CanCertorium patients he came to know well, of whom, so he tells me, five died and the other two are apparently going the same way."

This warning, spread in the pages of a magazine of immense circulation, must have had an immediate and powerful effect on the

CanCertorium. Mr. Adams sought to use the article to shame the press for the part it played in promoting quackery. He closed the article by referring to Dr. Kilmer as representing "an old, picturesque and fast-disappearing tribe of bunco-artists, and when his side-whiskers disappear from the pages of the small city dailies, those publications will be the less amusing, though the more respectable for the loss."

Again and again, in the ten long articles of The Great American Fraud, Adams referred to the part played by the press. In a summary which may well have caused him pain to write, but which had to be written by a reporter as honest as he was magnificent, he brought up the matter he called "The Magic Red Clause."

"With a few honorable exceptions," he wrote, "the press of the United States is at the beck and call of the patent medicines. Not only do the newspapers modify the news affecting these interests, but they sometimes become their active agents." Mr. C. F. Cheney, who manufactured Hall's Catarrh Cure and who in 1905 was president of the Proprietary Association of America, had devised, said Mr. Adams, a method of making the press do the fighting for the nostrum vendors. On every advertising contract was a clause, printed in red, which provided that the contract should become void in event of legislation hostile to patent medicines. Adams reproduced one of these contracts with the article. It was between Cheney Medicine Company and the *Emporia Gazette* of Kansas, William Allen White's paper. Mr. Adams took pains to point out that Mr. White's paper had "since become one of the newspapers to abjure the patent-medicine man and all his ways." Yet it was "disheartening to note that in the case of one important and high-class daily, the *Pittsburgh Gazette*, a trial rejection of all patent medicine advertising received absolutely no support or encouragement from the public. So the paper reverted to its old policy."

The medical press itself, Mr. Adams found, was not wholly free from outside influences. "The control is as complete," he wrote, "though exercised by a class of nostrums somewhat differently exploited but essentially the same." Only "ethical" preparations were permitted in the representative medical press. These were articles not advertised in the lay press. Yet Adams had noticed that this distinction was not strictly adhered to. There was Syrup of Figs, for instance, which made a pretense in the daily press of being an extract of fig, which it was not; while in the medical journals it was advertised for what it was, a preparation of senna.

Adams thought the physicians seemed to have "awakened, if somewhat tardily," to counterattack the nostrum makers. He cited the American Medical Association, which had "organized a Council on Pharmacy and Chemistry to investigate and pass on the ethical preparations advertised to physicians." The council had already issued some "painfully frank reports on products of imposingly scientific nomenclature, and more are to follow."

The last of the ten articles appeared in September, 1906. To illustrate them Adams used facsimile reproductions of various documents, medicine labels, faked testimonials, death notices of persons whose portraits were simultaneously appearing in patent-medicine ads telling of their cures, and much else. With the articles, too, were cartoon-type pictures by the artist Edward Windsor Kemble, who could do wonders with a death's head labeled the Patent Medicine Trust, with its eyes of Laudanum and Poisonous Alcohol, and a row of grinning teeth composed of bottles.

The over-all effect on the public was staggering. Adams had attacked 264 concerns and individuals by name. The cries of the wounded were terrible and were reported in hundreds of small and several large newspapers. One could read that this or that medicine company had "instructed its legal counsel" to sue Adams and *Collier's* for damaging remarks on an "old established business." The favorite sum was $300,000. Yet the Proprietary Association of America, described by Adams as "the body for mutual help and protection of all the more powerful quacks and frauds," did not threaten or even intimate legal action. Instead, the nostrum makers instituted a continuous bombardment against *Collier's* and Adams "in the newspapers they controlled."

Everybody was soon getting into the act. The staid *World's Work* spoke portentously of "this nefarious business." *Life's* funny men and artists began to satirize cure-alls and adulterated food. Wallace Irwin wrote some verses, entitled "A Testimonial," which were widely copied or plagiarized, telling how he had been taking Z-Ru-Na and Lydia Pinkum until his pains disappeared in the happy fog of a wonderful jag.

In its summing up, *Collier's* remarked that Adams, though he had rightly enough spoken bluntly, had been careful and fair. He had applied "murderers" to some, using the term "because they were taking their profits at the cost of human lives." Others he had "designated merely as thieves, because no other term describes them." Only two suits for libel had materialized. One of these was dropped before it could come to trial. The other, brought by Pink Pills for Pale People, was still (1907) in the courts.

Before the Fraud series was done, the American Medical Association was bringing pressure to bear on Senator Nelson W. Aldrich, of Rhode Island, who was leading the fight against passage of the Pure Food and Drug Act. Dr. Charles A. L. Reed, the AMA's spokesman, told Aldrich that backing Reed were "some 135,000 physicians, organized into 2,000 county units, each member instructed not only to act for himself but to ask patients and friends to bring pressure on the Senate." The bill passed the Senate 63-4; the four negative votes were cast by Southern Democrats, less fearful of doped medicine and adulterated food than of Federal encroachment on the constitutional powers of the states.

In the House, the bill was referred to committee, and there it slept, a sleep induced by the combined lobbies of food processors and makers of patent medicines. At this point Upton Sinclair's novel of Packingtown, *The Jungle*, appeared, to upset the stomachs of much of the United States and to infuriate President Theodore Roosevelt because, if bad meat was being sold, the Federal inspectors were at fault. It turned out that bad meat indeed was being sold. The President set off an uproar almost to deafen that about patent medicines, and to tip the legislative scales in favor of the Pure Food and Drug Act, which finally passed 240-17, was signed by Roosevelt, and on January 1, 1907, went into effect.

It was a triumph greater for no one than for Dr. Harvey W. Wiley, long head of the Bureau of Chemistry in the Department of Agriculture, who since 1883 had been seeking a law to regulate the labeling of foods and medicines. "Tell the truth on the label," said Wiley, "and let the consumer judge for himself." In 1929, after twenty-nine years of active service during which he probably made more powerful enemies than any other man in government, Dr. Wiley resigned his post. He died in 1930, and his memory should not wholly fade so long as drugs and processed foods are made to carry descriptive labels.

During his campaign against quackery, Mr. Adams was given every possible aid by the American Medical Association. This group, as intimated, was already roused to curb an evil that existed within the medical profession itself; namely, the prescribing of certain proprietary medicines. It had become almost a custom to introduce a nostrum to the public, the association admitted, "through such undiscerning, uncritical or even venal physicians as would prescribe it, or recommend it in testimonials calculated to impress laymen." And now, in 1906, the association was prompted by Adams's campaign to extend its investigations to include the more widely promoted patent medicines.

To take charge of this new effort the association established what was first known as its Propaganda Department and which later became the present Bureau of Investigation, in charge of Dr. Arthur J. Cramp, who for thirty years was to work closely and ably with the Food and Drug Administration, the Better Business Bureau, and all other public and private agencies seeking to protect the public from the ever alert and often ingenious con men of medicine.

This is the place to mention that Samuel Hopkins Adams, aside from his exposé of medical frauds, also took after certain processors of foods. They protested that he was out to ruin them, and began libel suits, while Adams compounded his crime by printing new and worse charges. But that story does not belong in this book.

What does belong here, if only to indicate the complete independence of one of the great reporters of all time, is a statement Mr. Adams made in connection with his research for The Great American Fraud. "Since entering upon this field of work," he told an interviewer, "I have received enough fundamental misinformation, *from physicians*, to have kept me in jail for the rest of my natural life on libel charges, had I accepted one-tenth of it."

Having said as much, he turned his attention to other things, while the makers of patent medicines turned theirs to complying with the provisions of the Pure Food and Drug Act, or to possible means to circumvent them.

PART TWO

The Beginnings

The Alliance: Medicine and Ink

What impressed Samuel Hopkins Adams most of all, when he had finished his campaign against The Great American Fraud, was that the American quality of shrewdness fails us when we go into the market to purchase relief from suffering.

"When the average American sets out to buy a horse," he observed, "or a box of cigars, he is a model of caution." But see him when he is seeking "the most precious of all possessions, sound health." He has become an inveterate gull. Anybody's word is good enough for him here: "An admiral whose puerile vanity has betrayed him into a testimonial; an obliging and conscienceless senator; a grateful idiot in some remote hamlet; a renegade doctor or a silly woman who gets a bonus of a dozen photographs for her letter —any of these are sufficient to lure the hopeful patient to his purchase. He wouldn't buy a second-hand bicycle on the affidavit of any of them, but he will give up his dollar and take his chance of poison on a mere newspaper statement which he doesn't even investigate."

Mr. Adams believed that the incomparable asset to the exploiter of patent medicines, as well as to drugless nostrums, was printer's ink. He also believed devoutly in a free press, even while he worked to some purpose to purify it from "a fraud whose flagrancy and impudence" were of minor importance "compared to the cold-hearted greed with which it grinds out its profits from the sufferings of duped and eternally hopeful ignorance."

Just when the first American ink was used to advertise what later would be called a patent medicine is not certain. As early as 1692 there appeared in the *Boston Almanac* an announcement of "That Excellent Antidote against all Manner of Gripings called Aqua anti torminales, which if timely taken, it not only cures the Griping of the Guts, and the Wind Cholick; but preventeth that woeful Distemper of the Dry Belly Ach. Sold by Benj Harris at the London-Coffee House in Boston."

Although the medium is not cited by name, one writer states that "in 1711 the first patent medicine advertisement appeared. It was called Tuscarora Rice and was sold by a Mrs. Masters as a consumption cure." For well more than a century consumption was the most feared and probably the most prevalent disease in the United States; and one of the best known of the early imported medicines had to do with coughing. In 1733 the celebrated Peter Zenger, who was to win the first major victory for the freedom of the press in the colonies, printed in his *New-York Weekly Journal* "An Abstract of the Patent Granted by His Majesty King George . . . for Dr. Bateman's Pectoral Drops" which in New York province were "to be sold by James Wallace." Notice was given that a ten-guinea reward would be paid to anyone who "shall discover any person that Counterfeits this Medicine, or sells a Counterfeit."

It seems probable that American use of the word "patent" applied to medicines stems from these royal patents of colonial days. It is true that when later the United States Patent Office came into being a few nostrums were patented, but only a few. Most American medicines for sale over the counter were registered by name and trade-mark, a sort of copyright, and were thus proprietary. This system was used because exclusive rights to a *patented* formula would expire at the end of seventeen years, after which anyone could appropriate both the formula and the name. An example was to be seen in the case of Pitcher's Castoria. Once Pitcher's patent had expired, half a dozen different castorias were promptly on the market, and "castoria" was for all commercial purposes a generic name.

But a copyright could be renewed every twenty years; and it is no exaggeration to say that the formula of any so-called patent medicine was of less value than its name. For instance, there was never any secrecy about the ingredients of Lydia E. Pinkham's Vegetable Compound. In its early days this wise woman went to considerable expense to describe each step in its manufacture, a fine homely touch for a product whose proprietor was shrewd enough to play up the kitchen stove, with Grandmother brewing the honest herbs for her neighbors. Let those who would, copy the formula; they could not name it *Lydia E. Pinkham's* vegetable compound.

No matter whether patented or registered, the word "patent" in the United States came to mean what technically are proprietary medicines.

As Adams intimated, the swift rise of American patent medicines came largely from newspaper and periodical advertising. It was synchronous with and dependent upon the spread of education which made it possible for a majority of Americans to read, a condition not present in early colonial times. Newspapers *made* the patent-medicine business, which in turn supported the newspapers.

Early nineteenth century newspapers in the larger centers got their income largely from storekeepers. The more numerous country papers had to do the best they could with such public printing as their managers could get from publishing legal notices, laws, and so forth. It is not astonishing that editors welcomed the paid announcements of nostrums and found room also to run in the news columns, and without extra charge, the so-called "reading notices" expected of them by the nostrum vendors. (Reading notices for patent medicines were those items known in the trade as the saved-from-a-horrible-death type.)

The ethics of the nostrum manufacturers were clear and simple; the nostrum that sold best was the best medicine in its field. The ethics of the newspaper publishers were no more complicated; the nostrum vendor who always paid promptly for his advertising was the best kind to have in the paper.

By 1820, to choose an arbitrary date, there was not only a nostrum for every ill; there were a dozen nostrums for every ill. It was a wildcat business from the first. All the schools of patent-medicine therapy operated in the manner of empirics, basing their practice on experience alone; and the business gradually developed several divisions, or types. Patterns that were to endure for more than a century were forming.

For instance, there were those who claimed to be privy to the "secret" herbal formulas of American Indians who were usually described as Indian Chiefs. Closely allied with this school, though leaving the Indians out of it, were nostrums called Nature's Remedies, a sort of botanic folk wisdom from time immemorial, whose exploiters more often than not liked to use "vegetable" in their advertising.

Occasionally, too, this Nature or Vegetable School sought public confidence by claiming that their remedies were the work of Quakers, a sect reputed for honesty. There was also at least one concern formed to sell Shaker Remedies. Shakers were an offshoot of Quakers, and had the same reputation for honesty as the parent group.

Then there were the aggressive eclectics who claimed any and all medical knowledge as their own. These were the go-getters, the mass-production men of the period. They might begin with one registered-name medicine which they built up by repetitious and blatant advertising until it became almost a generic word; then, when the nostrum was rolling high, they added one or several items until they had what was popularly known as a complete line of Family Remedies, good for man and child, internal and external.

Lastly, and comparatively few in number, were the "drugless" healers, the engineers of health whom the American Medical Association came in time to designate as operators of "mechanical fakes." The most sensational of these drugless miracle workers was also the most successful, and came into being almost with the Republic itself.

The United States Patent Office opened for business in April of 1790. It waited only a little more than six years, or until the 17th day of February, 1796, before it had to consider, for the first but not last time, the matter of therapeutics, when Dr. Elisha Perkins appeared before the Commissioner to pray for recognition, and was granted a patent carrying with it the exclusive right for seventeen years to manufacture what he called his Metallic Tractors.

Dr. Perkins was no itinerant "Indian doctor," no suddenly conceived fraud, but one of New England's most highly regarded physicians. He might have been termed an eminent practitioner, like his father, Dr. Joseph Perkins. Elisha had been one of the founders of the Connecticut Medical Society. His practice in Windham County was large. He had done no little surgery, at which he was most skillful, and it had been from this field of his profession whence had come the idea that resulted in his application for a patent.

During operations Dr. Perkins had noticed that when his metallic instruments were brought into contact with muscles, the muscles contracted; he had "witnessed the cessation of pain when instruments were used to separate teeth from the gum prior to extraction."

Reflecting on these things, he determined to apply to medical practice the principles discovered by Luigi Galvani commonly known as animal electricity.

Dr. Perkins's tractors came in pairs, and consisted of two metal rods, some three inches long, made of brass and iron, rounded at one end, pointed at the other; half round on one side, flat on the other. With these implements the patient was to extract the disease from his body by stroking the affected part first with one, then with the other tractor. The directions for use varied with the malady.

More than a year before he approached the Patent Office, Dr. Perkins reported his discovery to the Connecticut Medical Society but gained, says one account, "little encouragement from his professional brethren." He was not wholly discouraged, but went promptly to Philadelphia, the American metropolis, where he performed public tests of his tractors in hospitals. The results are said to have been most successful. Congress being then in session, many of the prominent men of the country were attracted. One report has it that George Washington purchased a set. Chief Justice Ellsworth was sufficiently impressed to give Dr. Perkins a letter of introduction to incoming Justice John Marshall. At least three distinguished professors said in writing that they "believed in tractoration." Within a few weeks Dr. Perkins and his tractors developed into a public sensation perhaps never before known in the American medical field.

The professional brethren of Dr. Perkins were not happy. Two of them secretly made several sets of tractors which, though they looked like the patented set, were made of lead, of slate, and even of bone; yet, when used by patients, they cured whatever was ailing. In 1797 the Connecticut Medical Society expelled Dr. Perkins on the ground that he was "a patentee and user of nostrums." Whether or not the society members knew it, Dr. Perkins was also something of an ironmaster; he had been making the marvelous rods himself, in a small furnace "concealed within a wall of his house."

The expulsion must have been a blow to the doctor's pride, but it had no effect on the by then national enthusiasm for "Perkinsism." Dr. Perkins did not in any way guarantee the infallibility of his method. He merely recommended it for "Rheumatism, Pleurisy, Some Gouty Affections, etc., etc.," but stopped short of "the headaches that arise from drinking to excess." The fad was still at its height in the United States when the inventor's son, Benjamin Douglas Perkins, Yale College, 1794, went to England and opened an office in London.

The English were no more immune to Perkins's tractors than the Americans. Business thrived. It was thriving five years later when Dr. Elisha Perkins, who remained home to care for the American trade, announced a new remedy for yellow fever. This, too, was a simple specific: common vinegar dosed with muriate of soda; and Perkins had sufficient faith in it to go to New York City, during an outbreak of the disease, to prove its worth. Faith, however, was not enough. The cure seemed to have no effect, and Perkins himself contracted the fever and died of it.

In England, meanwhile, the Perkins tractors were increasingly popular. The younger Perkins published a book about them, and established in London the Perkinean Institution. It tells something of the status of tractoration that the institution was formally opened with the Right Honorable Lord Rivers as president and with Sir William Barker as vice president. Some five thousand patients were treated there before the fad passed. It seems probable that the fad wore itself out rather than that it succumbed to the attacks of medical men, like Dr. John Haygarth who, in 1800, published a treatise entitled "On the Imagination as a Cause and a Cure of Disorders of the Body."

The younger Perkins soon returned to the United States, where he died in 1810. By then tractoration was generally considered one of the follies of the past; yet this did not mean that galvanism was dead. Many an incipient quack must have read what Dr. Haygarth wrote about the connection between imagination and disease and cure. Within a little while, the fortunate people of the United States could buy one of Dr. Christie's galvanic belts and bracelets and even a galvanic fluid for the cure of all nervous diseases.

There seems to have been no complete stoppage in the galvanic business. As late as 1916 United States Patent No. 1190831 was issued to a Dr. F. C. Werner for his Galvano Necklace, which was advertised by the Cosmas Pharmacal Company as "the latest discovery for the relief of goiter by mild electric treatment." The Galvano Necklace did not bring on a national fad in the manner of Dr. Perkins's tractors. It was simply one of the later galvanic devices to be patented, and it seems not to have had much success. The field of mechanical nostrums had been taken over in large part by "Dr." Hercules Sanche, who called himself "The Discoverer of the Laws of Spontaneous Cure of Disease." We shall meet him later.

The fad of Dr. Perkins had pretty well died out in the United States, though not in England, when a Dr. Steers, then located in New York City, reached back into the mists of Swiss medical history for a name to describe his universal liniment. This was extensively advertised in American newspapers as Dr. Steers' Chemical Opodeldoc. The elixir's name originated with Dr. Paracelsus (1493-1541), described by the Medical Society of the City of New York as "that patriarch of quacks." Of his own version of Opodeldoc Dr. Steers said it was "remarkably pleasant to smell." It was a reliable specific for sprains, rheumatism, and whatever else came to mind under "etc. and etc." In case of "Sudden Head-Aches, it is Equal to any of the Volatile Essences."

This seems a modest claim. And though one was warned to "Look for Dr. Steers' name on the Label" because "None other is Genuine," the name Opodeldoc was in the public domain and Dr. Steers was only one of a long line of healers who used it. Robert Browning wrote a narrative poem about Dr. Paracelsus whose Opodeldoc soon went into doggerel, into plays, songs, and folklore. One of the first outdoor advertisements I recall was O-P-O-D-EL-D-O-C painted on fences in northern Vermont and New Hampshire. I do not remember whether Dr. Steers, or any of a dozen others, was sponsor to this particular brand. But the very name had something about it that stuck in memory. It was applied to favorite horses, oxen, and mules. It was applied to local "characters" as a humorous name. Many a melodrama had in its cast an *Old Opodeldoc*, a comedy part for relief from the play's dramatic violences.

Thus it was that Dr. Steers met a good deal of competition. A Dr. Fahnestock operated in the Midwest with something he called his Celebrated Vermifuge and Liquid Opeldoc (*sic*) which "could safely be administered to the tenderest infant." In the early 1820's New England newspapers carried a "Card to the Public" announcing "an improvement in a well known composition." This was J. P. Whitwell's Chemical Embrocation, or the Liquid Improved Opodeldoc, which contained "three of the most important articles in the whole circle of medicine never before employed in any other Opo-

deldoc." One may believe that by this time opodeldoc had become
a generic term for a liniment. But there were healers who dared to
depart from it and to strike out with new external remedies like
Mexican Mustang Liniment, Wolcott's Pain Paint, and Cram's Fluid
Lightning. Here was something named with imagination.

Cram's Fluid Lightning was nothing to treat lightly, and some
curious or envious healer took the trouble to have it analyzed, to find
it composed of "Oil mustard, oil cajeput, oil cloves, sassafras, ether,
tinct, opium, and alcohol."

Alleged Indian doctors were so numerous in the early nineteenth
century that one printer saw a chance to follow James Fenimore
Cooper into popularity by bringing out a book of the red man's
medical wisdom. This work was signed by "The Celebrated Indian
Doctor, John Mackentosh, of the Cherokee Nation," who, said his
publisher, Seth Holderwell, had "devoted his whole life to curing
diseases of the indigent." This good man treated dropsy with milk-
weed roots. His remedy for "fever" was a strong tea brewed from
alder and oak bark. He took cancer in stride with his prescription of
"berries of Poke Weed."

No matter who was responsible for the Indian recipes in publisher
Holderwell's book, the name of John Mackentosh surely is an oddity
in this school of medicine. Later practitioners, no few of whom were
credited to the Kickapoo tribe, included doctors named Chief Many
Horns, Chief Iron Bull, Chief Crow's Nest, and even Chief Sitting
Bull, whom American history remembers for his ability in a field
other than medicine.

By the time the small and most unfortunate Kickapoo tribe had
been libelously selected to father this quackery, the Indian medicine
business was being operated largely by corporate concerns. In the
early days, however, it was carried on in most part by individual
fakers such as Old Doc Hashalew who said he had formerly been
"Professor Popple, the Indian Healer," and claimed to know the
"Secret Arts and Herbal Virtues of the Great Indian Chiefs of the
Seneca and Cayuga tribes."

Just what this itinerant quack had done as Professor Popple and
why he publicly changed his name is not clear, though possibly he
wanted to rid himself, as Doc Hashalew, of the stigma of having, as
Professor Popple, performed as a fire-eater and magician at fairs,
muster days, and celebrations. In any case, as Old Doc Hashalew he

took to the towpath of the still incomplete Erie Canal because it was the best highway available from 1818 on. It was also free from the burdensome imposts of the turnpike tollgates. Travel by towpath was illegal for the public, but it was almost universal in the years when the canal was building, and in lesser degree later. The pathmaster had too much territory—fifteen miles—to be an effective deterrent.

Old Doc Hashalew's product, which he advertised extensively in Central New York weekly papers, was Hashalew's Elixir of Life. It was the cure-all type. It could be taken internally and externally. Nothing was beyond its therapeutic powers, and its discoverer more than intimated, in advertisement and lecture, that his Elixir brought a man's system up to the virile point and kept it there.

Such were the benefactions to be conferred by one who had learned the secret arts and herbal virtues of the Great Indian Chiefs of the Seneca and Cayuga tribes. One is quite ready to believe that Old Doc Hashalew's practice was enormous compared to that of lesser medical men of the time. But these fellows were trying hard.

For instance, there was the Medicated Oil Silk Bandage made and promoted by Benjamin Morang, who did not claim to be a physician but who had provided this "Infallible Cure for Gout, Colds, Rheumatism, and Stiffness of the Joints." The curative silk, loaded with various medicaments, was cut into bandages to fit the affected parts. It could be had by mail or from agents, was simple to apply, and was manufactured at "Mr. Morang's residence in his Factory in Greenwich Street, Opposite Fort Gansevoort, New York City."

Other specialists of the period were offering Chambers' Remedy for Intemperance; and various specifics advertised as Potter's Catholicon, Wilson's Panacea, Columbian Syrup, and the Syrup of Salza of De Angelis, the last named recommended for the awful "Secret Diseases of Men." These medicines, so the Medical Society of the City of New York observed, were "worthless or worse," adding that they "afford a striking example of the human mind to resort to secret and mysterious agents for the removal of disease."

While these and a hundred more nostrums were fighting hopefully for dominance in the trade, Thomas W. Dyott of Philadelphia was on the way to becoming the first Patent Medicine King in the United States. Back in the 1790's he had migrated from London, where he had been an apothecary's apprentice. In Philadelphia he rented a small room and basement in which to manufacture a liquid shoeblacking at night. By day he cleaned and polished shoes. Long before Horatio Alger's birth, young Dyott was performing perfectly in the upward-and-onward tradition of an Alger hero. Just as soon as he had saved enough money, he opened a drugstore in downtown Philadelphia.

Dyott prospered. As early as 1815 he was offering thirteen patent medicines, advertising them extensively all over the Eastern states, and was tapping virgin territory in Indiana. In that year it required three full columns in the *Western Sun* of Vincennes to describe the marvels achieved by his thirteen medicines. No other house had as yet aspired to so complete a line of Family Remedies to care for ills so varied as a specific for gout, another for female disorders, and still others ranging from constipation to deadly consumption.

Because most of his medicines were in liquid form, Dyott needed bottles; so Dyott, being a sort of period Henry Ford, bought the well known Kensington Glass Works to supply his needs; and a little later added another 400 acres to his property along the Delaware River, and expanded the factories until he was making five grades of glass in five separate furnaces. Some 450 hands were employed. Dyott hired expert mold designers, and by mid-century was turning out bottles decorated with locomotives and the slogan *Huzzah for the Railroad!* His bottles also came in the forms of trees, flags, and "the likenesses of celebrities, including Dyott himself."

Dyott rightly considered himself a celebrity. At the glassworks he had established a village for employees and their families, a flowering of conscious paternalism which he called Dyottville, often Temperanceville. (No liquor was permitted there, though many of his medicines had a formidable alcoholic content.) He told the press that he wanted "to combine mental and moral with manual labor." Thus Dyottville had a library, a singing school, concerts, lectures, and a hospital.

Discipline went with paternalism, and the activities of employees were regulated by bells ringing for rising, hours for baths, for meals, including a sort of cracker-and-water-break during working hours; for "the hour of leisure after supper," for prayers, for night school. The discipline in both factory and village was fairly strict, though kindly, and the moral tone of the community enjoyed high repute.

Dr. Dyott, who had felt the need to add the M.D. to his name, went on to make a startling announcement: Henceforth his factories would operate on a twelve-month schedule planned in advance; rain or shine, through boom or depression, Dyott employees were assured of a steady income.

Prosperous and presumably happy Dyottville, however, was not to last. It was not the patent medicines that let it down; it was Dr. Dyott's grave mistake in founding the Manual Labor Bank, an unchartered institution which failed in 1836; with it failed the medicine business. Dyott was indicted, found guilty of fraud in connection with his bank, and sent to the Eastern State Penitentiary. But he was pardoned before expiration of his term.

The now aging man was still something of a wonder. Emerging at sixty-seven from prison, he managed to open his old drugstore again and, says one of his biographers, "again acquired considerable wealth." It is unfortunate that one does not know if Dr. Dyott was addicted to his own patent medicines. If he was, then no patent-medicine king could have wished for a more glorious testimonial than that of Dr. Dyott himself, who died in 1861 at ninety.

Dr. Dyott was well in advance of his time as far as patent medicines were concerned. At the height of his career in 1835 no other concern in the field compared in size or prosperity with his company. His success may have inspired no few of the manufacturers who went into the business in that early period, like Dr. Benjamin Brandreth, another Englishman, who came to New York and in the mid-1830's began to make and sell Brandreth's Pills so successfully that within a few years he required an entire block on Broadway for his factory and offices.

But the golden age awaited the end of the Civil War, the completion of the first continental railroad, and the rapid settlement of the West. Above all it awaited the coming of the popular press, the basic medium to spread the word of new elixirs, balms, and cure-alls. The lone pioneer might carry in his gear a token supply of Epsom salts and calomel, but he was ready for the handy bottled and packaged miracles of therapy that would come only in the wake of the newspapers. A likely thesis still awaits some energetic candidate for a doctorate who will assemble statistics relating the rise of patent medicines to the increase in the number and circulation of daily and weekly newspapers. The one followed the other, almost automatically, to the far end of the frontier.

PART THREE

The Vegetable Kingdom

1

The Sarsaparillas

Of all the herbs adapted from ancient folk remedies by the patent nostrum vendors of the nineteenth century, none was more popular than sarsaparilla—as a trade name. Even in 1850, before the business had grown to something like a national phenomenon, there were at least ten brands of sarsaparillas being advertised. Thirty years later sarsaparillas were legion, though by then most of the early brands had disappeared; and superior advertising, if not the quality of the medicine, had made best-sellers of half a dozen, of which the two outstanding brands, Ayer's and Hood's, were manufactured in Lowell, Massachusetts.

By the turn of the century Americans were dosing themselves with bottled sarsaparilla allegedly because it "eliminated poison from the blood and tissues." It seemed to be more popular in the spring than at other times of the year, for it "purified the system" of all leftover infelicities of winter, and rehabilitated it for the months ahead. Sarsaparilla never wholly conquered sulphur and molasses as a blood purifier; youngsters were still dosed with the dreadful if cheap mixture when their elders had become ready converts, at one dollar a bottle, to the dark-colored, fragrant liquid which, to cite one satisfied customer, "cheered while it cured." Another sarsaparilla addict observed, though he was never quoted in a testimonial, that one of the many admirable qualities of the several brands he favored was that its therapeutic powers were independent of weather conditions. He had never known a bottle of it to freeze.

It seems improbable that many Americans knew anything of the history of sarsaparilla, the botanical *Smilax*, described as a thorny vine widely distributed throughout the tropical and semitropical world. Nice old ladies and, for that matter perhaps nice old men,

45

would have been shocked to learn that sarsaparilla had been introduced into sixteenth century Europe as a treatment for syphilis. It was found worthless, and dropped. Then, two centuries later, its use was revived, not specifically as a remedy for syphilis but for what medical men term an alterative, or something that tended to change a "morbid state into one of health." In this manner sarsaparilla became a "blood purifier," a "medicine for spring."*

In their advertising the sarsaparilla men usually got in a mention or two of the word *vegetable* and spoke of the Laws of Nature which, it seemed, could not be broken with impunity, although infractions might be mended if the right brand of sarsaparilla were immediately and consistently taken aboard. One of the earlier exploiters of this "natural remedy" was a C. C. Bristol, who did not attach M.D. to his name but who was eloquent in the pages of his "Free Almanac" in praise of Bristol's Sarsaparilla which, so he wrote in 1846, had been in use for ten years, and had triumphed over the worst cases, bringing approval of the medical faculty. During that decade the Bristol product witnessed the fate of a dozen mushroom quackeries which went down to defeat "in the mire of their purchased puffery and misrepresentations." Meanwhile, Mr. Bristol pointed out, "ten years is at least to [sic] long for a hoax to live," but his sarsaparilla had survived splendidly and achieved a celebrity almost without precedent.

Mr. Bristol may have spoken true, yet whatever celebrity his compound may have won, it was soon challenged by Dr. Townsend's Sarsaparilla, which was "A Wonder & a Blessing"; and Dr. Easterly's Sarsaparilla, which was not only "Six Times Stronger" than any other brand but which within three years had cured more than 25,000 cases of disease, including "3,000 of scrofula, 2,000 dyspepsia, 1,000 gout and rheumatism, 2,000 general debility, 2,500 liver complaint, dropsy, and gravel; 1,500 female complaints; and 6,000 syphilitic or venereal coughs."

These are imposing figures. But Easterly had to compete with Dr. Radway's Sarsaparillian Renovating Resolvent, a name, surely, to

---

* Though it is known that the tropical species of *Smilax* was imported for use in American proprietary medicines, certain manufacturers managed well enough with the native "wild sarsaparilla," *Aralia nudicaulis*, the long aromatic roots of which look much like the true "official" herb.

give pause to invalids who were foolishly doddering along with a mere sarsaparilla.

Neither the trade names of these early nostrums nor their immense popularity could have meant much after a native of Connecticut named James Cook Ayer appeared to demonstrate the innate possibilities of a one-dollar bottle of the *right* kind of sarsaparilla compound. Here was the genius of *Smilax medica,* and also the rightful heir of the place recently vacated by the unfortunate Dr. Dyott, the King of Patent Medicines.

Fatherless from the age of seven, young Ayer was sent to live with an uncle, James Cook, an eminent citizen of Lowell, Massachusetts, who was responsible for his namesake's fine education. The lad wanted to be a physician. He was accordingly prepared by studying medicine with Dr. Samuel L. Dana, of Lowell, then sent to the University of Pennsylvania, where he got his degree in 1841.

Returning to Lowell, young Dr. Ayer bought Robbins's Drugstore with money borrowed from his uncle and which, it is worth noting, he repaid in three years. He had also devised a remedy for pulmonary ills which he registered under Ayer's Cherry Pectoral. He now began to advertise, then to build up a typical line known as Family Remedies. These included sugar-coated pills, an ague cure, a hair invigorant, and Ayer's Extract of Sarsaparilla. With every new remedy he doubled his advertising.

As early as 1857 it must have been evident that Dr. Ayer was well on the way to great things. In that year he moved his patent-medicine business into an immense building which grew steadily in proportion to the steady increase of his advertising appropriation. Alert to the changing times, he caught the vision of an enormous future for patent medicines in the Western movement set off by the end of the Civil War, by the first continental railroad then under construction, and by the offer of free land by passage of the Homestead Act.

In later years Dr. Ayer told an interviewer: "Earlier generations had lived in fairly close settlements, with doctors in their midst. But now Americans in the West were dispersed. Even on horseback a doctor could not carry enough medicines to meet the needs. The settlers must doctor themselves." Though he did not do so, Dr. Ayer might have commented on the state of the medical profession,

which, as late as 1870, left a good deal to be desired. In that year
the head of the Harvard Medical School was quoted to the effect
that "written examinations could not be given because most of the
students could not write well enough."

If, as Dr. Ayer put it, the new settlers in the West must doctor
themselves, he meant that these pioneers should have opportunity
to know the ready relief offered by his several nostrums, the leader
of which became and remained Ayer's Extract of Sarsaparilla. To
this end Ayer's advertising grew until, as early as 1870, he had contracts with 1,900 newspapers and periodicals. His annual output of
circulars and almanacs would "if laid end to end" stretch for 1,894
miles. He asserted that there was "hardly a village in far Australia
where his remedies could not be bought." To meet this demand his
factories were "daily making 630,000 potions or doses of Ayer remedies."

Dr. Ayer possessed abilities in other fields. A biographer wrote
that his versatility was "remarkable," for there was scarcely a machine in his factories that he "did not either invent or improve."
He ran his own paper mill in order that "his wrappers and labels
should be difficult to counterfeit."

Money rolled in faster than he could spend it for advertising,
and he used some of the surplus to buy large interests in several of
Lowell's textile mills. When he came to suspect that the Boston
and Lowell railroad was charging greedy rates to carry his sarsaparilla
and textiles, he chartered the Boston and Andover Railway Company, then built the line "to provide his factories with a parallel
and competing route between Lowell and Boston." It did not do to
tangle with this physician whose nostrums had made him one of the
foremost capitalists in Massachusetts.

Though he seems never to have lost the least interest in the
patent-medicine business, Dr. Ayer bought vast timber lands in
Florida and built sawmills there which he operated from Lowell.
He bought into iron mines in upper Michigan, and was soon
awarded patents for an ore-reduction process. At the time of his
death he was promoting a project to build an interocean canal between Panama and Tehuantepec.

Active though he was, Dr. Ayer may well have given some thought
to immortality, for in 1871 the town of Groton Junction was re-
named in his honor, and five years later a fine town hall, the gift

of his family, was dedicated there. "He died in 1878," says an obituary, succinctly, "worth many millions." In Lowell Cemetery, where he was buried, a massive lion marks his grave. It was a proper enough memorial, though unneeded, so long as the village of Ayer, Massachusetts, should stand.

What went into Ayer's and the other extracts and essences of sarsaparilla whose popularity waned ever so slowly after the attacks of Samuel Hopkins Adams and other crusaders? In its late eighties a trade magazine, *Chicago Druggist*, printed an alleged formula of Ayer's Sarsaparilla as follows:

Take of—
Fluid extract Sarsaparilla .... 3 oz.
          "   "   Stillingia .... 3 oz.
          "   "   Yellow dock .... 2 oz.
          "   "   May apple .... 2 oz.
Sugar .... 1 oz.
Iodide potassium .... 90 gr.
          "   iron .... 10 gr.

In 1911 the Connecticut State Agricultural Station analyzed nine proprietary sarsaparillas, to find they were "of a most complex composition, containing not only sarsaparilla but yellow dock, stillingia, burdock, licorice, sassafras, mandrake, buckthorn, senna, black cohosh, pokeroot, wintergreen, cascara sagrada, cinchona bark, prickly ash, glycerin, iodids of potassium and iron, and alcohol."

Commenting on this analysis, the *Journal* of the American Medical Association observed that "the only possible value of this combination of drugs is the cathartic action of the well-known senna and cascara sagrada, etc., the tonic action of the iron, the appetizing action of the cinchona, the very potent action of the potassium iodid, and the possible *desired* effects [italics added] of alcohol. It will be seen that the sarsaparilla is so overloaded that if it had any action it could not be found."

The *Journal* went on to speak of the "mistaken belief of laymen" in the therapeutic powers of sarsaparilla, which by itself was as harmless as it was useless, but that "potassium iodid can generally do harm in large doses, and may do harm in small doses."

At least a decade before these reports on sarsaparillas were published, the small James W. Foster Company of Bath, New Hampshire, had apparently come to the conclusion that common everyday sarsaparilla alone could not conquer all of the many diseases which "arise from an impure blood or low condition of the system." Thus early in 1898 the Foster Company announced Cloverilla, a "Powerful Blood Purifier that contains no opiate, but the best selected Honduras Sarsaparilla Combined with the Best RED CLOVER," then went on to list the twenty-six ills it would cure. Possibly because of a niggard advertising program, Cloverilla seems not to have enjoyed much if any success.

In an essay on the various sarsaparillas, the *Journal* of the AMA said it was extremely improbable that they had any value as a medicament. (This was perhaps as mild a rebuke as the medical association ever gave to a patent-medicine formula.) It could hardly account, even if widely publicized, for the decreasing demand for all sarsaparilla compounds in the past forty years. They are now (1958) comparatively rare as a medicine sold over the counter to the consumer. Possibly they were a victim of the war of Science against Nature; or possibly they were ousted by newer nostrums of no more value than sarsaparilla but promoted by advertising techniques more appealing to new generations. Patent medicines cannot be any more immune to fad or fashion than automobiles, whisky, or cigarettes. (How long is it since you saw a Pope-Toledo, a bottle labeled *Gibson's*, or a package of Perfections?)

When during the *Collier's* crusade Adams got around to investigating those remedies which he termed "The Bracers," he found Ayer's Sarsaparilla to contain considerably more alcohol than was justified simply to keep the liquid from freezing in northern Maine, where it was highly thought of. Another leading brand, Hood's Sarsaparilla, he noted, managed to defy winter with only 21 per cent alcohol.

Yet in another article Mr. Adams spoke well of the Ayer Company for "dealing fairly and squarely with the public." What brought such astonishingly good words from the hard-hitting reporter concerned another of the Ayer medicines which contained a derivative of opium. This was the Cherry Pectoral, and printed on its label, as required by the new law, was the proportion of heroin it contained. "More than this," wrote Mr. Adams, "Ayer prints the proportion of

every ingredient in the medicine. A full open formula." He went on
to say it was "pleasant to note a company which not only obeys
the law, but goes much further than the law required in open dealing." Then he turned from this unusual incident to the "surprising
and ugly disclosures" that had been forced from other vendors of
nostrums.

For instance, something called Dr. J. C. Fahey's Pepsin Anodyne
was packaged in a carton on which were printed in large type the
legend "Absolutely Harmless" and also the statement that "this
valuable preparation contains no laudanum or any injurious article."
However, the same carton showed on minute inspection one line of
very small type, so placed that when the carton was opened the line
was wholly invisible. What the tiny hidden letters spelled out was:
"Each ounce contains Chloral Hydrate, gr. 2½; Sulphate Morphia, gr. 1-10."

Observing that Fahey's Pepsin Anodyne claimed to "pacify the
most fretful child," Mr. Adams called Dr. Fahey "a very conspicuous scoundrel, even in the dope nostrum business." Which must
have indicated to his million or more readers that Crusader Adams
had quickly returned to his usual form, after being refreshed briefly
by the honesty of the Ayer Company.

2

The Celeries

In the materia medica of patent remedies celery occupied an insignificant place compared to sarsaparilla. This is understandable. Sarsaparilla, as indicated, began life as an allegedly absolute specific for sixteenth century syphilis and, if it failed as such, it nevertheless went on to success as a blood purifier. Celery, on the other hand, was claimed to be "good" for what were vaguely described as nervous diseases.

Nervous diseases were virtually an abstraction. But "poisons in the blood" were something the imagination could deal with. They had drama. Even a clod could comprehend and fear such enemies. Driving them out and purifying the blood was a proper regimen for spring, the time when all nature was renewing itself. With Man, *that* was sarsaparilla's job.

For these and doubtless other reasons celery waited in obscure places in the vegetable kingdom of patent medicines while sarsaparilla made fortunes for Dr. Ayer, Dr. Bristol, Dr. Easterly, and many more, including Dr. Townsend whose tonic made it possible for him to buy the home of Merchant Prince A. T. Stewart, described as the costliest mansion ever built in New York City.

But if the magic properties of celery were delayed many years from proper revealment, they burst full-bodied upon the patent-medicine world with the appearance of Paine's Celery Compound. The paternity of this remarkable nostrum is clouded, but not so the remarkable men who composed Wells & Richardson Company, of Burlington, Vermont, proprietors of this "Nerve Tonic and Alterative Medicine, which can justly be called one of the Great Things in the line of Aids to Health and Happiness."

Formed in 1872 to deal in wholesale drugs, the firm came to include the several Brothers Wells, together with A. E. Richardson and W. J. Van Patten. Of the brothers, all of whom had served in the Civil War, the most prominent was William, who commanded the leading battalion charge on Round Top at Gettysburg, and came out of the war brevetted a major general. He was known to later generations in the form of a vigorous, full-bearded cavalry officer, wearing a sword and, in spite of cast iron, striding confidently forward from his pedestal in Battery Park overlooking Lake Champlain.

Wells & Richardson were doing quite well as a wholesale firm when they purchased the formula of a celery medicine from a Burlington widow, a Mrs. Paine, and began cautiously to manufacture it. Paine's Celery Compound must have filled a need in this Land of Steady Habits where untold numbers of apparently self-reliant Vermonters were actually suffering from nerves.

The manufacturers, who from the first made no secret of the nostrum's ingredients, but who, like Mrs. Pinkham, printed the formula in their advertising matter, declared their Celery Compound to be made of celery extract, hops, and coca. Alcohol was not mentioned, although the firm planned that so good a medicine should neither spoil nor freeze by adding 21 per cent of pure spirits; but the coca content was stressed. This was described as "the famous medicinal plant" found in the mountains of South America which, long before the Spanish conquest, had been used by the aborigines and was considered by them to be an incomparable nerve tonic. They chewed its leaves and immediately "felt strengthened, their misfortunes forgotten." This was not at all astonishing. Of coca, medical dictionaries say it is "the source of cocaine and several other alkaloids."

Though it is best to leave the medical faculty to judge the effects of cocaine and alcohol combined, it is not too much here to say that Paine's Celery Compound made a host of people feel strengthened and cheered. By the 1890's imitations of it were on the market. Then or later these were registered variously as Celery Bitters, Celery-Vesce, Celery Crackers, Celerena, and even a soft drink or tonic named Celery-Cola. Sears, Roebuck had taken the nation's pulse and responded promptly with a house-brand Celery Malt Compound which it called "a Recognized Nerve and Brain Medicine."

None of these, not even Sears' which aided the brain as well as the nerves, was in the same class with Paine's. By the late eighties Paine's had burst national bounds and was going abroad. Its modest, even retiring sort of trade-mark was familiar to illiterates. The label showed nothing pictorial except a fine, healthy-looking bunch of common garden celery, over the leaves and stalks of which was imposed the trade name. (It is doubtful that a picture of the coca shrub would have been recognizable in the United States.) Here was the very essence of the magic word Vegetable, comprising Nature's Own Remedy, gathered in Field and Forest, which Wells & Richardson said was "A Permanent Cure for Nervous Diseases," along with an imposing list of subsidiary or related complaints.

In their advertising Wells & Richardson naturally used daily and weekly newspapers, the religious press, and both popular and quality magazines. In about 1883 they issued a neat pamphlet to be given away free at drugstores. It was here that this somewhat off-the-beaten-track concern showed originality. Entitled *Great Things, What They Are, Where They Are*, one quickly learned that "Health is the Great Thing in this life of ours," and two paragraphs later discovered exactly what was best to promote health. Then, with the pitch delivered, the booklet took up, with picture and text, the Seven Wonders of Antiquity; the Great Wonders of America; even the Great Lighthouses of the World, and on to the Great Bridges, Great Ships, Great Discoveries, Great Bells, Great Monuments, Great Diamonds; and a list of the Richest Men of Today.

Wells & Richardson were proud of their pamphlet, and mentioned that in preparing it "all the best cyclopedias, histories and atlases have been laid under tribute." Only then did they bring up the matter of their testimonials which were "undeniably genuine, and will warrant investigation." They closed with a less than subtle effort to connect the Great Things of Life with Paine's Celery Compound "which, as a Nerve Tonic and Alterative Medicine, can justly be called one of the Great Things" in regard to health and happiness. This became a sort of punch line.

All in all, Wells & Richardson's pamphlet was admirably intellectual when compared to the many patent-medicine almanacs a majority of which were little more than a combination of testimonials, descriptions of fatal diseases, and jokes straight from Joe Miller.

Now that a leading nostrum had been found, it would have been typical—in the business—if Wells & Richardson had proceeded to build up one of those complete lines of Family Remedies. Ayer,

Herrick, Hood; Jayne, Radway, and many another house had done so to their great profit. But these villagers of Burlington, Vermont, took a different tack. From the home of Celery Compound came a sudden burst of scintillating colors—Diamond Dyes, brilliant, durable, simple, and economical: "A Child Can Use Them."

Along with a blinding spectrum of thirty-three colors, all ten cents a package, came an advertising campaign staged by the now seasoned experts of Wells & Richardson. These were "the only pure, harmless and unadulterated dyes." One should beware of all other dyes which were made of poisonous and useless adulterations. Just why "Vegetable" was not used with Diamond Dyes is not clear. No matter, Diamond Dyes were a success equal to if not exceeding that of Celery Compound. And, though Wells & Richardson could not have guessed it then, Diamond Dyes were to outlast the Compound and other products of the company.

One might have thought, what with the tremendous popularity of Celery Compound and Diamond Dyes, that Wells & Richardson would have rested content. But they did not choose to do so. One day from their factory in the pretty lakeside city there came forth the first carload of Lactated Food for Infants and Invalids. This product was packed in square tin boxes, the label fairly teeming with: The Physician's Favorite . . . Sure Cure for Cholera Infantum . . . Perfect Nutrient for Invalids . . . The Best Food To Use in Partial Nursing . . . Unequaled for New-Born Infants.

Even then Wells & Richardson were not quite content to sit back and load freight cars of the Vermont Central and Rutland railroads with their Lactated Food and Celery Compound and Diamond Dyes. These were not big-city men. They were Vermonters, country boys reared in rural surroundings where cows were more plentiful than steers and butter was the leading product of the farms. Now there appeared Wells & Richardson's Improved Butter Color.

Though less a national than a local product, the Improved Butter Color found a ready market in all regions where during long winters dairy herds had only hay for fodder, and butter came pale from the churn. A few drops of Wells & Richardson's new product changed everything, and into the tubs and molds went December butter as bright as June's, the year round.

As to this product's genesis, I like to fancy some bitter, leaden day in a Vermont December, when a Mr. Wells or a Mr. Richardson contemplated the pallid spread on his griddlecakes, and his mind recalled the rich beauty of last summer's butter, and then, by a rapid association of ideas, leaped to the gorgeous Canary Yellow of Diamond Dyes. Could not something be done for the aesthetics of the American breakfast? I am sure a stout proposition could be supported connecting environment, climate, and industry alone on Wells & Richardson's great contribution to the herds of lovely Jerseys in Vermont.

Such was the complete if strangely assorted line of Wells & Richardson. Paine's Celery Compound managed to survive the terrors of the Pure Food and Drug Act, though it took a beating at the hands of Samuel Hopkins Adams. In his crusade, Adams put Paine's in the category he called The Bracers, or the alcoholic stimulators. In a chart illustrating one of his articles was shown the strength of three selected nostrums compared with the alcoholic content of whisky (50 per cent), champagne (9 per cent), claret (8 per cent), and beer (5 per cent). Of the three patent medicines, Paine's Celery Compound was a poor third, with 21 per cent alcohol. Peruna did much better with 28 per cent. And the all-conquering Hostetter's Celebrated Stomach Bitters ran to a staggering 44.3 per cent. All three remedies were about to suffer acute attritions as to claims of therapy, and also content of spirits. All three survived the Prohibition years, then began to decline, and Paine's Celery Compound disappeared.

Of the several estates in Burlington built from the enormous profits of Celery Compound and allied products, the most imposing was that of Frank Wells, a son of the Civil War hero. "It occupied the better part of a large city block," recalls Ralph N. Hill, a native of Burlington. "This mansion stood among sweeping drives, formal gardens, tall elms and maples. Mr. and Mrs. Wells often opened their swimming pool, one of the few in all Vermont, to neighborhood children. Mrs. Wells was a handsome, gracious woman. In her later years she invariably wore a large purple hat when out driving, and I can still see her and Mr. Wells passing our house in their Pierce-Arrow, which looked to stand a good seven feet high and was mostly of glass. They naturally had a uniformed chauffeur, and were attended at home by several servants including a butler."

(Something of The Gilded Age had at last come to this outpost in rural Vermont.)

"The Wellses, indeed," recalled Mr. Hill, "could be said to be the complete Moguls, for they bought an island in Lake Champlain to which they repaired in season in their yacht." They appear to have been the last of the second-generation of Celery compounders to pass from the scene. When they passed, so did their mansion, which fell into disrepair. The estate was subdivided into building lots.

Searching back into the history of Wells & Richardson, Mr. Hill came across some long-forgotten promotional literature that will give a sample of the expert advertising that leads, charmingly enough, from one to another, then to still a third of the company's products. "A lady," it begins, "uses some Diamond Dyes, and finds that they do more than she expected. This gives her confidence in the manufacturers, and when she begins looking for a food that will make her baby healthy and strong and hears that Wells & Richardson Company make Lactated Food, also prepare Paine's Celery Compound, she has confidence that this is a reliable remedy, and purchases a bottle."

This surely is the homey touch so often attempted but not always achieved by the ad boys of the time. It is also a distinct switch from the standard method of leading off with the Big Number, then going on to lesser products. And although Daddy or the man of the family appears to have been forgotten in this instance, one may confidently surmise that Wells & Richardson knew what Paine's Celery Compound could do for *him*.

3

The Lady of Lynn, Mrs. Pinkham

Of the hundreds of successful manufacturers of proprietary medicines only one became a legend. She was the most widely known woman of nineteenth century America, neither Louisa May Alcott nor Frances Willard, but Lydia Estes Pinkham, born in 1819 in Lynn, Massachusetts, who lived but sixty-four years yet achieved a celebrity that is as lustrous three-quarters of a century after her death as it was in her lifetime. The fact that more than $40,000,000 has been spent to run her picture and her message in the newspapers surely has some bearing on her celebrity, though not all by a good deal.

Young Lydia Estes was a child of her era. She taught school in her native town, an occupation for which she was eminently fitted, both because of a good education and an engaging personality and also because she was of striking appearance, being five feet ten inches tall, with reddish hair and fine dark eyes. She was a devout Grahamite, a worker for Temperance, Abolition, and Woman's Rights. In 1843 she married Isaac Pinkham, a widower. He was reputed to be a kindly and affable man, filled with various ideas to make money but of "no great vigor."

Vigor or no, children began to appear in the Pinkham household until there were three sons and a daughter. Meanwhile, Isaac tried farming, "trading," and the manufacture of many different products, including kerosene. Nothing worked out quite the way it should, and the family, though never in want, lived sparingly and were not even able to have a hired girl in a period when hired girls were common enough in New England villages. Yet, by a pleasant irony it was one of Isaac's several follies that led directly to the Pinkham fortune.

Never a man to refuse a friend, Isaac had signed a note for one

George Todd, a Lynn machinist, and had to make good on the note to the extent of twenty-five dollars. The best Todd could do as reimbursement was a formula which he described vaguely enough as a "cure for the weaknesses of females." This Isaac turned over to Lydia who had an active animus for physicians, especially those of the calomel-and-bleeding school.

It is worth knowing that Lydia had been much impressed with the ideas of Dr. Jacob Bigelow, of Harvard Medical School, who had published *American Medical Botany*, and *Discourse on Self-Limited Diseases*, the latter work embodying the proposition that many disorders if left to the natural recuperative powers of the patient would disappear more rapidly than from dosage with drugs. Lydia had long been brewing home remedies for herself and her children. She now tried the Todd formula herself. It was pretty good, she thought, but she could better it. At her elbow, these many years, had been her own copy of Dr. John King's *The American Dispensatory*, a massive compendium of botanic lore, the handbook of the eclectic school of therapeutics. Like any good eclectic, either cook or physician, she subtracted from and added to the Todd formula. Among the additions were two items, True Unicorn (*Aletris*) and Pleurisy Root (*Asclepias*).

Now she had the "finest remedy of her experience," and she gave it away, gallons of it, in the neighborly manner of small-town America. There was no thought of *selling* it. That is, not until 1873, when the nation-wide panic wiped out Isaac Pinkham's latest effort, a real-estate promotion. The Pinkhams were now virtually penniless.

Whether or not the Pinkhams held to the favorite Yankee belief in the "interposition of Providence," this was the very time, almost the very hour, when two strangers drove up to the Pinkham home "in a handsome carriage" to inquire about something called, so they had understood, "a vegetable compound." The only detail marking the transaction as extraordinary in any way, so the late Miss Jean Burton, Mrs. Pinkham's incomparable biographer, points out, was that these visitors were not only willing but anxious to pay for the remedy. "To the accompaniment of considerable embarrassment," says Miss Burton, "a price of five dollars for six bottles was set."

Was it the hand of Providence? The compound not only had its first sale, but even its name. Less than two years later Lydia E. Pinkham's Vegetable Compound was making a stir in the drugstores of New England, and heading for a dizzy success such as few if any patent medicines have known.

Even so, Mrs. Pinkham's remedy had hard going until she and her highly competent sons and daughter began to advertise. Then it began to sell in such quantities that even son Daniel, the most enthusiastic of the lot, was continually astonished. The Pinkhams were a closely knit family and they turned all of their remarkable energy and high intelligence into one channel. Sales often threatened to swamp production until much later the first unit of what was to become the immense main factory went up in Lynn, where some 450 employees were eventually needed.

Until her death in 1883, the advertisements were written by Lydia in close collaboration with her sons and daughter. It is not too much to call them inspired. Consider: "A FEARFUL TRAGEDY, a Clergyman of Stratford, Connecticut, KILLED BY HIS OWN WIFE, Insanity Brought on by 16 Years of Suffering with FEMALE COMPLAINTS THE CAUSE. Lydia E. Pinkham's Vegetable Compound, The Sure Cure for These Complaints, Would Have Prevented the Direful Deed."

Such tragedies were common, and what clergyman or, for that matter, what layman would oppose his wife's need for something that would prevent her from committing a capital crime? For another thing, Mrs. Pinkham's checks for advertising were notably prompt. The Vegetable Compound did not, however, depend solely on horror stories and on quick payment for services rendered. Mrs. Pinkham herself composed a four-page folder, *Guide for Women*, which described, in language plainer than that of a family physician, the physiology of the female and the many disorders she was heir to. The author's tone of quiet assurance, some of which doubtless came from her intelligent use of Dr. King's *Dispensatory*, proved most effective. Two Pinkham sons, their knapsacks loaded, managed to distribute an average of 3,500 of their mother's *Guides* daily in Boston, and did even better in Brooklyn. These were not dumped in bundles in drugstores; they were distributed one by one at individual homes, and at the many doors of tenements.

The Pinkham *Guide for Women* turned out to be a basic item of the Compound's success. Reprinted over the years by the millions of copies, and enlarged, by 1901 it ran to sixty-two pages in five languages, and its back cover showed an enormous manufacturing plant described as The Home of Lydia E. Pinkham's Remedies. On the front cover was the comforting likeness of "Yours for Health, Lydia E. Pinkham."

By this time Mrs. Pinkham's was the best-known female face in the United States. For a quarter of a century this face, "so full of character and sympathy," had been consistently on view in the press. The fortunate newspaper first to run it was the *Boston Herald*. Dan Pinkham had dropped in one day and, acting on impulse, asked what it would cost to run his mother's picture as an advertisement. "On the front page," he specified. "Sixty dollars," said the man in the *Herald* office. It was a lot of money, but it happened that Dan had just collected that amount from a drugstore. He placed the order and paid the cash.

The effect can be termed nothing less than electrifying. Within twenty-four hours several Boston wholesalers, who had been getting along with one dozen bottles at a time, each ordered one gross. Next week the picture went into the paper again. The results were such that, after a family conference, young Dan Pinkham went back to the *Herald* to offer the paper a $1,000 mortgage on the Pinkham home as security for $1,000 worth of front-page advertisements. Never again was there the least doubt as to the road to success. "Here," as Dan remarked, using a favorite Yankee superlative, "Here was a real stem-winder!"

The next thing was a trade-mark. Advised by William H. Gove, a young lawyer soon to marry the Pinkham daughter, Aroline, Mrs. Pinkham decided to patent neither her formula nor her process, but to register her trade-mark under the copyright law. If imitators chose to use her formula, let them; they would have to name it something other than Pinkham's Vegetable Compound. Exclusive rights to a patent would expire at the end of seventeen years, after which anybody could appropriate it, as witness the melancholy case of Pitcher's Original Castoria, one of the early American patent medicines.

Thus the Pinkham Vegetable Compound was, like most other so-called patent medicines, technically a proprietary, with a trademark protected by registration. The Pinkham trade-mark was a portrait of Lydia E. Pinkham. Whether or not by design, the portrait selected in 1876 was inspired, as Miss Burton pointed out, to the last detail—"the neat black silk dress, the tortoise-shell comb, the white lace fichu fastened with a cameo brooch."

Mrs. Pinkham's mature face was handsome, sagacious, composed, and kindly. Here, aged fifty-five, was everybody's dream grandmother.

In that day, a majority of grandmothers were able to perform miracles with home remedies which, one should bear in mind, were simples. Simples were *vegetable* drugs. Vegetables were Nature. Nature cured all ills. Who, indeed, was Nature but Omnipotence?

Mrs. Pinkham's picture went into folklore along with the medicine. When Queen Victoria died, many a small-town newspaper in the United States, hard-put for illustrations, merely routed out the signature and ran Mrs. Pinkham's portrait over an obituary of the good queen. The same likeness allegedly served when death removed Lucretia Mott, Carry Nation, Mrs. James G. Blaine, and even Miss Lizzie Borden, formerly of Fall River, Massachusetts. Once, so the story went, a make-up man on the *Boston Herald*, deep in liquor, set the likeness of Mrs. Pinkham at the top of every column clear across the page. *That* was a startling morning for *Herald* subscribers. And the Pinkhams, though they had not ordered such profusion, gladly paid for the space, and reckoned the money well spent.

By the late seventies Mrs. Pinkham, who had no little insight into psychology, began to reply, without interposition of secretary or machine, but in her own copperplate hand, to the thousands of letters that came from readers of the *Guide for Women* in all parts of the country, asking her advice. Both of her major biographers say that much of Mrs. Pinkham's advice was sensible, perhaps much the same as would be given today by a psychiatrist. Of even greater value to many of her correspondents was the direct and wholly unsentimental way in which she described the phenomena of puberty, conception, birth, and the menopause. "Her physiology," as Miss Burton observes, "was accurate and she used (this was rare) the correct scientific terms for the parts and functions of the body. Ignoring the prevailing morass of superstition and unhealthy mystery, she did a realistic and lucid job."

Mrs. Pinkham's advice on problems apart from sickness of the body was on the whole, as Robert Collyer Washburn remarked, "wise, kindly, and generally shrewd," and cites the example of a young married woman greatly anxious "for a quick cure" because she wanted to become a mother. Mrs. Pinkham wrote her: "Wait, do not be in haste to bear children; build up your health in this general way I have indicated, and the desired result will be brought about." To another correspondent Mrs. Pinkham wrote that "sterility is not always the fault of the wife—many husbands are sterile. The spring of the year is the most favorable to fecundity. The repose of the woman on the bed after the act of generation also helps conception."

Although at first Mrs. Pinkham unaided was able to reply to all queries, the volume later became too great, and she asked for help from daughter Aroline and the wife of a Pinkham son. Mrs. Pinkham herself continued to read all letters and to note on each the reply to be made; and the younger Pinkhams became so expert in her lore that they could answer themselves, still under Lydia's supervision. Still later, female clerks were trained. Mrs. Pinkham was determined that this feature of the business should be perpetuated. And so it has been. "As far as there can be continuity in human institutions," wrote Mr. Washburn in 1931, "it is to be found here in the group of antique females in the correspondence department of the laboratory at Lynn, who still today answer in strictest confidence all questions of all comers."

While his mother, sister, brothers and in-laws combined to run the factory and its several departments, young Dan Pinkham developed into a sales force of remarkable power. Almost without fail people liked him. Among his many friends was Charles Nelson Crittenton, the New York City magnate of the wholesale drug business. Was ever a Horatio Alger hero better chosen than this dedicated and hustling son of Lydia E. Pinkham? Mr. Crittenton not only went more than once to visit the Pinkhams at their home in Lynn, but placed immense orders for the compound.

What mattered it to young Dan, brought up on Universalist teachings, just then tinged with the theories of Charles Darwin, that Crittenton was rather boringly orthodox in religion, that he believed the world to be flat? This merchant prince was buying—and selling—more Vegetable Compound than any other wholesale druggist in America. A little later he became known as the Merchant Evangelist, and founded an organization for "saving unfortunate women," named the Florence Crittenton Mission. One is tempted to some graceful analogy connecting the saving of unfortunate females in both moral and medical categories.

Dan Pinkham died at thirty-three, a martyr, said a Lynn obituary, without exaggeration, "to the cause of the great business he had helped to start." Will Pinkham, another son, died two months later, aged almost twenty-eight. The remaining son, Charles, and daughter Aroline formed a corporation in which they were presently joined by Aroline's husband, William H. Gove. In 1883 Lydia E. Pinkham died, to be followed six years later by Isaac.

Death could remove the Founder, but the Vegetable Compound went on to new and greater glories, with the younger Pinkhams and the Goves often fighting each other yet closing ranks to meet all enemies. They were also agreed on one other thing; that their advertising manager, John T. Wetherald, was a genius. So he must have been. He not only caught the fine flavor of the late Mrs. Pinkham's prose, but was more subtle and markedly more genteel, as befitted the new times.

Under Mr. Wetherald's bold promotion the Compound captured Canada, Mexico, Spain, China, and other foreign parts, where weak women grew less weak than of yore, or at least were much comforted in their weaknesses. There was one bad moment in China when it was discovered that only married women were buying the Compound. Investigation showed that the trouble lay in the Chinese name for Vegetable Compound which had been most ineptly translated as "Smooth Sea's Pregnancy Womb Birth-Giving Magical 100 Per Cent Effective Water." This not only filled the bill, but was a far from subtle warning to those who did not *want* such effective water.

There was another bad moment in 1902 when the *Ladies' Home Journal*, which had abjured all patent-medicine advertising and was now attacking patent medicines by name, reproduced a Pinkham advertisement which more than intimated that Mrs. Pinkham herself still lived and was giving advice to women who wrote to her. Beside the reproduced ad, the *Journal* ran a good clear photograph of Mrs. Pinkham's gravestone in Pine Grove Cemetery at Lynn, with the date, May 17, 1883, indicating her death twenty-two years before.

After a momentary slump, the sales of the Vegetable Compound soared to new heights. Ten years later it was selling a little more than twice the amount before the attack.

Mrs. Pinkham had long since entered American folklore. Ten years before the *Journal's* attack, Eugene Field, the wit and newspaper columnist of the *Chicago Daily News*, had connected her with the *Journal's* noted editor Edward Bok. Bok and Field were close friends, and the fact that Bok was unmarried appealed to Field's sense of humor. So did Bok's widely known opposition to all patent medicines. Then, one remembered day, the *Daily News* ran a story, written by Field though not for his column, which appeared as a straight news story in the paper's general content. Field also had it put on the Associated Press wire.

In the dull factual manner of news writing, the story said that Edward Bok, famous editor of the *Ladies' Home Journal*, and Miss Lavinia Pinkham, granddaughter of the late Mrs. Lydia E. Pinkham, of the patent medicine, were engaged to be married. The account went on to describe Miss Pinkham as young, good-looking, and talented, and hinted at her wealth. Still all unsuspected, even by his own or other papers, including those of Boston, Field followed the sensational announcement with a second story, this one announcing Bok's secret arrival at a Boston hotel, and the sailing for Paris, to buy her trousseau, of Miss Pinkham.

The hoax was soon discovered, though not before Bok, sworn enemy of all patent medicines, was fairly swamped with telegrams and letters. Bok was understandingly flustered and vexed. There was not, however, any complaint from the Lydia E. Pinkham Medicine Company of Lynn.

If the *Journal's* attack had little or no effect on the Vegetable Compound, neither was its sale seriously injured by the uncomplimentary remarks about it made by Samuel Hopkins Adams. The claims on the label, true enough, were notably reduced; the alcohol content was cut from 18 to 15 per cent. The Compound's great curative properties, however, seemed to be in no manner changed. At the present time (1958), it appears as if the happy users of it are getting not merely a mild dose (13½%) of alcohol, but a surprisingly good herb remedy, as indicated by independent analysis which reputedly showed an estrogen content.

Women still sing Mrs. Pinkham's praises in print. Men sing them in bars and clubs:

> Oh, we sing, we sing, we sing of Lydia Pinkham,
> And her love of the human race.
> How she sells her Vegetable Compound,
> And the papers they publish her face.

Even physicians are not immune to the charm of the likeness on the registered trade-mark that still appears, as it has these eighty-odd years, on each and every bottle. They have been heard at medical society conventions to chant the Lydia Pinkham song in full voice and with no little harmony.

The Golden Age of Quackery

PART FOUR

Manhood Was Lost

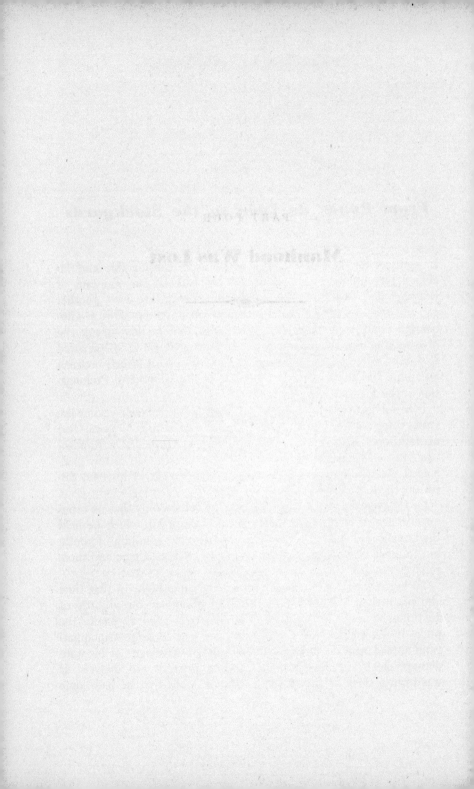

1

From Ponce de León to the Stockyards

In spite of his legendary labors, which were considerable and included the discovery and exploration of Florida, the fountain of youth eluded Ponce de León. Man was obliged to wait another 340-odd years before Dr. William M. Raphael set up shop in Cincinnati, Ohio, with the glad, glad tidings that *he* had drunk the invigorating cordial of its waters; and was now, in 1858, prepared to discuss confidentially at his office, 24 East Fourth Street, between Sycamore and Main, what he described as the Wonderful Prolongation of the Attributes of Manhood.

It is not to be thought that other men had not been seeking the same thing during the intervening centuries. Indeed, some had made so bold as to intimate they had found it, though Dr. Raphael paid them no heed, not even to deny their claims. He merely challenged the world to produce anything comparable to his own discovery; Dr. Raphael's Cordial Invigorant.

Of Dr. Raphael the lay historian may be certain only that no other quack, then or later, could match the low esteem in which he held the human intelligence, not only in regard to the fountain of youth, but to many another hoary myth which, in 1858, had here and there survived the hard wear of centuries.

To begin with, Dr. Raphael's Invigorant came high. In that time and place three dollars was a great deal of money for a bottle of anything; so much so that the proprietor felt need to justify the price. It was only a few months since he had come to Cincinnati from abroad, and his pitch included a sort of travelogue of his wanderings, chiefly in the East, the land of mystery and marvels. It was from a sheik of the Bedouin tribe of Arabs that he had come by the recipe of the Cordial Invigorant, a specific, he said, which for many years and with unvarying success had been used for producing and restoring sexual competency.

Getting down to cases, Dr. Raphael identified the sheik as Ben Hadad who, when he presented the doctor with the formula, was himself 109 years old, yet erect and active. By "active," Dr. Raphael did not mean merely that the aged sheik could walk. Not at all. "When I last saw him," said the doctor, "he had a babe on his knee, born to him only a week before by one of his female slaves." The vigorous Ben Hadad attributed his continuing interest in such things wholly to the Cordial Invigorant. "By then," added Dr. Raphael, "his children by his several wives numbered seventy-seven."

Although one might have thought that Ben Hadad's experience indicated the panacea to be potent enough, Dr. Raphael said that "in its Arabian form it was infinitely less powerful and certain in its operation than it has since become under the magical influence brought into requisition in its manufacture by the mightiest of modern Astrologers." By which he meant Dr. Raphael himself.

Three dollars a bottle? Were ever Balm in Gilead and a written "Guarantee of Parental Joys" offered for so little? And lest innocent bachelors miss the point, Dr. Raphael raised his voice a bit and called italics to aid: "The Cordial stimulates the sluggish animal powers to healthy action, and with vigor comes *natural desire*. It brings the system up to the virile point and *keeps it there*."

What he called his Galvanic Love Powders occupied a lesser position than the Invigorant in Dr. Raphael's pitch, but not because of any doubt as to their potency. "Courtship may fail," he observed, "devotion may fail; wealth, beauty, all ordinary inducements to love may fail, but these powders *never*." They had been revealed to him, naturally enough, "while sojourning at Teheran, in Persia, a country where Love is the great aim and end of life . . . and where in harems the means of its development are thoroughly understood."

The formula for these love powders was invented by one Zerlina, a "beautiful slave of the present Shah, who was anxious to secure the undivided affection of her lord." She succeeded, then informed the Shah of the charm she had used and its ingredients." It was only because Dr. Raphael "had cured his Highness of a severe bilious fever that the Shah, who already had enriched him with presents, also gave him the recipe, saying at the same time no human could resist it."

So, here in prosaic Cincinnati, at 24 East Fourth Street, was this essence that "creates love as infallibly as the dew and sunlight promote vegetation." For some reason or other the price of the Galvanic Powders was not listed. And the doctor could not give purchasers a Certificate (testimonial). Ethics prevented. The "names of persons applying for this article are considered a sacred trust never to be divulged under any circumstance."

It is impossible to know how Dr. Raphael made out with his monumental pitch for the lost-manhood trade. There seems to be no record that his code of ethics attracted attack by a medical society. Perhaps local physicians considered him beneath their attention if for no other reason than that he described himself in print not only as a physician but as "the renowned Astrologer, Philosopher and Magician." That he was out to get both a local and a mail-order trade is clear from his advertising, which stressed his ability to diagnose and cure by post. That he was appealing to the least sophisticated is also clear; he was operating on approximately the same medical level as that of charms, conjures, and the High John magic of voodoo.

It is abundantly clear, too, that Dr. Raphael had, no more than Ponce de León, found the fountain of youth. Two decades after Cordial Invigorant passed from the scene, the Lost-Manhood and the Secret-Diseases-of-Men racket had grown into organized big business. By the turn of the century it was progressing along two general lines. There were the mail-order operators who diagnosed, treated, and cured sufferers by way of the post office or express; and the museum operators who might also use the mails but who depended chiefly on the walk-in trade at the "free anatomical educational museums" they maintained in the Skidroad or Bowery-type districts of towns and cities. There were also, of course, both lone pitchmen and traveling medicine shows offering various wares, switching as it pleased them from special or all-purpose liniments to Vital Sparks and other suggestively named nostrums.

The appeal (the pitch) of the medicine shows seldom rose higher than that perfected by Dr. Raphael. The mail-order houses, however, sought to capitalize on the "new scientific discoveries" in the field of medicine. As for the museum crowd, they went after their naive clients with the plain and fancy horrors displayed in their street-level waxworks.

Of the many mail-order concerns specializing in the apparently unlimited supply of Weak Men, none had a more fetching pitch than the Packers Product Company with offices in the San Diego Building, Chicago, whose literature and stationery declared that its business was the manufacture of Orchis Extract, and that Orchis Extract was specifically for Weak Men. If weak men did not happen to be familiar with Classic Greek, and hence missed the promise implicit in "Orchis," they surely could fathom the significance of the Packers Product Company's graphic letterhead.

Here was revealed the unmatched sagacity of the company's promoter: full across the top of Packers Product Company's stationery was a picture of Chicago's vast Union Stockyards. In the middle distance was the plant of Armour & Company. This was not one of those "artist's conceptions," but an actual photographic panorama of the famous stockyards; and *there* loomed the potent name of Armour, one of the Big Four of American meat packing.

It is important to bear in mind that the meat packers had achieved the reputation of almost complete utilization of the animals they killed. Armour & Company, for instance, were making buttons from bones, glue from feet, combs and ornaments from horns, curled hair from tails, fur from wool, while the fats went into soap, the blood into fertilizer. Though it possibly belonged to folklore, it was widely believed that the Big Four packers had not overlooked the possibilities for utilization of the reproductive organs of male cattle and sheep.

If the connection between the teeming slaughter pens of Armour & Company and an extract advertised by the Packers Product Company as "the Greatest Known Treatment for Weak Men" was still not too clear to the slow-witted, the company's literature casually mentioned Orchis Extract to be "a substance from the testicles of rams."

Although the name of no packing house appeared in Orchis Extract literature, except of course for the panoramic letterhead, where Armour was spelled out in huge letters across one side of the big plant, the alert men of Armour & Company were not pleased. They protested to the United States Post Office Department, whose agents set about to look into the personnel and background of the Packers Product Company.

The Post Office men were not surprised to find that the moving spirit of Packers Product was an old acquaintance. Fred A. Leach had "been in the mail-order business for many years" during which he had operated, first as Distributors Guarantee Association, then as The Vacuum System Company, then, in turn, as David Kuno, the Ausin System, and Wade Manufacturing Company. In all of these enterprises Leach was selling a device described as a "Vacuum Developer for Men." Fraud orders had been issued by the Post Office against one or more of Leach's concerns. And, now that Leach had abandoned mechanical therapy for "medical science," the Post Office issued still another fraud order against him in his new guise of Packers Product, which thereupon went out of business.

Within months Fred A. Leach was in business again, still in Chicago, at 11 West Randolph Street, which was the "Main Office and Mail Order Dept. of Organo Product Company." This time, however, he was without the splendid if phony connection with Armour. He was also tiring. After all, that superb imagination may well have spent itself. In any case, the text of Organo's come-on letter was identical, word for word, with that of Packers Product for Orchis, except for that panoramic view of thousands of rams in the slaughter pens, patiently awaiting their turn to restore the vigor and vitality of millions of Americans.

In spite of which, the Post Office, in August, 1919, issued a fraud order against the Organo Product Company.

It is not to be supposed that the imaginative Fred A. Leach would long be permitted to enjoy a monopoly of his alleged connection with Armour & Company's unlimited supply of rams. His Packers Product Company was still a new thing in the male debility trade when a still newer outfit came into the market under style of the American Animal Therapy Company of 152 Lake Street, Chicago, which offered "Lymph Compounds" and various other items allegedly derived from animals whose species were not described in the literature.

The Animal Therapy Company was a new corporation, but its promoters were old hands, being Dr. James M. Rainey and Louen

V. Atkins, who for many years had operated as Men Specialists in the mail-order field, using the same Lake Street address for two concerns—the Dr. Rainey Medicine Company and the American Home Treatment Company. The partners had frequently quarreled over methods of conducting the business. Late in 1909 their differences became so acute that Rainey withdrew from partnership, but not from 152 Lake Street. On the next floor below Atkins, who retained the Dr. Rainey Medicine Company, the American Home Treatment Company, and the American Animal Therapy Company, Rainey opened for business as Dr. James M. Rainey, Inc.

It was a handful for Chicago's letter carriers. And the complications inherent in the situation were too much even for the ex-partners. Two concerns using the Rainey name at the same address meant trouble. Rainey and Atkins accused each other of opening the "wrong" mail. Then, on the afternoon of September 16, 1910, matters came to a head. Said the *Record-Herald* next day: "As a dramatic climax of a quarrel that was to have been carried into the courts this morning, Dr. James M. Rainey yesterday shot and killed Louen V. Atkins, head of the Rainey Medicine Company, in the offices of the corporation, 152 Lake Street. After killing the corporation chief, Dr. Rainey calmly walked back to his own office in the building and telephoned the police to come and arrest him." Atkins died in an ambulance on the way to Cook County Hospital.

Two days later a coroner's jury was convinced Rainey was justified in killing Atkins. The physician was released. Evidence indicated Rainey had gone into Atkins's office about a disputed letter containing five dollars. Atkins reached into the drawer of his desk where he was known to keep a revolver. Rainey drew pistol and shot him full in the forehead.

That the several Atkins concerns were doing a good business was evident from a witness who declared that "the shooting caused a panic among" the *thirty girls* employed by the medicine company. Other witnesses said both Rainey and Atkins used lists of names of prospective clients which they purchased from letter brokers. They both sold the original letters of their own clients to brokers.

The *Journal* of the American Medical Association took no little satisfaction because "the sordidness and general disrepute of the mail-order medical business has been brought to public attention." The editor thought that occurrences like the Rainey-Atkins affair "turned the spotlight of publicity into the dark and noisome pit of quackery and made clear the miserable fraud inseparable from it." Doubtless they did, yet the *Journal's* editor said he did not think that "the hapless victims" of quacks like Atkins and Rainey would remember very long "the sham, the ignorance, the utter disregard for the patient" shown by mail-order doctors.

Even while the *Journal's* editor was composing his little homily about one quack shooting another, the *Chicago Tribune*, aided and abetted by the American Medical Association, had begun an aggressive campaign against the numerous "medical institutes" in that city.

For Men Only: The Medical Institutes

By the end of the nineteenth century "medical institute" was almost a generic name for a type of specialized quackery, whose field was the Secret Diseases of Men. Whether it was staffed by one man or twenty, the faculty members were men's specialists. The institute might or might not have a correspondence department to treat patients by mail. It was almost certain to maintain a front called a Museum of Anatomy, advertised as Educational and Free. Known to old-timers in the trade simply as The Store, no other pitch equaled the fascination which the anatomical museum had for young men and unsophisticated males of all ages. It was the old reliable, sure-shot deadfall of walk-in quackery.

The ideal spot for a museum was the waterfront of a city, or the area near a railroad station, or whatever part of town was most frequented by itinerants. There it stood and leered from amid the fifty-cent hotels, the ten-cent lodging houses, the shooting galleries, penny arcades, employment offices, saloons and other dives seeking the custom of sailors, loggers, harvest hands, of miners, laborers, and farm boys out to see the world.

The medical institute's consultation rooms might be on the second floor, but the museum must be at street level. In its window was a waxworks display of eye-arresting quality; and leading back into the building was a short corridor lined with glass cases of human figures to show the early stages of various diseases of men. After ten or twenty feet the corridor opened into the museum proper, and the prospective patient suddenly found himself in a large room facing approximately one hundred wax effigies. These displayed the *later* stages of the more or less Secret Diseases of Men.

He was an unusual man indeed who did not, as he moved around the museum, begin to feel small chills chasing each other up and down his spine. He may, as a boy, have seen the pictures in his school physiology purporting to show the progressive hell through which a drunkard's stomach moved from healthy pink to an ominous mottled black and purple. But they were no sort of preparation for the horrors now confronting him.

It is improbable that realism in any other art form has quite equaled that of the talented worker in wax or papier-mâché and bright colors. No actual corpse is so striking as a wax corpse done by a master. And no other wax figure, not even a corpse, could exceed the horror that emanated from a standard fixture of the anatomical museums known in the trade simply as The Boy. As the museum visitor moved from one exhibit to another, he eventually came to a glass cabinet completely dark inside. If he paused a moment, the inside automatically and instantly came ablaze with electric light, and the fearsome face of an idiot boy leered out hideously at him. Above this terrible apparition was a warning: LOST MANHOOD.

It was time now for the "floor man" to go to work. His cold sharp eyes had been watching the tip, or crowd, to judge which were live ones or potential marks. The visitors' reactions to The Boy were often the deciding factor. If favorable, the floor man approached the by then well prepared customer to ask a few questions in a most sympathetic tone, then to lead him upstairs to the medical institute where the eminent specialists had their consulting rooms. Because the wages of floor men depended largely on their persuasive talents, the visitors selected for the trip upstairs were not likely to get off the hook for less than five dollars, and often paid ten or even twenty dollars for "consultation and medicine."

At least one chain of men's specialists had an extra-powerful chamber of horrors upstairs, next to the consulting rooms, which was brought into play if at the last moment the victim hesitated to become a paying customer. This chain, operated by the Reinhardt Brothers, of whom more presently, was also noted in the trade for having conceived one of the most splendid attractions ever used in connection with a Museum of Anatomy. This was in the street-level window of their Minneapolis store on Washington Street near Pioneer Square.

It was a remarkable waxworks scene called The Dying Custer. Flat on his back in mid-window lay the commander of the Seventh Cavalry. That he was still among the living was clear from his blue-

clad chest which, owing to a concealed apparatus, heaved slowly up,
then down, as if from the measured breathing of him who was
about to enter the legendry of the American West. No more ghastly
or effective stopper of pedestrian traffic could have been imagined.
There was a hypnotic quality about it. Young men and old stood
as if transfixed, breathing deeply in unison with the expiring hero
who had made his last stand, and his last mistake, on the banks of
the Little Big Horn.

The aforementioned Brothers Reinhardt, together with their numerous relatives, comprised a crew of medical-institute operators as
hardy as they were imaginative. "The Dying Custer" was only a
sample of the talents which, within little more than a decade,
brought them into controlling ownership of between thirty and
forty institutes, each with a fine museum, in the Midwest. There
were three brothers: Wallace A. and Willis F., twins, and the elder
Frank A. H. Reinhardt. Wallace was a graduate (1896) of the College of Physicians and Surgeons, Minneapolis. Willis, though often
referred to as "doctor," seems not to have had a degree from any
recognized medical college. Frank was not even called doctor. As a
young man he had followed the trade of blacksmith.

At some time in the nineties the Twins opened in Minneapolis
their medical institute, which quickly became so successful that the
Hennepin County Grand Jury was moved to investigate its practices; and in July, 1900, the Minnesota Board of Medical Examiners
revoked the license of Dr. Wallace Reinhardt. Whereupon the Twins
sold the institute, complete with Custer, to their elder brother,
Blacksmith Reinhardt, and immediately took off for Europe.

The Reinhardt twins found travel invigorating and educational.
In 1901 they returned to the United States, this time to settle in
Milwaukee, Wisconsin, and to open two modest medical institutes,
one styled The Leipzig Doctors, the other The German-American
Doctors. Neither corporate name was likely to be semantically harm-
ful in Milwaukee. The two young men had ambitions for greater
things; and a year later they and various in-laws incorporated the
Wisconsin Medical Institute, with offices in the Alhambra Theater
Building, Milwaukee, and began to advertise as specialists in the
diseases of men. Office hours took into consideration the afflicted

workingmen of eastern Wisconsin; the doors were open from eight to eight.

Blacksmith Reinhardt, who had managed to keep the Minneapolis institute running, was now imported to Milwaukee where all business matters were conducted in his name. Business was responding to extensive advertising, in two languages, in such volume that the Reinhardt Twins could not begin to handle it. They started the practice of hiring young M.D.'s just out of college, with preference given those who spoke both English and German. Within another two years still more help was needed, and an outfit was incorporated as The Master Specialist by J. M. Ruffner, William Hageman, and M. C. Wolf. The first two were brothers-in-law of the Reinhardts, the third was an employee. The president was L. J. Reinhardt, wife of Wallace. The secretary was F. A. H. (Blacksmith) Reinhardt.

It was a tight, cozy family group of varied talents fit to take charge of the several departments, the Electric Belts, Trusses, Collections, Politics, and so forth. In so far as possible they kept the Reinhardt name out of the public eye. The austere Vandyked specialist pictured in the ads was never given a name; he merely stood, one hand resting on an immense book labeled *Science*, the other arm thrown out in a gesture of welcome, while the text indicated a generosity well beyond average medical ethics: "I Make No Charge for Private Counsel, Call!"

In the realm of politics the Reinhardt interests were guarded by something named the Wisconsin Newspaper Association, whose secretary-manager was A. J. Wilson. Wilson was also on the Wisconsin Medical Institute's pay roll as "Advertising and Legislative Agent." It is getting a little ahead of the story, but one should know that when troublesome ex-patients of the institute took their complaints to the State Board of Medical Examiners, the officer employed by the board to investigate and secure evidence against the Reinhardts happened also to be in Reinhardt employ.

Despite this useful arrangement, so many complaints piled up that bills were introduced in the legislature to restrict the advertising and other practices of medical institutes. Though the Reinhardts gave generously to defeat such un-American laws, in 1906 a temporary restraining order was issued against the Wisconsin Medical Institute. Nevertheless, business continued as usual until the business manager,

Blacksmith Reinhardt, was hauled in for contempt of court and fined $150. Because criminal charges were being prepared against them, the Twins, their wives, and in-laws "had all disappeared and gone beyond the jurisdiction of the State of Wisconsin."

They had, indeed. They had taken residence in St. Paul, Minnesota, where at the corner of Seventh and Jackson streets they opened The Heidelberg Medical Institute, with the slogan "We Lead the Northwest in Curing Diseases of Men." The new institute's office hours were eight to eight. The connected Free Museum of Anatomy faced Seventh Street. In a supreme effort to match The Dying Custer, the Brothers Reinhardt produced several waxworks tableaux in their show window.

"Perhaps the nearest they came to the appeal of Custer," recalls a St. Paul newspaperman, "was a jungle scene in Africa. There were three figures. A white big-game, pith-helmet type hunter, and two native gun-bearers. Almost at the hunter's feet a huge snake coiled and uncoiled. The hunter moved forward. The snake struck. The hunter recoiled, yet did not lose his aplomb, for the pith helmet remained in place.

"This sequence occupied perhaps one minute, then the snake coiled again and struck. I remember that the gun-bearers never moved an inch. They stood with gaping mouths, fascinated at the drama. Like the office hours of the Heidelberg Institute, the animated waxworks operated from eight to eight. It was an eye-stopper, all right, though it seems not to have equaled Custer, who remained on view for many years, while the Heidelberg display was changed occasionally. I imagine that the hunter-and-the-snake deal was moved around the Reinhardt circuit in the manner of vaudeville acts on the Orpheum time."

While the main crew of Reinhardts were getting the new institute in St. Paul under way, the brave Blacksmith remained in Milwaukee to face the indecencies of the law. A court had issued an order permanently restraining both the Master Specialist and the Wisconsin Medical Institute, Inc., from doing business. The order was a little late. The alert Blacksmith produced evidence to show that both corporations had already been dissolved by a vote of their directors. Then, as soon as the court dismissed the civil proceedings, a new concern, the Wisconsin Medical Institute (not Inc.) opened for business at the old stand in the Alhambra Theater Building. The hours, one is glad to know, were eight to eight.

Next, the State of Wisconsin set out to extradite the Twins from Minnesota, to be tried on criminal actions for gross fraud and common-law cheat. After a lengthy contest the governor of Minnesota ordered the two Reinhardts surrendered, but habeas corpus proceedings defeated the move. The Twins stayed in St. Paul. Their Heidelberg venture was doing well. Their embattled brother remained on the firing line in Wisconsin where, for another two years, he continued "openly to defy not only the whole of the practice of medicine in the state," according to the American Medical Association, "but also the laws of the state and the authorities who were charged with the duty of enforcing these laws." Worse, Blacksmith Reinhardt came to be regarded by the public "as a victim of persecution" and was in the end, or on July 13, 1908, "able to compromise on the sole condition that he leave the state and agree not to defraud the people of Wisconsin any longer."

The compromise stipulated that none of the three Reinhardts, the Twins or the Blacksmith, would engage in any medical practice designated as an institute or corporation in Wisconsin, except that "Wallace A. is not prevented from practicing individually under his existing license."

Although their Milwaukee Institute and Master Specialist had been bringing the energetic Reinhardt group an estimated net income of $100,000 a year, the resolute family were not wholly cast down by this expulsion. Indeed, the four years after that event were to be fruitful beyond the dreams of most quacks and of all conventional physicians, even specialists. The Twins had built the Heidelberg Institute into a tremendously remunerative enterprise. Within a short time they opened another, named The Copenhagen, "Over Driscoll's Drug Store, Fourth and Brady Streets, Davenport, Iowa." Their ads led off with a new slogan: *Cured in Five Days $5*. The Twins must have felt assured of business, for in Davenport their office hours were radically reduced, being nine to five, save on Tuesdays and Saturdays when they stayed open till nine.

Back in the early Minneapolis days, the Reinhardts had become acquainted with Dr. E. N. Flint, whom they now engaged to help run the St. Paul Heidelberg. But they could not induce Wisconsin to issue Flint a license to practice. So the Twins prevailed on Flint to take charge of the new business they planned for Chicago.

This was the Vienna Medical Institute, 130 Dearborn Street, Corner of Madison, which Twin Wallace A. was to make the operating headquarters of perhaps the earliest and surely one of the biggest chains of men's specialists in the country. Bigness was in the air. Mergers were making big ones out of little ones. Such magnificent examples as Standard Oil and United States Steel showed what could be done. Competition was wasteful. Monopoly removed waste. The difference was pure profit. The Brothers Reinhardt were no more immune to the significance of trusts than they had been to the value of foreign names and Vandyke beards in their advertising.

What parts each of the various Reinhardts and in-laws were to play in building the Midwest medical-institute trust is not known. The Twins seem to have taken the lead. Where the Blacksmith was during the great years is regrettably obscure, but so stout a fellow must have been active and right in the middle of things. What is clear enough is that by 1912 the Reinhardt family had control and a majority ownership of medical institutes in seven states.

Unlike many manufacturers of patent medicines, the Reinhardts could see no commercial value in using their own name. But as the Vienna, Copenhagen, Heidelberg, Paris, and London medical institutes they were prepared to make men like new in Omaha, Nebraska; in Davenport and Des Moines, Iowa; in Rock Island, Peoria, Moline, Joliet, East St. Louis, and Chicago, Illinois; in St. Paul and Minneapolis, Minnesota; in St. Joseph, Missouri; in Gary, Hammond, Fort Wayne, and Indianapolis, Indiana; and, yes, in Milwaukee, Wisconsin. Other institutes in their chain rose and fell in smaller towns, but those were permanent fixtures until misfortune slowly caught up not only with the Reinhardts but with lesser rivals.

The Reinhardt chain was well organized. Each institute had a resident manager responsible to a triumvirate of directors to whom reports were sent daily in triplicate. These were Dr. Wallace (Twin) Reinhardt, St. Paul; "Dr." Willis (Twin) Reinhardt, in the Chicago headquarters; and an H. E. Johnson, who lived in Davenport and managed the two stores in Iowa and certain others in Nebraska, Missouri, and Illinois. Johnson was believed by employees to own a strong minority interest in the chain. There seems to have been no holding company. Exactly how profits were distributed is not clear.

In the Chicago office was a sort of instantaneous medical college

for the training of floor men to work in the museums of anatomy
that were a vital part of the institutes. One floor man and intern
recalled that his instruction occupied the best part of four days, during which Dr. Flint gave him a list of "medical lingo and other details of the business," then had him make himself familiar "with
300 wax models exhibiting diseases of various kinds in different
stages of development." Doc Flint thereupon "gave me a final examination and said I was ready for practical work."

The intern was shipped to the chain's institute in Gary. The
Gary store averaged forty callers daily. The new floor man managed
to hook his quota, which was set at eight by the manager, described
by the new employee as "an educated, cold-blooded and heartless
giant named Julius Sweizenthall."

The boss artist in charge of Reinhardt's waxworks department
was a Monsieur Brouillard, possibly a graduate of Madame Tussaud's
of Paris and London. He arranged a superb window for the Gary
store. It showed a nurse and doctor caring for a syphilitic baby. For
the store in Indianapolis he fashioned a group watching breathlessly
while a man worked "to resuscitate a nearly drowned person." It
proved most effective, possibly because, like the famous Dying Custer
up in Minneapolis, there was the same hypnotic repeated movement;
in this case the slowly pumping arms of the resuscitator. In a single
day, during the Indianapolis auto racing, The Drowning Man
hauled eight hundred visitors into the Reinhardt store.

Yet, for all their organization and discipline there was one thing
the Reinhardts apparently could not do—prevent their floor men
from talking out of class. Reporters of the *Chicago Tribune*, sent out
to pose as easy marks when the paper began its campaign against
medical institutes, soon had the floor men bragging of the amount
of business done, and telling with relish of the ease with which
healthy young men were induced to believe they had contracted
various diseases. The reporters also learned the ingredients in "our
popular come-back prescription" which according to one floor man
called for "four pounds of sugar, two and one-half pints of alcohol,
and Aqua Missourianas quantitat sufficiat ad cong II."

The floor man in the Gary store related how Manager Sweizenthall
had given him a "doctor-looking white coat" and suggested he let
his red whiskers grow, then trim them into a neat Van Dyke." He

did so, and found the effect most impressive. "I was told," he said, "never to say I was a real doctor, but if any of the customers called me doctor never to correct them." In good time the young fellow was dispensing medicine and preparing patients for "the electrical table." Once he caught the store's official M.D., an old alcoholic called Dr. Morse, going through a patient's coat and trousers while the patient was in the operating room.

Then, one day when Doc Morse and Manager Sweizenthall together were "digging around in the arm of a customer with a rusty needle, trying to strike an artery," the floor man felt he had had enough. He ran out of the room. In another instant the gigantic manager had him by the throat. "If you say a word about this," Sweizenthall warned him, "I'll kill you." The floor man took off his doctor's coat and left the store.

The *Tribune*'s series of articles, running through a period of two months, dealt not only with the Reinhardt stores but with other medical institutes as well as individual quacks. The campaign was effective in Illinois. The State Board of Health took action to revoke the licenses of many physicians who "had sold their services to these institutes." Federal authorities secured the conviction of others who had been using the mails for purposes of fraud.

Doubtless the campaign by the *Tribune* gave heart to medical societies elsewhere. It may also have pricked the conscience of many publishers of daily papers who for years had accepted the ads and the money of medical institutes. Yet the institutes did not disappear overnight. Several survived into the 1920's.

It was the steadily advancing pseudosophistication commonly attributed to automobiles and radio that gradually did away with the old-line medical institute and its museum of anatomy. If manhood was still lost on occasion, and secret diseases appeared, they might still be treated with nostrums, but the nostrums had to be advertised with a new kind of pitch. The Store, and even The Boy, were things of the past.

PART FIVE

Masters of the Monster Pitch

1

The Invalid's Friend and Hope

When Samuel Hopkins Adams was a youth in Rochester, New York, one of that city's most eminent businessmen was Asa T. Soule, proprietor of Soule's Hop Bitters, The Invalid's Friend and Hope, which by the late seventies was one of the six best sellers in the field of bottled therapy in the United States. By then, too, the Soule concern had opened branches in foreign parts, and added three sidelines to its Bitters. These were a Hop Cure for colds, a Hop Pad for upsets of the stomach, and "an Absolute & Irresistible Cure" for the victims of liquor, narcotics, and the tobacco habit.

Mr. Soule himself was a rather handsome man, astonishingly youthful for his fifty-odd years, alert of eye yet of pleasant manners, who was known to pay sixty dollars each for his tailored cutaway suits of conservative tone and style. His habits were said to be moderate, and it hurt neither his business nor himself, in Rochester, that he was a known Sabbatarian and a generous contributor to the Presbyterian Church. Mr. Soule seemed also to have a fine feeling for his relations with Rochester's long-established citizens. When Mr. Myron Adams, for instance, wrote Mr. Soule a letter commending his stand on the Sabbath, Mr. Soule responded by sending, with his compliments, a generous case of Hop Bitters to the Adams home. "Though my Grandfather was a militant foe of Demon Rum," wrote Myron Adams's famous grandson, "he was seldom without his three-a-day dosage of Soule's inspiring concoction."

Mr. Soule never chose to reveal the content of his remedy, though his advertisements consistently, if vaguely, stated Hop Bitters to be "no vile, drugged drunken nostrum, but the Purest and Best Medicine ever made. The greatest Blood Purifier, Liver Regulator, and Life and Health Restoring agent on earth, Tonic and stimulating WITHOUT INTOXICATING."

Asa Soule was born the eleventh child to a Quaker family. He had "inherited the commercial shrewdness of that sect without the handicap of its ethical standards." He had been a farmer, a patent-rights broker, a real-estate operator, and salesman for a cough cure, before he turned up in Canandaigua, New York, where he bought out the owner of Doyle's Bitters, an alleged extract of hops. Mr. Soule tinkered somewhat with the Doyle formula, chiefly to fortify it against the dangers of rigorous winter, and in 1873 moved to Rochester with what now was The Invalid's Friend and Hope. The much improved formula was just the ticket. Six years later Asa T. Soule was reputedly worth one million dollars.

What could a public-spirited citizen do for a town in which he had accumulated a fortune in half a dozen years? Mr. Soule looked around. He asked for advice. The city of Rochester, he was told, needed nothing so much as a rattling good professional baseball team. The local nine had done so poorly it had been disbanded at the end of the 1878 season. When the new season was about to open, nothing had been done to organize a team. "Must we go to Syracuse or Buffalo to see a game?" asked the *Democrat and Chronicle.*

Here was opportunity, and Asa T. Soule grasped it. At an emergency meeting of worried citizens, he announced that Rochester would indeed have a team in the league. Wildly enthusiastic response told him that here was the utmost benefaction an appreciative citizen could bestow. He forthwith bought the league's bankrupt Albany club, transferred it to his home community, and put the boys into splendid new uniforms of scarlet and gray.

Rochester was elated. What did it matter that instead of the city's name across the players' shirts there appeared the legend "Hop Bitters," or that the local field was rechristened Hop Bitters Park? Rochester had been saved the ultimate disgrace any real American town could suffer, which was to be without a baseball team. And when Hop Bitters Park was opened for the first game, Rochester's mayor delivered a warm address of welcome and the G.A.R. band delivered stirring music. What was more, the Hop Bitters nine won its first game.

It was a gorgeous beginning, yet by early July the Hop Bitters team had slid to ninth place in the league of nine. The *Democrat and Chronicle* was complaining, and asking editorially "Will somebody tell us what ails the Hop Bitters Team?" Mr. Soule responded, according to local talk, by doubling the pregame dosage of his tonic; and the players were inspired to climb into eighth place over Manchester, New Hampshire. In another couple of weeks, however, they were again in the league cellar, if only because the Manchesters, who had been having troubles of their own, disbanded.

What happened next is still obscure. Mr. Soule was charged, in the Troy and other papers—excluding Rochester's—with bribery and corruption, and after an embittered controversy he and his team were officially read out of organized baseball.

It was still only a little more than mid-season. Mr. Soule disbanded his team and organized a New Hop Bitters club, a wildcat team without league affiliations. He got a whiz of a new pitcher who not only was a left-hander but had only one arm. The new team could not be barred from nonofficial contests, and for the rest of the season it did well against Washington, Providence, Worcester, and also defeated Buffalo, Rochester's traditional enemy.

But Rochester was far from happy. Its team had done only fair, and by the very nature of its name and the business of its sponsor the Hop Bitters nine laid itself open to telling derision by the cruel sports-page writers of other cities. A Buffalo paper declared that "the Hop Bitters have already been challenged by the Castorias." From Amsterdam came the jibe that "Bull's Body Builders are billed to play Pierce's Pile Drivers, while the Worm Lozenges will tackle the winners." A Troy paper constantly referred to Mr. Soule as "the medicated sportsman." In Rochester the *Union and Advertiser* said, "Mr. Soule is very indignant at the Buffalo and other papers because they don't call his club by their right name." This had reference to vulgarities like The Rumbleguts, The Liverpads, and The Gambler's Friend and Hope, applied to the Hop Bitters boys.

When the 1880 season opened, Mr. Soule abandoned the Hop Bitters uniforms. The new shirts had Rochester spelled out. The team was officially named the Rochester Baseball Club, and restored to decency by admittance to a four-team league recognized by the National Baseball Association. It still did not do well. Mr. Soule finally gave up, and turned his interest to single sculling which, next to baseball, was just then perhaps the most popular sport in the United States.

Professional rowing was also a little more fraudulent than the baseball of that era, being controlled "in the interests of the lowest class of thieves, gamblers and cutthroats," according to a newspaper analysis. But Mr. Soule was induced to put up a $6,000 purse for a match race, to be rowed on Lake Chautauqua, and the press was soon building up the Hop Bitters Championship Prize Race. "In the character of a primitive five percenter," as Samuel Hopkins Adams told it, "Mr. Asa T. Soule exacted commission from railroads, excursion and sightseeing boats, grandstands, hotels and boarding houses."

The affair was a terrible bust, marked by the sabotage (by sawing) of one of the shells to be used, and the unique sight of only one man sculling in this "championship race." And when the "winner" went to the City Bank in Rochester, to collect the Hop Bitters Prize, he discovered that Mr. Soule himself had withdrawn the money. No race, no prize.

It seems probable that Mr. Soule's popularity in Rochester had been waning. So had that of Hop Bitters. A remarkable new remedy had appeared, Warner's Safe Kidney and Liver Cure, manufactured in Rochester by H. H. Warner, who had once been a manufacturer of safes. Being of a whimsical turn of mind, a picture of a Warner Safe appeared on the label of Warner's Safe Kidney and Liver bottles. Though Hop Bitters was a universal restorative agent, the United States was apparently undergoing a virtual epidemic of breakdowns owing to liver and kidney ills which did not respond to Mr. Soule's medicine. Warner's specific soon passed Hop Bitters in sales to such an extent that Mr. Warner, no less appreciative of Rochester than Mr. Soule, was moved to build on East Avenue a fine observatory for Lewis Swift (1820-1913), a local astronomer who had achieved an international reputation and was already honored here and abroad for the discovery of two intra-Mercurial planets.

The Warner Observatory was opened with fanfare, and Mr. Warner announced an award "of $100 for each new celestial discovery." While Lewis Swift settled down to bring further glory to Rochester —and to H. H. Warner—Mr. Soule pondered the possibility that culture, rather than a baseball team, was what Rochester really wanted. Well, then, he would endow the small University of Rochester with no less than $100,000. He went to see his friend Ernest Willard of the *Democrat and Chronicle*. "If there is a Warner Observatory," he said, "why not a Hop Bitters University?"

The newspaperman sat up in his chair. "Good God, no!" he cried. "People would call it Cathartic College. They'd bestow on you the degree of Bachelor of Booze. They'd make a guy of you in Latin, Greek, and Hebrew. Have you forgotten what the newspapers did to your Hop Bitters team?" This was plain talk, but it was wasted. Mr. Soule made advances to the university trustees. They turned him down "with an asperity that injured his feelings."

The rejection of Hop Bitters University, and the steadily falling demand for the universal restorative agent, combined to make up Mr. Soule's mind that his future lay elsewhere. Turning over $50,000 to his trusted nephews, Eugene and Lou Soule, he sent them west to seek out some underdeveloped region that might respond to the touch of a promotional genius. Within a short time the two young men reported that western Kansas looked ripe for a man of vision. Town boomers were operating catch-as-catch-can. A quarter-section could be bought from the United States Land Office for a few hundred dollars. The land could then be subdivided into town lots. Any old piece of the prairie could be declared to be a town, given a name, whooped up in the press, East and West, and a fortune made. If enough settlers came quickly, an alert promoter could clean up a million dollars before the pseudoboom collapsed. If enough settlers came and stayed, why, there was no end to the possibilities.

Asa T. Soule was as charmed with the prospects as his nephews. Like many another dedicated city slicker before and since, the Soules held the mistaken belief that Kansas, and all other great open spaces, were inhabited by wholly unsophisticated people—rustics who liked to buy gold bricks in whatever form they appeared. This was an error. Kansas in 1887 may have harbored a considerable number of simple folk unused to the ways of the larger world, but they were probably there because of the wiles of as sharp a crowd of promoters as ever platted a town overnight and then sold it as Metropolis complete with city hall, skyscrapers, railroad, streetcar lines, churches and schools. All of these, to use a favorite term, were "projected." In other words, incorporated illusions.

The scene selected by Asa T. Soule for his Kansas operations was Gray County, where three incipient towns had been feuding for the county seat. Cimarron had been so designated temporarily when the county was organized. The original promoters of both Ingalls and Montezuma had not given up, but were bending every effort to take over the seat of government just as soon as the first election could be held. Mr. Soule looked all three over, then bought up most of the real estate in Ingalls.

Possessed now of approximately enough land to have held both the New York City and the Boston of 1887, he turned his mind to many projected improvements. Being Asa T. Soule, these were no small affairs. First came a ninety-mile irrigation canal starting at Ingalls. Then he actually began laying track for a railroad from Dodge City to Montezuma, chiefly as a bribe for the later settlement to drop its contest for the county seat. Though nothing was done about a baseball team, Mr. Soule had not forgotten H. H. Warner's easy fame derived from education, and so here on the plains of Kansas he announced the founding of Soule University.

In the fall of 1887, as time for the Gray County election approached, Mr. Soule, having heard of the rowdy and even bloody county elections in Kansas and other parts of the West, took steps to guard the polls. To be captain of these good-government men, he engaged Bat Masterson, long the celebrated marshal of Dodge City; and with him Bat brought some able pistoleers, including Bill Tilghman and Ben Daniels. The election was orderly enough, according to Masterson's biographer, Richard O'Connor, and a majority voted for Ingalls as the county seat.

Cimarron had not, however, given up the battle. It would not even give up the county records. The controversy wound through the courts, and at last the Kansas Supreme Court found for Ingalls. Cimarron started an action seeking a rehearing of the case. Mr. Soule decided not to wait any longer. His agents were told to recruit a force of the toughest gunfighters available. Again the formidable Bat Masterson was chosen to lead the good-government men of Ingalls. Among his helpers were Jim Marshall, George Bolds, Ed Brooks, Neal Brown, Fred Singer, and Bill Tilghman, every one capable of holding his place in any collection of Western peace officers or, for that matter, in any collection of men seeking trouble.

What in movie Westerns is known as the walk-down, the climax, took place on a cold Sunday in January, 1889. The Ingalls mob invaded Cimarron. Masterson and Marshall entered the courthouse to throw the files out of a second-story window to their men waiting below in the wagon. Quiet Cimarron, enveloped in a Sunday-morning hangover, suddenly came to life. Several hundred men gathered

around the profaned courthouse. Shooting started promptly. The
Ingalls men in the wagon took off in a hail of lead, several of them
already wounded.

Up in the courthouse chamber, the beleagured Masterson and
Marshall put up a stout defense throughout the night and next
morning. "By noon on Monday," so Masterson's biographer wrote,
"they ran out of ammunition and had to surrender. Bat took off his
stiff-bosomed white shirt, now blackened by gunsmoke, and waved
it as a token of capitulation."

One man had been killed in the street. Several more were
wounded, and another had a close call when a bullet pierced his hat
and clipped a lock of his hair. "If my hair hadn't been standing on
end," he explained, "it wouldn't have got shot off that way."

A few years later, when it obviously didn't matter which town in
Gray County won the battle, Cimarron was awarded the county
seat. By then Gray County's total population was less than 4,000.
Cimarron could boast less than 800. Ingalls's count was officially
213.

Disillusioned with the unsophisticated West, which in one way or
another had taken his million dollars, Asa T. Soule returned to
Rochester to die. Because he had neglected to devise any funds for
the support of Soule University in Kansas, he left no monument.
Rochester did not erect one for its once favorite son. The Invalid's
Friend and Hope disappeared from drugstore shelves. Collectors
of antique bottles are only mildly interested in the rather handsome
amber bottles, with an agreeable bas-relief of the fruitful hop, which
used to contain Asa T. Soule's remarkable product. The market
price has never risen to above half a dollar each, no higher than the
current rate for the unadorned, utilitarian square face of the all-
conquering and justly celebrated Hostetter's Stomach Bitters.

2

Dr. Hartman's Peruna

By the time Asa T. Soule abdicated his Hop Bitters and Invalid's Friend, with the idea of founding a city in Kansas, one of the rising new patent medicines was Peruna. Empty Peruna bottles, unlike those of Hop Bitters, were never to be in demand as antiques. There were just too many of them. Peruna made fortunes for its exploiters beside which Mr. Soule's million was pretty small change.

In 1905 Peruna was one of the giants. It was made in Columbus, Ohio, by the Peruna Drug Manufacturing Company, whose founder and president was Dr. S. B. Hartman. The Peruna Lucky Day Almanac for 1904 shows on its pale green cover a sort of pictorial history of the marvelous growth of what Samuel Hopkins Adams called "the most conspicuous of all medical frauds." Four graphic scenes mark Peruna's steady progress to eminence.

The first is captioned "Where Peruna Was First Made." It is a tiny log cabin, thus indicating not only the imposing lineage of the remedy, but also its birth in what then and now is generally if mistakenly believed to be America's first contribution to architecture. Though Swedish immigrants brought it with them in 1638, when other settlers were living either in wigwams or in English frame houses, the log cabin quickly became the favorite abode of the American pioneer. Long before Peruna was born, the log cabin had also become the classic home where our Presidents were born. Nothing connected with this honest and strictly 100 per cent American structure could be other than of honest merit itself. The implication is clear enough: Peruna was born in a log cabin.

The second scene on the Almanac's cover shows a small frame building, two stories high, over the main entrance of which is the simple legend PERUNA. One tall chimney is smoking, telling of the activity within. The picture is captioned "Second Peruna Labora-

94

tory." Scene Number 3 shows steady progress. The factory is now of brick, three stories high, and with three chimneys, all belching. Yet these three early homes of America's fastest-selling medicine pale beside the picture of "Present Peruna Laboratories."

Here, covering two solid blocks of Columbus, Ohio, stands a tremendous plant. Beyond it is the towered and crenelated "Hartman Sanitarium," and still beyond this haven is another large building labeled Hospital Wards. It seems an odd location for a sanitarium. Two lines of streetcars are pounding by the doors, while from the factory just across the street rumble big wagons loaded high with what must be Peruna. The sidewalks are cluttered with pedestrians.

Inside the Almanac is a likeness of the founder of the enterprise, Dr. Samuel Brubaker Hartman. In a day when beards or at least mustaches were considered the badge of solid worth, he is smooth-shaven, thus daring convention. Dr. Hartman appears to have been unconventional also in diagnosis. To his way of thinking the all but universal trouble of the human race was catarrh. One line of bold black type at the top of every other page in his Almanac told how it was: Peruna Cures Catarrh of the Head; Peruna Cures Catarrh of the Lungs; Peruna Cures Catarrh of the Stomach; and so on down through the Liver and Kidneys, the Bladder, Epidemic Catarrh (or La Grippe), Pelvic Catarrh and, at last, Systemic Catarrh.

It was Dr. Hartman who discovered the wonderful formula he called Peruna. And because he was a veritable M.D., we must credit to him also the discovery that all or most ills stem from universal catarrh. If this diagnosis seems arbitrary, then all we can do, after reading the thousands of signed testimonials he published over the years, is to say either that several million people were cured of catarrh by Peruna or that the United States was inhabited by a race of hypochondriacs. Right here we come to the all but unknown name of Frederick W. Schumacher, "the fabulous merchandising genius who made Peruna a household word all over America."

Mr. Schumacher burst upon the world of Peruna in a most astonishing manner. The exact date is not now known, though local legend places it during the early nineties of the last century, a time when Dr. Hartman had moved into the building described in the Almanac as "Third Peruna Laboratory," and was struggling to get enough orders to keep his still small force busy. It happened suddenly. With no warning there came to Dr. Hartman an order, not for one gross but for one *carload* of Peruna. It was from a Mr. F. W. Schumacher of Waco, Texas.

How many gross of Peruna were needed to fill a freight car was something not even Dr. Hartman had figured out. But he knew what to do. He put his factory crew to working overtime. And then, because he was already indoctrinated with the great destiny of American business, Dr. Hartman got aboard the first train that would take him to Waco, Texas.

The rich story of Peruna is regrettably filled with barren spots. There seems to be no account of this most pregnant meeting of Dr. Hartman and Mr. Schumacher. What had caused the monstrous order for Peruna? What kind of business was the latter operating in Waco? Was Waco suffering an epidemic? All is vague. What is not vague is that on the spot Dr. Hartman engaged Mr. Schumacher to return to Columbus with him and to take charge of the promotion of Peruna. From that day on, one is quite ready to believe, Peruna began to fulfill its great destiny. In a little while, so overwhelming was the barrage of advertising developed by Schumacher, the "Third Peruna Laboratory" was unequal to the demands put upon it. Construction was begun on Scene Number 4 of the Almanac's cover. This in all its immensity was the Present Peruna Laboratories and Hartman Sanitarium.

In the Hartman Sanitarium were "all the great Water Cure Facilities of Karlsbad, Nauheim, Kissinger, and Vichy"; and these, according to the Schumacher advertising copy, were "Modified and Grouped Under One Roof for the treatment of heart disease, rheumatism, anemia, rickets, erysipelas, nervous prostration and paralysis." Worthy of note, too, said the ads and brochures that went out by the millions, in the Hartman Sanitarium "all regular examinations were made with the Dynamometer."

One is not to think that Dr. Hartman charged a fee for diagnosis. Free medical advice to all was his motto. The ever fatter Almanac, year after year, invited its readers to consider the "List of Symptoms which will be found in these pages." Mark them, said Dr. Hartman in his first person, and send them in a letter to me. He cautioned against cutting out the symptom list, or otherwise mutilating the Almanac, which "you may need for future reference."

For a quarter of a century no patent medicine in the United States used so much newspaper space as Peruna. No little of this space was given to testimonials. Perhaps Peruna copy was not quite so fetching as Mrs. Pinkham's, but the sheer bulk of it, its insistence, more than made up for its failure to catch that assured everybody's-grandma flavor of the Vegetable Compound's appeal.

But in the matter of testimonials Dr. Hartman was not content with the female nonentities who wrote to Mrs. Pinkham dead or alive. Hartman, or rather Schumacher, went after Big Names. Among the Big Names suffering from catarrh were congressmen: Ogden of Louisiana, Powers of Vermont, Dungan and Meekison, Ohio; Zenor, Indiana; Sparkman, Florida; Wilber, New York; Worthington, Nevada; Snover, Michigan; and Barham of California. Among the afflicted United States Senators were Butler, South Carolina; Rice, Oklahoma; Mallory, Florida; Thurston, Nebraska; Sullivan, Mississippi; and Call, Florida.

Governors often spoke fair if somewhat cautious words for Peruna, accompanied by their portraits. So did eminent statesmen and celebrated Army and Navy men. One of the latter, Admiral Winfield Scott Schley, a hero of the Battle of Santiago Bay, was much embarrassed at the national uproar which followed his signed statement in a Peruna ad:

"Mrs. Schley has used Peruna and I believe to good effect."

Though the admiral could hardly have said less, he had said too much already. For some reason, the poor man was set upon by editorialists, commentators, and writers of letters all over the country. He was abused most shamefully. The incident grew into a sort of Affair Peruna-Schley that is cited by social historians even today as an example of vulgarity in high places and of the brashness of patent-medicine exploitation.

But the Peruna exploitation did not lessen or change. Schumacher-Hartman developed a status value of testimonials and a systemic method of keeping their testimonialists in line that will be treated in a later chapter on such matters. For the present it need be said only that the attacks on Admiral Schley did nothing to decrease the sales. Neither did an attack by the influential *Ladies' Home Journal* aimed specifically at Peruna and two other nostrums.

Edward Bok, the *Journal's* editor, had long since announced that his magazine would not accept any advertising for patent medicines. In its number for September, 1905, he now ran a story and pictures to describe a "scientific experiment" conducted by the eminent

Dr. A. J. Read of the Battle Creek Sanatorium. The pictures show Dr. Read's apparatus, the purpose of which was "to test the alcoholic content of patent medicines." Four metal containers, holding three different nostrums and one of beer, were attached by rubber tubes to a gas burner and mantle. Heat was applied, the liquids simmered, and "the vapor gave bright illumination."

According to a chart accompanying the pictures, the results were as follows: Hostetter's Celebrated Stomach Bitters kept the light burning an even 4 minutes. Peruna was second with 2 minutes, 40 seconds. Lydia E. Pinkham's Vegetable Compound was third with 2 minutes, 35 seconds. The ration of standard lager beer was a poor fourth; with such slop the light burned only 20 seconds.

Mr. Bok could announce what he had long suspected—that a great deal of stuff bottled as medicine was nothing more or less than "cheap whisky." This may have troubled the conscience of many females of middle and later years who, according to Mr. Bok, were given to sipping patent medicines while they also worked faithfully for Temperance, but the exposé had no discernible effect on the three remedies, unless it might have caused a slight shifting of brands among the male population in favor of Hostetter's, whose label at that period declared it to contain "25 per cent of Alcohol by Volume."

All was going wonderfully well in Columbus, where Frederick Schumacher, a most personable man—a Prince of Pilsen type, according to one who knew and liked him—had become a prominent citizen, respected for the magic he had devised for Peruna, and beloved by Dr. Hartman, whose daughter Maribel he had wooed and won. It was a splendid marriage, and presently the Schumachers took up their residence in a castle the like of which was hardly to be seen nearer than Sewickley, Pennsylvania, where the young vice presidents of the new United States Steel Corporation had been building mansions.

This magnificent monument to the healing powers of Peruna was built to last. It still stands, in 1958, and I am in debt to Mr. Bill Arter, of Columbus, for his unmatched description of what one day soon may fall to the wreckers. "Mr. Schumacher," writes Mr. Arter, "gained wealth in a notoriously heartbreaking business. The mansion is the product of a period when architectural hysteria was dear to those who could afford its manifestations. The house itself and its huge adjoining coach house display nearly every beloved feature of the time. A square tower in front sprouts a smaller tower corbeled into its corner. Still other towers, ornate false façades, and soaring chimneys create a skyline of sharp finials. French and Italian details grafted onto lingering Gothic marble, green stone and slate, all combine to form a bewildering whole."

It was a castle fit for this prince of patent medicines. Its day and his have now passed; and Mr. Arter, obviously a man of feeling for Time and the mutations it brings to all things, takes a last look at the hulk of echoing corridors. "Steadily marched upon," he writes, "and passed by encroaching places of business, the great, gray-green mansion still stands aloof in its spacious grounds, behind the high iron fence around which so many stories have been woven. . . ."

It is not to be thought that Dr. Hartman was meanwhile living in poverty. He, too, built a palatial home, though of less striking appearance than the Schumachers' castle. The doctor also erected the Hartman Building, in the center of Columbus, housing the Hartman Theater, one of the finest legitimate houses still standing in Ohio. It was a fortunate community that could and did boast of two citizens like these. Yet, even while whole freight cars loaded with Peruna were leaving the factory every day, a tragedy of some size was taking form.

It will be recalled that Samuel Hopkins Adams had fired a salvo or two at Dr. Hartman and Peruna, and had published in *Collier's* a government order forbidding the sale of the nostrum on Indian reservations. "As a medicine," said the order, "something else can be substituted; as an intoxicant it has been found too tempting and effective." Mr. Adams put the matter more brutally. "In short," he wrote, "the internal revenue authorities bade old Doc Hartman either to put some real medicine into his drink or to open a bar." These unhappy events occurred in mid-1906.

Dr. Hartman decided it was best to comply. But first he must prepare his several million customers for the change. The Peruna company published a booklet in which Dr. Hartman was quoted: "For a number of years requests have come in to me from a multitude of grateful friends, urging that Peruna be given a slight laxative quality." The booklet then went into the third person to expand on matters, explaining that "Dr. Hartman has always been a strict temperance man himself, and when the government proposition was made to him that he must either manufacture and sell Peruna as an alcoholic beverage or change the formula he was shocked beyond all measure . . . He could not bring himself to engage in anything that looked like liquor traffic."

But something had to be done instantly, and what was done, according to a chemical analysis of the new Peruna of 1907, was to add a substantial dose of senna and buckthorn. The results were appalling. Once the new and improved Peruna had reached the grateful addicts, these poor people found themselves in what a learned man in the Pure Food and Drug Administration described happily as the Great Borborygmus Era.

Strong men in Bangor and Wichita cried aloud in perplexity that something obviously, and most terribly, had happened to their sovereign remedy. Sales of Peruna dropped alarmingly. They did not recover. No appreciable number of Peruna customers could have read Dr. Hartman's warning. They might read on the new label that alcoholic content had been reduced from 27 to 20 per cent, which was bad enough in itself; but that would hardly account for the truly ghastly reaction that now came in the wake of a dosage which before had brought only comfort.

Something would have to be done, and quickly. And it was. A new announcement was broadcast by the Peruna Company:

> Ever since the new Peruna was offered, thousands of people who had used Peruna as a family medicine for many years began to complain of the change. . . . The new taste acquired by additional drugs, the new effect that the drugs produced, was all strange and caused them to hesitate and some of them to be actually afraid to use it. Thus it was that the sale of the new Peruna fell below the sale of the old Peruna.

Indeed, it was time something was done, and Dr. Hartman put it on the line:

> The continuous requests of such a multitude of people have caused him [Dr. Hartman] to relinquish in so far that he allows the old Peruna (now called KA-TAR-NO) to be manufactured and sold as an alcoholic beverage.

In 1912 Ka-Tar-No appeared in a list of proprietary medicines, published by the Commissioner of Internal Revenue, for the sale of which a liquor dealer's license was required. It was one of 240-odd nostrums that could be sold legally only over the bar.

In 1912, too, Samuel Hopkins Adams contributed two articles to *Collier's* in which he reported on the changes made in patent-medicine manufacture and advertising brought about by the Pure Food and Drug Act. Of Peruna he noted that its claims had been radically reduced to what Mr. Adams called the "following confessions": "No one claims Peruna is a cure for dyspepsia. . . . It is not claimed that Peruna will cure rheumatism. . . . Peruna does not cure." That the curse of the Great Borborygmus Era was still strong was indicated by a statement quoting the proprietor "of a large wholesale drug house in the Middle West," who told Mr. Adams: "Peruna is nowhere. We used to get a carload, even two carloads a month. Now we hardly handle a carload in a year."

As for Ka-Tar-No, apparently it was not a lively number. Mr. Adams did not mention it.

Yet there was still some future for Peruna. As late as 1927, the American Medical Association observed that "this alcoholic nostrum seems to have taken on a new lease of life due to radio advertising." What the hucksters of the air were able to do for this once top seller of nostrums is beyond the province of this book. I think it is worth knowing, however, what the home-town people think of the late Dr. Hartman.

"Doctor Hartman," writes a long-time businessman and prominent citizen of Columbus, "was never called 'Doc' by local people. He was a tall man, well nourished and of the extrovert type. The Hartmans were accepted and liked by all the better people in the city, and held in high regard by the banks and other institutions." His numerous philanthropies are remembered. The Schumachers "lived in the grand manner and entertained lavishly," and though later divorced were always well liked. "Mr. Schumacher lived on for many years, alone in the great mansion save for Cartigan, his man Friday, and a cook whose name was Katurah." He died as recently as 1957, "leaving his fortune of about $50,000,000 to the Columbus Gallery of Fine Arts," according to local report. Peruna was not the sole source of this immense sum, for Schumacher had "also prospered as the result of a gold-mining operation in Canada." Yet it appears that a substantial share of his fortune came from his brilliant mining in the field of the all but universal catarrh, which afflicted so much of the United States before passage of the Federal Pure Food and Drug Act.

3

Favorites of the South

As early as the 1840's a few patent medicines of local manufacture existed in the Southern states, and at least one of them, Black-Draught, was already in wide use before the Civil War. In great part, however, the distribution of nostrums was a postwar phenomenon. It came into being with the appearance of thousands of country stores in a region where there had been virtually no stores outside the larger towns.

In prewar days peddlers had ranged the nigh impossible roads in two-horse buggies. Then, about 1866, began the sudden spurt, almost a fad, as one historian judged it, of storekeeping. These new merchants of village and crossroads were mostly ex-Confederate soldiers who, returning to a wrecked economy, could see little opportunity in the professions. They opened stores instead.

No matter the amount or the variety of merchandise, the new stores had one thing in common, a generous shelf of patent medicines. Three years after the war ended, the makers of Old Plantation Bitters were bragging in print that below the Potomac they were selling annually five million dollars' worth of their alcohol-laden product.

This immense appetite for nostrums had obviously been awaiting the easy availability of back-country emporiums; and now, among others, came Black-Draught, the wondrous medicine already compounded for years by Dr. A. O. Simmons, a Tennessee frontiersman of the time of Davy Crockett. On Dr. Simmons's death, the recipe for Black-Draught passed to his son-in-law, J. H. Thedford, who in 1856 had begun large-scale manufacture of it.

Thedford must have known just what his fellow Southerners wanted. From that day to this no other Southern patent medicine has enjoyed a greater sale than Black-Draught, a laxative equal to the standard diet of the rural regions. This diet, according to Thomas D. Clark, native historian, consisted chiefly of "fat meat, corn bread, hot biscuits, molasses and white gravy," which "clogged the whole system with poisons of constipation."

At about the time Black-Draught became supplementary to Southern food, one R. L. McElree offered a new medicine which he called Wine of Cardui and described succinctly as Woman's Relief. Here was something to challenge the Yankee woman of Lynn, Massachusetts, Mrs. Pinkham. Both Black-Draught and Wine of Cardui were selling well if not sensationally by the end of the war, when two Federal soldiers, Z. C. Patten and T. H. Payne, were mustered out of the Union Army at Chattanooga, Tennessee.

Patten and Payne decided to remain in Chattanooga. They formed a partnership to sell writing paper, blankbooks, and the miscellany common to stationery stores. They were doing well enough, but Patten, the more aggressive partner, had been eyeing the sales of Black-Draught and Wine of Cardui, both of which were made in Chattanooga. He bought the formulas. Then he organized the Chattanooga Medicine Company and began production.

The energy that Perry Davis of Rhode Island, the Ayers and Pinkhams of Massachusetts, and the Jaynes of Phildelphia were putting forth for their remedies, Z. C. Patten expended to place Wine of Cardui and Black-Draught on the shelves of the thirty thousand rural stores in the South. Both became virtual folk remedies, and have remained so for almost a century.

"Wine of Cardui for Women" and "Black-Draught for All the Family"—these were the messages, painted always in black and yellow, that crawled along nobody knew how many fences, and covered the sides of more barns than one would have readily believed. Indeed, the gracious agents of the Chattanooga Medicine Company stood ready to paint your entire barn, or your store, if you could accept the slogans and the combination of colors. (Mind the slogans or the colors? Why, bless you, mister, the Hand of Providence works in many ways. . . .)

It was evident, too, that the Hand of Providence also had something to do with Wine of Cardui itself, for on each of the millions of black-and-yellow cartons was the picture of a white woman standing beside a kneeling Indian maid. The latter was pointing to a tall, leafy plant, and speaking. "Take and Be Healed—The Great Spirit Planted It," she said.*

It is improbable that many of the users of Wine of Cardi recognized, if ever they had heard of, the plant to which the Indian maid was pointing on the label, nor did it matter: Indians knew all the God-given herbs, and that was enough. The plant was commonly called Blessed Thistle, known to the educated as *Carduus benedictus*, from which the nostrum derived its name. But it was the little squaw that gave importance to the scene on the carton. She, plus the promise set clear and bold beneath the picture spelled Woman's Relief.

With no trouble at all the agents of the Chattanooga Medicine Company were able to corral all the testimonials needed to keep the Cardui department of its factory busy; and though there was no Mrs. Pinkham, living or dead, to confide in, the women of the South were as filled with Female Complaints as those in the North, and just as subject to writing letters about their troubles and the miraculous cures performed. The Chattanooga Company's "Ladies' Birthday Almanac" was running full of the testimonials and portraits of Cardui's grateful friends.

The very nature of Cardui's purpose lent itself to imaginative advertising without limit. This was not so when dealing with Black-Draught. After all, this was a laxative. You could say it did its work well, but there were none of the veiled mysteries connected with Female Complaints. The copywriter could speak a good word, and honest, too, for Black-Draught's tonic effect (in its liquid form) if only because a generous percentage of alcohol made one feel better almost immediately. Still, as much could be said for any other of a score of Southern brands of bitters and compounds. Yet, by some means or other, Black-Draught, as Historian Thomas Clark pointed out, "became practically a folk remedy." It was used, said he, for almost everything. Was it a boil on the leg? Using the powdered

* Though mentioned elsewhere in this book, the poor red man, like the Quaker, has been singularly a subject of libel; the latter for what was believed to be his innate honesty, the former because he was a simple savage of no book learning, and hence was directed in his therapy by the Great Spirit. Both red man and Quaker were thus favored subjects with quacks.

form, the customer made a poultice. The sting of a bee? Dampen a pinch and slap it on the spot. More than a few aging veterans of the Confederate Army attributed their continued excellent health to a constant use of chewing tobacco and Black-Draught.

Even though the genius of the Chattanooga Medicine Company, Z. C. Patten, had been a Union soldier, he was not so embittered as to hold fast to any grudge. Let bygones be bygones was his motto. And thus it came about that the most popular piece of patent-medicine literature in all the South was the aforementioned "Ladies' Birthday Almanac," distributed free in the interests of the Patten nostrums. Some of its popularity was doubtless due to the qualities of its testimonials and the physiological editorials which Samuel Hopkins Adams declared to be unmatched for "loathsome and gratuitous indecency"; but the "Birthday Almanac" made another bid for custom; it tended in its chronology of notable dates to stress Confederate triumphs rather than defeats; and to remember such things as "June 3, Birthday of Jefferson Davis; Confederate Memorial Day in Tennessee."

In the matter of remembrance of things past, in relation to deeply held prejudices, however, Wine of Cardui could not match the efforts of the manufacturers of Kookman's Bitters who "advertised their product and their political spleen" at the same time. In commenting on the most hated Southerner then living, who was Hinton Rowan Helper, author of *The Impending Crisis*, Kookmans ran an ad in the *Carolina Watchman*: "This gentlemen [Helper] is not radical enough to please his [Republican] party and has been removed as Postmaster at Salisbury—Use Kookman's Bitters."

Down in Georgia, the up-and-coming outfit making a compound registered as B.B.B. liked to spread the revered name of Alexander H. Stephens across the top of its advertisements. Stephens had served the Confederacy as vice president and as firebrand and martyr, and could do no wrong. But Georgians who read the fine text of the advertisement learned that the Alexander H. Stephens who had been cured of cancer by B.B.B. was not the hero but a distant and, until discovered by the B.B.B. agents, obscure relative. Yet despite the subterfuge, the feeling of Georgians for kinfolk, even unto the utmost traceable relationship, was probably strong enough to identify the remote sufferer from cancer with the immortal "Little Ellick" Stephens and to promote sales of the patent medicine.

It was in Georgia, too, where the segregation of patent medicines achieved a sort of perfection in the advertising of a liniment prepared by a Dr. Allen of Columbus. The Allen copy led off with "War! War! is Declared Against Pains of any Kind by Dr. A. W. Allen's SOUTHERN LINIMENT!" and continued: "Every Southerner will be satisfied by using One Dollar's Worth, that they have no further use for Northern Liniments." Then it listed Allen's as a cure for "Rheumatism, Neuralgia, Sprains, Burns, Bruises, Fresh Cuts, Pains in the Back of Limbs, Colic in Man or Beast"; and declared, with a bow to the late Confederate cavalry, that it was "the only Certain Remedy for BLIND STAGGERS IN HORSES." At the end of this superb announcement came a "Caution to Everybody!—Don't use any more Northern Liniment until you have given Southern Liniment a fair trial."

A few patent medicines manufactured in the North made attempts to capture a market in the South. One of these was Fletcher's Castoria, the soother of babies, which made good at crossroads stores. So did several of the nostrums of Chicago's H. E. Bucklen & Company, who made an Arnica Salve as well as Dr. King's New Discovery for Consumption. So too did Perry Davis, as witness Mr. A. W. Lafferty, former congressman from Oregon, who in 1958 recalled that "in my youth, nearly eighty years ago, nearly every plank fence in Missouri was painted with the legend Perry Davis's Pain Killer."

But neither these nor other Yankee nostrums were ever able to capture the tremendous market provided by the victims of malaria and chills and fevers of the Southern swamp country. In this field the old and sizable firm of Spurlock-Neal Company of Nashville reigned supreme with its Rich's Tasteless Chill Tonic and King of Malaria. Spurlock-Neal also met and defeated the Yankee threat present in many Northern tonics, restoratives and blood purifiers which sought to aid the distressed South, by introducing Phyto-Gingerin, a "most powerful, efficient and pleasant remedy for ALL diseases arising from an impure state of the blood."*

Spurlock-Neal was privy to every cozy practice of the patent-medi-

---

* Much later came Hadacol, the inventor and herald of which was State Senator Dudley Le Blanc of Lafayette, Louisiana, who had already given Happy Day Headache Powders to the South. During the peak year of Hadacol, the tonic reputedly had sales approaching $75,000,000.

cine business, and invented a few improvements. In a special letter
to retailers, it pointed out that "we are extensively advertising our
Phyto-Gingerin," and that "no price is marked on the bottle, therefore make your own price." The company possibly did not need to
stress the fact that it invariably referred to Phyto-Gingerin as "The
Great Southern Tonic." Spurlock-Neal also made Gray's Ointment,
the Patriarch of Salves, which antedated the War Between the States;
and Spurlock's Quick Hair Dye, with every bottle of which went a
free brush.

In the matter of hair, Historian Clark observed that "one of the
quickest ways to make a small fortune in the postwar South was to
manufacture and distribute a reasonably satisfactory hair straight-
ener." Hundreds of these pomades came and went. To assure any
success they must withstand the entangling influence of damp
weather, and "remove from the head of the colored female the tight
string-wound rolls of hair" and replace them "with fluffy locks."
The hair straighteners were promoted with the same vivid text and
before-and-after-using pictures common to the ads for ague cures and
blood purifiers.

In describing the talents employed by Southern patent-medicine
concerns, Mr. Clark wrote that "literary men of a base but exceed-
ingly clever stripe filled the patent columns with advertisements of a
most seductive nature." Store signs proclaimed universal biliousness.
Southern roadsides were given the look of "civilization" by fence
and barn signs many of which "were as sensitive to regional lines as
the Southern Democratic party."

It is true that Texans were to absorb no little of Dr. Hartman's
Peruna, made in Columbus, Ohio, but the literary men employed
by the makers of the true Southern Simmons Liver Regulator were
not slow to meet the competition by capping Doc Hartman's own
ability to associate a remedy with famous, or at least notorious, people. Whereas Doc Hartman printed rather perfunctory testimonials
from governors, congressmen, admirals, and people of the stage, the
lads in the pay of Dr. Simmons told what was going on with the
really great American heroes:

"The Cowboys carry Simmons Liver Regulator with them and
take it when they feel bilious," came the word from Texas, and continued: "They use the dry powder, taking a pinch of same and wash-
ing it down with a little water, it having a satisfactory effect." Other

advertisements in this series told sufferers in the cotton and cattle belts exactly who these "cowboys" were; and cited Judge Roy Bean, Wyatt Earp, Doc Holliday, and even the Clanton Gang, every last mother's son of whom had been saved from bilious attacks by taking Doc Simmons' grand Southern specific.

In some of Doc Simmons' copy was a stout play for Temperance. The cowboy whose liver was kept in fine trim found that his stomach was in shape to resist the morbid longing for something to stimulate and excite it; and a man with a pure stomach and an unclouded brain had "no desire to become a Drunkard." Was not Doc Simmons thus "promoting the cause of Temperance in an effective manner?"

Perhaps the Dr. Simmons of the Liver Regulator was the same worker of wonders who so long ago composed the formula of the magnificent Black-Draught,* which was responsible for at least one-half of the success of the Chattanooga Medicine Company. Of all the nostrum makers, North and South, none has enjoyed a longer or more illustrious history than this venerable firm. Its Black-Draught and Wine of Cardui seem to be the only Southern remedies which held the line against invasion by Northern patents and went ahead to invade the North. By the time of World War I, Cardui and Black-Draught were a part of the civilization of the South. And because Southerners possess above all Americans the admirable quality of loyalty, not only to their own kin but to familiar things, they took with them, when they began to move by the hundreds of thousands to the industrial North, the remedies of their youth and the youth of their fathers. In their new homes in Detroit and other centers they demanded Wine of Cardui and Black-Draught. And got them. For more than two decades past, these two patent medicines have been available in Portland, Maine, and Portland, Oregon, and most of the cities in between.

Although the American Medical Association included the Chattanooga Medicine Company in its over-all war against nostrums, this battle resulted in libel suits that dragged through the courts for years and were decided in favor of the medicine concern. Still, Wine

* The current (1957) label of Black-Draught says the ingredients are: "Senna, Rhubarb, Anise, Peppermint, Cinnamon, Clove, Nutmeg, and Other Aromatics in sugar syrup."

of Cardui's claims to therapy, in both advertisements and labels, have undergone notable mutations. It is no longer a "cure" for anything. It is not even "recommended" for anything. Its alcoholic content is no longer the 20 per cent which organized medicine considered "an unnecessarily large amount." It has been cut to 10 per cent.

Both Wine of Cardui and Black-Draught went into commercial manufacture 119 years ago, and in their altered forms are still among the living on the shelves of drugstores throughout the United States. There cannot be many other nostrums with so long and illustrious a history.

4

The Natural History of Swamp Root

The originators of Swamp Root, on which was based a family fortune estimated at from ten to fifteen million dollars, were two brothers, S. Andral Kilmer and Jonas M. Kilmer, natives of small Cobleskill in Schoharie County, New York, who in 1879 moved to Binghamton. They had no capital, but their energy and ambition were of Horatio Alger size. They had also prepared themselves for the task ahead, which was the manufacture of patent medicines. Jonas had attended the Bryant and Stratton Business School in Albany. Somewhere along the line Andral had picked up a degree in medicine.

The brothers seem never to have bragged, in the manner of so many self-made men, about their early struggles on the way upward to those several millions of dollars. They were particularly chary about dates and vague about many seemingly vital matters until a family rift brought the brothers into the courts. Even so, a couple of lawsuits did not prevent the accumulation of Binghamton's largest fortune.

What is certain about the early days is that the brothers had not been in the city very long before Dr. S. Andral Kilmer was practicing medicine and he and Jonas were making and putting medicines into bottles. Their plan was doubtless to build up what was known in the trade as a Line of Family Remedies, something for every ill, be it cancer or constipation. In good time they were putting out Indian Cough Cure, and an Autumn Leaf Extract for Females, and Ocean Weed Heart Remedy, the (graphically named) Prompt Parilla Liver Pills, and Swamp Root.

The sequence in which these various compounds reached the market is no longer known, but it could not have been many years before the brothers recognized that in Swamp Root they had a winner. What happened to the others doesn't matter. Possibly they were dropped one by one until, in 1905 or thereabout, only the Prompt Parilla, along with a new item called A & O Anointment, were mentioned in what by then was the magnificent "Swamp Root Almanac," its cover bright in four colors.

Long before this time the Kilmer business had been moved into what was generally admitted to be "the finest business block in Binghamton." Rising eight stories in the heart of the downtown district, the Home of Swamp Root, described in company literature as "The Largest and Most Complete Laboratory in the World," was a structure marked within by marble columns, marble mosaic floors, hand-carved moldings and cornices, and the spaciousness which, half a century later, many architects are prone to deplore as "wasted space."

Wasted? It is safe to say that the Kilmers never considered anything about the Home of Swamp Root wasted. Consider the vast floors of the Laboratory proper. "Here," said a company brochure, "nothing could exceed the care which each of the army of young women has bestowd upon her working toilet, and thereby done her share toward investing each stage of the process of preparation with the safeguard of an absolutely clean environment." Wasted? Were not employees and visitors alike impressed with the spaciousness and cleanliness? It was "within the point of strict veracity to say that the skirt of the whitest, most delicate fabric could sweep unsullied through the engine room. . . . There are twenty-two miles of wiring in the building—just think of it! The telephone communicates with every department. . . ."

Such was the imposing Home of Swamp Root, known everywhere as "The great kidney, liver and bladder remedy," a result of the "scientific research and study of Dr. Kilmer, who graduated with honors and is now actively engaged in the practice of his profession, which calling he has successfully followed for many years."

All of which was doubtless true, but not the entire story. The building no longer knew the magnificently whiskered face of Dr. S. Andral Kilmer. A rift had already parted the two brothers, and now, though the corporate style was Dr. Kilmer & Company, there *was* no doctor. The senior partner was plain Jonas M. Kilmer, and the junior partner his son, plain Willis Sharpe Kilmer. We shall come in a moment to the family troubles, but first let us consider Swamp Root and its genius.

Dr. S. Andral Kilmer composed the formula, probably named it, and contributed his own benign not to say bewitching countenance to the label. I fancy he also selected the distinctive pale orange tint that gave tone to the package and, no matter where it was placed on the long drugstore shelves of the period, set Swamp Root apart from the countless bitters, sarsaparillas, liniments, and other nostrums bidding for attention. And then, as if this were not enough, S. Andral one day in an inspired moment let go a cry worthy a Paracelsus or a P. T. Barnum:

Thousands Have Kidney Trouble and Don't Know It!

There it was—pure, uncomplicated, matchless—the perfect answer to explain those first faint twinges in the interior of the middle-aged man or woman. In the eight easy words of that warning lay the glittering future of Swamp Root: *Thousands Have Kidney Trouble and Don't Know It!*

Yet, just in case among those thousands there were some with sluggish imaginations, S. Andral composed a list of fifty-six symptoms which exactly filled one full column in the "Swamp Root Almanac." They are as effective today as they were when the scientific S. Andral thought them up. I read them through one day in 1957 and again a year later, and on each occasion I discovered in my system no less than forty-two of the fifty-six symptoms. It was a sobering diagnosis, and it gave me to understand how, as Dr. Kilmer himself said it, Swamp Root had come to "fulfilling its great mission."

It has been mentioned that S. Andral dropped out of the firm of Dr. Kilmer & Company. In 1906, he was conducting a CanCertorium in Binghamton, billing himself as Cancer's First Conqueror. Five years later he was pressing two lawsuits against his brother and nephew, charging among other things that the corporation had been opening his mail. What was worse, said he in the complaint, the Swamp Root concern

holds out and represents to the public that plaintiff Dr. S. Andral Kilmer is the duly licensed, qualified and acting physician in charge of the medical department of said defendant; that it represents, holds out and pretends to give medical advice and prescribe medicines for disease which it pretends to diagnose.

In reply the Swamp Root Kilmers admitted using the name of Dr. Kilmer, the title "Dr." and the affix "M.D." and made no pretense of any right other than that, years before, they had license and authority to do so. The lawsuits were of particular interest to Samuel Hopkins Adams who, in 1912, was making a return visit to Binghamton to check information he had received in regard to the current practices of Dr. Kilmer & Company in its promotion of Swamp Root. Mr. Adams hoped to learn why a Post Office fraud order against Swamp Root had never been issued. Such an order had been earnestly recommended by a Post Office inspector. Most important of all, Adams was looking for evidence to support his suspicion that what he termed the Patent Medicine Trust had far too much influence with American newspapers.

The Post Office inspector had read in Swamp Root circulars how simple it was for anybody to learn whether or not he had kidney trouble. "Take a bottle or common glass," said Dr. Kilmer & Company, "fill it with urine and let it stand for twenty-four hours; a sediment or settling usually indicates an unhealthy condition of the kidneys."

Knowing that it usually indicated nothing of the sort, and that all urine deposits sediment after standing, the Post Office man decided to accept Swamp Root's advertised offer to make free analysis of urine samples and prescribe proper treatment. From different places he mailed samples addressed to Dr. Kilmer at the Swamp Root Laboratories. Some were weak tea. Some were horse urine. Promptly, as fast as the mails could bring them, came replies signed "Dr. Kilmer"; in every case the sample showed "a dangerous condition of the kidneys"; in every case Swamp Root was the remedy prescribed.

The Post Office man next went in person to Binghamton, presented his credentials to the general manager at the Swamp Root Laboratories, and said he should like to tour the place. The manager asked what he wanted to see. "Everything," he replied. He was shown through Swamp Root's home but observed nothing in the nature of analytical work. "Where is your laboratory?" he asked.

"Laboratory?" the manager repeated, obviously puzzled. "You mean where we compound our medicines."

"No. Where you make your analyses."

"Oh, *that*," said the manager, and led the visitor to a small room in which a number of employees were processing letters. There he pointed out a young woman, perhaps eighteen or nineteen years old, who he said was in charge of the analytical work. She was a Miss Maillette. Rigid questioning by the inspector failed to bring any satisfactory information. He returned to Washington and recommended to his chief the issuance of a fraud order. It was never issued.

Now, in 1912, Mr. Adams began his investigation, beginning with the seemingly extracurricular activities of the two Swamp Root Kilmers, Jonas M. and Willis Sharpe. They were owners of the *Binghamton Press*, which "enjoyed the largest circulation of any daily in that part of the state." The paper's advertising manager was Willis S. Kilmer.

Then there was the People's Bank, of which Jonas Kilmer was president, and Willis S. Kilmer vice president. Jonas Kilmer had also served a term as police commissioner of Binghamton. Mr. Adams concluded that in every phase of life in the city, "except perhaps in the social phase," the Kilmers were "powerful and feared." Adams thought it of interest, too, to discover that Miss Maillette, she who only recently had been "in charge of analysis" of Swamp Root "patients," had been promoted to a new job. She was now Society Editor of the *Binghamton Press*.

Adams was less interested in society news than in the possible political influence of the Kilmers' newspaper. Delving into the business of the nonissuance against Swamp Root of the fraud order, he found that at the time the Post Office agent recommended stopping the Kilmers' mail, he had also laid evidence before George Curtiss, the United States District Attorney at Binghamton, as basis for criminal prosecution. It seemed that Curtiss immediately agreed to prosecute. Instead, he forwarded the evidence to Washington together with a recommendation not to prosecute.

Mr. Adams now went to see Mr. Curtiss to ask why the Kilmers had been let off. Curtiss replied that "the case against them was not strong enough to warrant criminal prosecution." Adams went to work. He found that at the time of the Post Office agent's visit, the *Binghamton Press* was conducting a lively fight against the old-line Republican machine of which a George Dunn was leader, and whose chief lieutenant was District Attorney Curtiss. Dunn and Curtiss and the Kilmers had "got together." The result: Curtiss recommended dropping the case against Swamp Root; and Swamp Root's newspaper ceased its attacks on the Dunn-Curtiss political machine.

Mr. Adams also found reasons to believe that the Kilmers started the *Binghamton Press* because they were unable to control the long-established *Herald*, an evening paper, whose editor, Guy F. Beardsley, had refused to support political friends of the Kilmers even when Swamp Root advertising was suddenly removed from the *Herald*. The *Herald* had also seen fit to publish a news item when Willis Kilmer was charged with assault upon a bicyclist, and convicted. The cyclist had failed to give what Kilmer, a sporty young fellow, thought was right-of-way due his tandem rig in traffic; and Kilmer had horse-whipped the offender.

Only a little later, and with no explanation, the Kilmers resumed Swamp Root ads in the *Herald*. The mystery quickly cleared, however, when Mrs. Willis S. Kilmer brought a divorce suit against the junior Swamp Root partner. And the *Herald*, as Mr. Adams remarked, "declining to regard the Swamp Root business as a bribe for the suppression of news, printed an account of the divorce proceedings with the list of fourteen co-respondents."

Within a year after the Kilmer divorce, the first issue of the *Binghamton Press* appeared; and soon the *Herald*, which no longer had Swamp Root among its ads, also lost the Lydia E. Pinkham Vegetable Compound business, along with that of Dr. Pierce of the Golden Medical Discovery and the Favorite Prescription, and Hall's Catarrh Cure.

Having aired these facts (*Collier's*, May 11, 1912), Mr. Adams resumed his efforts to learn just what happened to the fraud order the Post Office agent had recommended so long before. The order charged Dr. Kilmer & Company with using a device to obtain money under false pretenses with at least three fraudulent phases:

1. Purporting to report findings from analysis of urine that was not made.
2. Diagnosing and prescribing for diseases without a license to practice medicine.
3. Selling Swamp Root to persons entirely free from kidney disease, on false representation they were suffering from such disease.

The trail of the indictment was long and devious as it wound from one subagency of the government to another. Early in 1909 the chief inspector of the Bureau of Chemistry had recommended prosecution for misbranding. In May, 1909, Dr. Wiley himself had recommended that Dr. Kilmer & Company be cited for a hearing before the Board of Pure Food and Drug Inspection, which consisted of Dr. Wiley and George P. McCabe, the board's solicitor, and F. L. Dunlap. At this point Mr. Adams paused briefly for an aside.

"At this time," Adams wrote, "there was developing, with Secretary of Agriculture Wilson's aid, that scandalous plot to nullify the Pure Food & Drug law and to hamper and discharge Dr. Wiley." The plot had been exposed and frustrated on the floor of the House by a congressional committee which showed McCabe to be Secretary Wilson's agent and Dunlap to be McCabe's echo. "Against these two," Adams pointed out, "Dr. Wiley was powerless." Now began a long series of procrastinations. These were the work of Attorney Warwick M. Hough whom Mr. Adams described as "the legal prop and bulwark of the patent medicine fakers and brought into the case as counsel for Swamp Root."

The hearing had been postponed, once in September, twice in October, again in November and December, and at last turned over to McCabe for legal preparation. It was now January 8, 1910. Postponements continued—in March, in April, again in May. The delay was being used by Swamp Root to revise its label. And finally, one year and three months after the farce began, Swamp Root's lawyer Hough submitted a new label which, Mr. Adams said, "is a model of deceptiveness and fraudulent intent, but which, nevertheless, does not lie specifically enough to bring it within the scope of the law." In July, 1910, the government accepted the new, revised label.

"Thus the Swamp Root fraud had," observed Mr. Adams, "by a series of special favors and privileged delays, beaten the law in its very stronghold, and victoriously reestablished its immunity, not only from punishment for obvious lawbreaking, but also from the more feared process of facing a court ordeal which would have officially proclaimed its fraudulency."

Comparison of the old and the new Swamp Root labels showed "cure" to be replaced by "remedy," and the old claims of therapy in their new form appeared as "numerous testimonials to the effect that Swamp Root has been used in cases etc., etc."

Mr. Adams made reference to the Proprietary Association of America, which he called the Patent Medicine Trust, and repeated charges he had made in the past against this outfit and its Red Clause advertising contract which provided that the advertiser might withdraw his business from a newspaper "if any legislation inimical to patent medicines" was passed by a state legislature.

Reporter Adams said he was happy that "a large majority of American papers refused any longer to bow down to this form of tyranny and . . . that the Red Clause has lost most if not all of its potency." Just to make sure his readers might think the revised Swamp Root label had had any effect on the nostrum, he closed his article by asking them to keep three facts in mind:

Swamp Root will not and cannot cure kidney, liver or bladder disease;
If used in such disease, it will often be harmful; and
That it may sometimes even kill.

"The way to end Swamp Root's career of fraud," he wrote, "is to spread understanding of what it really is—a compound of false promises, protected by political pull, and backed by a conscienceless newspaper; in all the realm of medical knavery, the most dangerous and law-destroying combination extant—the copartnership of quackery, blood-money, and fraud-nurtured journalism."

Swamp Root did not die. About the time of Jonas M. Kilmer's death, in 1912, only three days after *Collier's* published Mr. Adams's article, the *New York World* carried a large advertisement of Swamp Root. And though at this period most of the old-line nostrums had begun to feel the pinch and pressure of new laws, as well as the changing style of advertising generally, Swamp Root still had many prosperous years ahead of it.

The surviving Kilmer, the sporty Willis S., became noted for his racing stable, and for his private railroad car, the Remlik, in which he traveled to meetings the country over. At the time of his death, the press reported that his will, in addition to a $250,000 cash legacy, provided a trust fund to the widow, and no less than $400,000 to be apportioned "to business associates and servants." To the City of Binghamton he left "the Kilmer Pathological Laboratory as a permanent memorial." To the Brady Institute of Johns Hopkins University he bequeathed $10,000.

The assets of Dr. Kilmer & Company were sold by the executors to a concern headed by A. R. Diebold, Owen Willis, and R. R. Land. A reorganization resulted, according to the Pure Food and Drug Administration,* in Diebold Products, Inc., of Stamford, Connecticut, which became "the manufacturing end of the business, and Kilmer & Company, also of Stamford, a sales affiliate for distribution of Swamp Root and one other product."

* In a letter to the author, dated Nov. 19, 1958.

PART SIX

Therapy by Pipe and Wire

1

Dr. Hercules Sanche

Almost a century intervened between the patent issued for the Metallic Tractors (1796) of Dr. Elisha Perkins, and a patent for The Oxydonor granted in 1892 to Dr. Hercules Sanche. Other medical humbugs were patented during those ninety-six years, but none enjoyed so great a vogue or deceived so many people as the psychologically ingenious devices of Perkins and Sanche.

Dr. Sanche called his first effort the Electropoise. It was a metal cylinder three and one-half inches long, and weighed five ounces. The cylinder was sealed at both ends and to one end was attached an uninsulated flexible cord. At the free end of the cord was a small disc which, by means of an elastic band and buckle, could be fastened to the wrist or ankle. The cylinder, when broken into by prying physicians, was found to be hollow and empty. The Electropoise sold for $10. It was on the market by 1893.

Although the name of the device indicated electricity, Dr. Sanche soon applied for and received a patent for an "improvement" and changed the name to Oxydonor, the giver of oxygen. It was obvious that its inventor was still seeking just the right pitch to catch attention. His earlier claim was that the Oxydonor *forced* oxygen into the system. Reflection may have caused him to drop the idea of *force* as semantically wrong. In place of "forces" he now said the Oxydonor "causes the human organism to thirst for and absorb oxygen, the vitalizer of the blood, through the myriad pores of the skin." It was a most happy conceit. It was what academics like to call a seminal idea. The Oxydonor ushered in an era of mechanical therapy which reputable physicians and makers of patent medicines alike were to ridicule as the wire-and-gaspipe lunacy.

The new improved Oxydonor differed somewhat from the pioneer model. The cylinder was shorter. Instead of being empty, it now

123

contained a stick of carbon. It was now, too, "the New Life-Saver for Self-Treatment." The stick of carbon Dr. Sanche added to his invention must have given him a new and clearer vision of the powers of the Oxydonor. It could now not only "cure all fevers, including yellow fever, in a few hours," but "it cures all forms of disease."

Ten dollars was far too little for such a boon. The price of the improved rig was $35.

Putting the Oxydonor into action was simple. The cylinder was placed in a bowl of plain cold water. The disc was attached to an ankle or a wrist of the patient. That was all, except to relax while the instrument, as silent as it was potent, set the body to absorbing the life-giving oxygen.

Most Americans who were born early enough to recall when the advertising pages of magazines were populated with the Uneeda Biscuit Boy, the Pear's Soap Baby, and Sunny Jim of the breakfast cereal, must retain the nostalgic vision of a Gibson-Girl type reclining gracefully on a sofa, reading a novel and displaying a shapely ankle. From the ankle the eye was led cleverly along a cord to a table on which was a bowl of water. In that bowl, said a line in bold Spencerian script, was the Oxydonor, patented by Dr. Hercules Sanche.

There she lay, year in and out, reading Bertha M. Clay, reading Mrs. E. D. E. N. Southworth, reading on through Elinor Glyn, absorbing healthful oxygen with no more physical effort than the mental strain imposed by her favorite authors. Time gave her classic stature. Into and out of the White House moved Cleveland, Harrison, McKinley, Roosevelt, and Taft. Still she read, taking vital oxygen through the same shapely ankle. Age she did not. President Woodrow Wilson found her unlined, unwithered, and unknowing, even while agents of the United States Post Office Department were closing in on Dr. Sanche.

It was a sales pitch that had few equals, and along with the Gibson Girl tethered to the Oxydonor went a continuous barrage of pamphlets in which Dr. Sanche revealed his discovery of Diaduction, a force as elemental as that of gravity. Here, in Diaduction, was an end to all known diseases.

Because no great innovator—neither Whitney nor Morse nor Edison—has been able to escape infringers, Dr. Sanche's epochal invention was soon a target. By the time Oxydonor's enormous success was clear, a whole foundry of imitations was coming into the market one after the other. First was the Oxygenor King, then the Duplex Oxygenator, then the Oxytonor, the Oxypathor, the Oxybon. All looked very much like Dr. Sanche's patented invention; and one and all may have been just as efficacious in destroying disease. Yet, even in that simple time, long before the automotive industry felt the need for "improvements," the aggressive competitors of Hercules Sanche were advertising some trifling difference to stress the superiority of their models. Some had cylinders seven inches long; some models contained black sand, others yellow sand, still others pulverized chalk. At least two models were double-headers, that is, one cord and disc for the ankle, another for the wrist.

Dr. Sanche was not dozing. He came out with an attachment for his Oxydonor by which two persons might derive the same benefit from one instrument. But if he thought that would put an end to the copycats, he was quickly disabused when a competitor announced a really stunning new feature. This was no less than a whole set of changeable discs specifically labeled for as many different diseases.

One would think that so much and so aggressive competition would have brought lower prices; and one manufacturer did make an effort to get business with a cutrate $10 model. But the other brands held fast at $25 and $35.

Neither the reaper-harvester nor the telephone could have been more quickly and numerously infringed than the original Oxydonor. And stout Dr. Sanche was ready to meet the danger. Though he automatically threatened court actions against the infringers, it seems probable he was not anxious to invite too close a study of his own patented invention; and his major attack on imitators abjured the courts in favor of a campaign worthy a knight-commander of the ancient Christian Crusaders.

Dr. Sanche's first step was to found the Fraternity of Duxanimas, a "Cosmopolitan Organization of the Beneficiaries of the new Method of Curing Disease." This, of course, had reference to the newly revealed Force of Diaduction, as advertised by Dr. Sanche, its discoverer. For some reason or other, Sanche's numerous imitators did not see fit to plagiarize Diaduction, but were getting along as best they could with Oxypathy, Oxygenation, and other variations on the theme, although the Oxypathor was declared to be a "Thermo-Dia-magnetic Instrument."

Dr. Sanche considered Diaduction a good-enough word for his new method of healing; but now, as he prepared to raise his legions of crusaders, he felt need for a touch of classicism. Diaduction was scientifically *duxanimae*, he announced. His gathering of knights comprised *Fraternitas Duxanimae*; and their Vow, which was "the prime and inflexible condition of enrollment," was, of course, *Votum Fraternitatis Duxanimae*.

That his knights should be on familiar terms with "The School and Practice of Duxanimae," he published a brochure dealing with "certain Natural Forces and Principles of which I am the Discov-erer." In it he displayed an imagination that would do credit to Paracelsus himself. It is far too long for reproduction in all its com-plexity, yet one ought to know that Dr. Sanche made clear that the *only* manner by which those Natural Forces could be brought into play was by his Diaductive Connectors, which was to say, the Oxy-donor. He even gave a brief summary, in several thousand words, of exactly what the Oxydonor did. In one reiteration he put it thus: "The Oxydonor instantaneously arrests the chemical process of dis-ease, and rekindles the physiological Combustion of Life."

Here was a man fit to lead any crusade. And Dr. Hercules Sanche now got down to the business in hand, which was *Fraternitas Duxanimae*. The Vow of this order began: "Almighty God, I sol-emnly promise the following: . . .

"With all peaceful means at my command, I will oppose the sale and use of the imitations of Diaductive Instruments. . . .

"I will in like manner oppose all existing and proposed legislation everywhere I may be, that gives preference or any kind of advantage to medical or other Practices over the Practice of Scientific or Popu-lar Diaduction. . . ."

There is a great deal more to the Vow, but successive portions of it do nothing to modify the opening declaration. Indeed, along with printed forms of The Vow of Duxanimae to prospects went printed forms entitled "Donations to the Cause of Duxanimae by Induction, In Trust with Dr. Hercules Sanche, its Discoverer." Donations were to be sent direct to Dr. Sanche, 261 Fifth Avenue, New York City, and were specifically "for his own use in paying his personal and other expenses in travel and other incidental costs incurred by his promoting the general cause of Duxanimae by Diaduction . . . to be used by him to the best advantage, according to his own best judgment and discretion, upon his honor we trust implicitly herewith."

Was ever genius beset with infringements and competition better girded for battle? At the head of these crusading knights, vowed to a man to lay infidels by the heels, was Dr. Sanche, a Godfrey de Bouillon, Lord-Protector of Duxanimae. The possibilities were, like the imagination displayed, infinite. It is most unfortunate that there seems to be no readily available record of how many knights took the Vow and gave moral strength and possibly cash to what, after all, was the Oxydonor. There must have been a good many of these fellows, and their women, too, for Dr. Sanche's invention outlasted all the imitations.

A sort of knell for pipe-and-wire therapy, however, sounded in 1914, when one E. L. Moses, of Buffalo, New York, general manager of the copycat outfit making the Oxypathor, was convicted of using the mails to defraud, and sentenced to eighteen months in the Federal penitentiary at Atlanta, Georgia. To this particular infringement of Dr. Sanche's device, the American Medical Association had called attention, noting its singularly vicious advertising. "Diphtheria," said Oxypathor's pamphlet, "finds its supreme master in the Oxypathor. No earthly power except the Oxypathor can take the slowly choking child, and with speed, simplicity and safety bring it back to health." This, said the AMA's *Journal*, was "a cruel and criminal lie."

An interesting fact brought out at the trial of E. L. Moses was that 45,451 Oxypathors had been sold in three years at a price of $35 each. Evidence indicated the manufacturing cost to have been $1.25 each.

One by one, all of Dr. Sanche's imitators either gave up of their own accord or were forced out of business by the Post Office Department. Then, late in 1915, the busy Fraud Order division at last got around to the old master and his Oxydonor. The company was denied use of the mails. But one fraud order was not sufficient to handle Hercules Sanche, who moved deviously that his great therapeutic discovery should not die of Philistine attack. Other fraud orders followed, being issued at various times to cover concerns obviously doing business for Sanche and Oxydonor, first at two addresses in Chicago, and one in Detroit, and lastly at several places in Montreal, Canada.

The Post Office also felt it necessary to issue fraud orders against the Aid Committee for Vindication of Oxydonor, the Oxydonor Aid Committee, and Theodore T. Boyle, secretary, all of Detroit. These were patently surviving hardshell knights of *Fraternitas Duxanimae* who, like the Old Guard, might die but did not surrender. And lastly, mail was banned to Dr. H. Sanche, Gen. Del., Detroit.

Somewhat later, in commenting on Dr. Sanche, the American Medical Association spoke tartly of the registered physicians who had permitted their names to be used in "this very elaborate and ingenious separating the fool from his money." It referred to Dr. Sanche as "the original J. Rufus Wallingford," who was the leading character and con-man hero of a popular play of the period.

Both the AMA and the Post Office probably thought they had heard the last of Dr. Hercules Sanche. They had *not* heard the last of him. In 1946, or thirty years after he left Detroit, Dr. Sanche issued a come-on type of booklet from his office at 127 Milton Street, Montreal, comfortably entitled "Established in Montreal over Fifty Years." Still later, when I enquired of the United States Pure Food and Drug Administration, they wrote that in 1952 something named The Hydrotonic Company, which they had reason to believe was nobody but Dr. Hercules Sanche, was operating from a box-number address at Riviera, Florida. In May, 1958, however, a Pure Food and Drug agent reported that Hydrotonics, Inc., Blue Heron Boulevard, Riviera Beach, Florida, had "gone out of business."

I have no idea what The Hydrotonic Company was up to, though it sounds as if Dr. Sanche had dropped oxygen in favor of water; but one had best not assume *anything* when dealing with this old master of therapy. I am sure it was he, if only because of the delicate change from Hydrotonic Company to Hydrotonics, Inc. This shading of semantics was the touch of an artist.

Two other able men with pipe and wire were to follow the path clearly blazed by Pioneer Sanche. One of them made more money from his invention than did Dr. Sanche; the other possibly made less. Both, I feel sure, were greatly in debt to Dr. Sanche who had done no little to prepare the ground for Dr. Albert Abrams and Mr. Gaylord Wilshire.

2

The Electronics Man

Early in 1924 the American Medical Association paid homage to memory of the late Dr. Albert Abrams, who had recently died in San Francisco, by observing in an obituary notice in its *Journal* that Abrams "easily ranked as the dean of all twentieth century charlatans." This was no small distinction. If the ranking of Dr. Abrams seems arbitrary, his place in the hierarchy of successful operators got solid support from the newspaper estimates of his estate, which was given as "approximately two million dollars."

It is doubtful if any of the most eminent specialists of the time left a comparable estate, yet the fortune of Dr. Abrams had come unquestionably from the field of therapy in which, at the time of his death, he was either a genius or a very monster of quacks, according to what you thought of Electronic Reactions. (It is most regrettable that Dr. Hercules Sanche, the Oxydonor inventor, seems not to have commented publicly on Dr. Abrams.)

Quack or genius, Abrams began his career as a conventional physician with a degree of medicine from the University of Heidelberg (1882), then carried on postgraduate studies in Berlin, Vienna, London, and Paris before returning to practice in his native San Francisco, where he had been born in 1863. Here for several years he was chief of the medical clinic at Cooper Medical College. His first departure from traditional medicine came in 1910 with the publication of *Spondylotherapy; Spinal Concussion,* which the California Medical Society and similar groups elsewhere declared was "a hybrid of up-stage osteopathy and chiropractic."

If this churlish reference damned Abrams in many eyes, it gave him added status with others who had tried doctors of medicine and found them lacking in ability to fetch the wanted cures. The Abrams book went rapidly through five printings, and created such a stir that Dr. Abrams himself began a tour to give clinical courses in Spondylotherapy in several parts of the country. The course cost $200. Two years later there came into being the American Association for the Study of Spondylotherapy. But things were humming. New discoveries were being made. Presently the Spondylotherapists had regrouped as the American Association for Medico-Physical Research.

Progress waits on no man. Least of all it had to wait for Dr. Abrams, who now announced a revolutionary discovery he called Electronic Reactions. Possibly inspired by other scientists, who had offered the theory that disease causes change in the electrical skin potential, Abrams conceived the idea that the electron—the new unit of matter in general—was to supplant the cell as a biological unit. What was more, he proposed to do something about it.

In a book entitled *New Concepts on Diagnosis and Treatment*, published in 1916, Dr. Abrams said that because disease is a disharmony of electronic oscillations, diagnosis must detect and measure the alteration. Each disease has its own vibratory rate, hence treatment must restore equilibrium. And, since all cures make use of this principle, Dr. Abrams pointed out, this new method must of necessity supplant all others.

Almost overnight, it seems in retrospect, a new cult was born, and its devotees, with the easy familiarity of club membership, quickly abbreviated its name to E.R.A., meaning the Electronic Reactions of Dr. Abrams. Although the region of San Francisco was well north of the happy hunting grounds of most American cults, southern California did not disappoint Dr. Abrams; one of the best known and also most eloquent of the early converts was Upton Sinclair, an old resident of the charmed land of prophets and healers.

Almost simultaneously with appearance of the new cult's advance criers, Dr. Abrams founded a house organ, *Physico-Clinical Medicine*, and announced the perfecting of two new instruments. One was an electronic device for diagnosis. The other, called an Oscilloclast, cured the disease as diagnosed. Taken together they comprised the American ideal of the way all things, including therapy, should be carried on: by the push-button method.

It is unlikely that anything since Dr. Elisha Perkins's Metallic Tractors (Pat. 1796) had created so great a noise as Dr. Abrams's claims for his Electronic Reactions. "A drop of blood," said he in effect, "represents the entire individual and suffices for diagnosis, although it is necessary to place a healthy control subject in the electrical circuit and test his skin reactions, which conform to the vibratory rate of the disease." With neither capital letters nor italics, Abrams went quietly on to say that by means of his diagnostic device he could also tell the sex of a patient he had never seen, and also to what race he belonged.

Then, just as matter of factly, Abrams took his machine into the rare upper air of metaphysics; from that one drop of blood "religious belief may be determined." He realized, he said, that "reception of this fact" might be termed as "stultiloquence" on his part. He need not have worried. Genius though he may have been, he misjudged the enormous credulity of his public; his public was so ready to believe that within a short time more than 3,500 electronic practitioners were hard pressed to attend to the hordes of the afflicted anxious to forswear medicine for the quick, the positive, the incomparable relief of E.R.A.

The disciples were ready to accept the machine's identification of an unseen subject's disease, or even of his religion by that one drop of blood or his autograph. About this time a commentator wrote that "Dr. Abrams' colleagues came to think him unbalanced." Perhaps they did, but because Abrams was of established professional reputation—so this most careful commentator noted—"it is not easy to disprove his basic claims." As with all new systems of treatment, "remarkable cures are not lacking." Could this seemingly fantastic theory mark a revolutionary discovery? Had not his contemporaries laughed at Dr. William Harvey? And who had not sneered at Louis Pasteur?

And yet it was difficult, save for congenital cultists, to go the whole way with Dr. Abrams's claims for what we might as well call his Electronic Assembly. How this imposing piece of machinery went about its work was described by an investigator for the American Medical Association:

"All that was needed was a drop of blood from the patient, who might be any number of miles away. (His autograph was just as suitable for the purpose.) The drop of blood on a piece of white blotting paper, or the autograph, was put into the diagnostic machine which in turn was connected by means of a wire to a piece of metal pressed to the forehead of a healthy individual while Abrams

or his disciple tapped on the abdomen of the individual who, incidentally, had to stand facing west in a dim light. According to various 'areas of dullness' that were found by tapping on (percussing)
the healthy subject's abdomen, there was determined the disease
from which the patient who had furnished the blood, or the autograph, was suffering and also the location of the diseased area."

This seeming miracle was brought about when the machine's operator followed the instructions given by Dr. Abrams in his rule
book: "Conduct the energy at V R 6 and use the S V reactions."
The machine hummed. In another moment the diagnosis was complete.

If the still-absent patient was suffering from one disease or another, which was likely, he could now go to the nearest electronic
practitioner, of necessity also a lessee of the Abrams Electronic Assembly, for treatment by an Oscilloclast. The cure was accomplished
by applying to the patient the same vibratory rate as that of the
disease from which the soon-to-be-happy man had been suffering. It
is perhaps proper to mention that though the diagnosis took but a
moment, the cure could call for any number of treatments and run
into money.

By the time Sunday-supplement medical advisers were swamping
newspapers with typical gee-whiz articles, and magazines with oh-
the-wonder-of-it pieces, most of them in praise of Dr. Abrams, a
factory was making the first of some four thousand electronic machines "authorized by Dr. Abrams." These were for lease, not sale,
at good stiff rentals. Each machine was sealed, and the lessee signed a
contract not to open it. Each machine, almost as soon as it came
from the production line, was snapped up by the primitive electronic
engineers of the day, a majority of whom, said the American Medical
Association, were osteopaths who "by this means prolonged the life
of their dying cult."

The high-water mark of the E.R.A. cult was probably mid-1923
when, as said, more than 3,500 of the Abrams machines were in
operation; and the lessees, according to one estimate, were finding
E.R.A. a gold mine, "taking in from one to two thousand dollars a
week." There was not a cloud in the Abrams sky, though clouds
were soon to form. Both the American Medical Association and the

Scientific American were separately and possibly jointly looking into the phenomenon.

"The absurdity of the E.R.A.," said a report in the *Journal* of the Association, "was demonstrated at various times by sending some of Abrams' disciples specimens of blood purported to be from patients who were ill but actually taken from animals." One case was diagnosed as general cancer and tuberculosis of the genito-urinary tract. Another blood sample came from a sheep. The diagnosis said the patient was suffering "from hereditary syphilis and the E.R.A. man wrote to offer a guaranteed cure for $250."

In another article the AMA periodical said that the Abrams machine had "forced the chiropractors to bring out *their* piece of mechanical hokum, the Neurocalometer, in order to meet the competition of the osteopaths with their Oscilloclasts and other Abrams magic boxes."

Beginning in October, 1923, the *Scientific American* brought out an adverse report on Dr. Abrams and E.R.A. which, added to the many strictures published over a period of years in the AMA's *Journal*, served to cool many of the cult's members as well as to discourage current and prospective patients of the several thousand E.R.A. operators. When in January of the following year Abrams died suddenly, the shadows were already forming which in time were to obliterate the last remnants of the Electronic Reactions of Dr. Albert Abrams.

One would like to know what became of all that imposing mass of machinery. I like to think that, somewhere or other, in the attic of a house that has belonged to four or five generations of a dedicated faddist family, there is grouped a now dusty and rusting display of the mechanical nostrums which, periodically over the years, have brought temporary comfort and hope to their users.

In this museum of obsolete therapy the oldest exhibit would of course be a pair of Dr. Perkins's Metallic Tractors; and surely one of Dr. Raphael's Famous Electro-Magnetic Chains, "endorsed by Prince Albert of England." There must be a collection of the patented works of Dr. Hercules Sanche, the Discoverer of the Laws of the Spontaneous Cure of Disease, which began with his basic Oxydonor, and flowered into the elaborate attachments known as the Animator, the Novora, the Binora, and the Vocorbis. There would have to be a copy of Dr. Chas. A. Tyrrell's J.B.L. Cascade, The Internal Bath of Continuous Good Health; and perhaps several unmentionable devices, patented or otherwise, which had come in Plain Sealed Wrapper from mail-order houses with names like the Ponce de León Appliance Company.

Then, within reach of an electric socket, would stand the wonderful showcase of Dr. Abrams, a complete Electronic Assembly, its levers, buttons, and flashing lights reminding one today less of therapy than of a small-size computer, or Thinking Machine, as it is called by the glibber writers about The World of Tomorrow.

But the Abrams machine, though the most impressive in this attic museum of science, would not be last chronologically, for at almost the same time that the faddists were ready to give up the E.R.A., they were offered, and you may be sure gladly purchased, the magnetic life buoy named Ionaco by its inventor, Gaylord Wilshire. This remarkable thing would not take up much room. It could easily hang from a nail in the studding, and it would look to the uninitiate like a new type of lifebelt, or perhaps a horse collar. It had one great merit lacking in the Abrams electronic assembly. Whereas the E.R.A. must diagnose before it could cure, Wilshire's I-ON-A-CO simply cured. Anything.

3

Gaylord Wilshire's I-ON-A-CO

Ink is a pale medium, and weak, in which to do justice to Gaylord Wilshire. He belongs by right to Technicolor. He was perhaps the only therapist worthy of that medium, and Technicolor might well have claimed him had it not been for his untimely death in 1927, before Hollywood had quite achieved prismatic perfection.

Because therapy occupied less than three of the man's dynamic sixty-six years, it is best to approach him in the same manner in which he himself approached the profession of healing, by an indirection unmatched by any other eminent charlatan. Wilshire was born in 1861 in Cincinnati where, only a little before, Dr. William M. Raphael had set up in business as an "Oracle for All Who Desire Health, Wealth, Happiness and Long Life." But there is no connection, other than spiritual, between Wilshire and Raphael.

To his father, George Wilshire, his son always referred as a prominent citizen, president of a local bank, and "among those keen-eyed men who sensed the tremendous future of oil," "one of the original Standard Oil stockholders." A cousin was "president of the great Fleischman Yeast Company." Another cousin was vice president of "the largest coal company in the world." These forebears or relatives, Wilshire intimated, accounted for his own career as "a doer and go-getter"; his mother was "Clara Clemens, the same name borne by the mother of Mark Twain, and there is a family connection." Which of course took care of Wilshire's intellectual inheritance.

If there are such things as inherited abilities, then Henry Gaylord Wilshire was fit to go far in almost any direction. He seems to have paused briefly in Cambridge, Massachusetts, as a student at Harvard where, as he told it, he "specialized in economics, and at times even addressed the class at the request of the professor." Although there are as many reasons for being chary of Wilshire's biographer, who signed himself George J. Duraind, as there are about the accuracy of Wilshire's memory, there can be no doubt that here was a remarkable fellow.

Sometime in the late eighties Wilshire arrived in Los Angeles, California, where in 1890 he was an unsuccessful candidate for Congress on the Socialist ticket. He was undismayed. Just how he managed it is not clear, but Wilshire recalled for his biographer, that he had "stood for Parliament" in 1894 as a Socialist candidate from Manchester, England; and again "for the Canadian Parliament in 1902," though the constituency is not named; and still again, and still as a Socialist, "for Congress from New York 1904."

Meanwhile, however, he had made a small fortune in billboard advertising, according to his long-time friend Upton Sinclair, and founded *Wilshire's Magazine* in Los Angeles. He soon moved with the periodical to New York and there, in 1902, converted Sinclair to Socialism. "It was like a falling down of prison walls about my mind," Mr. Sinclair remembered. "Wilshire's Socialist periodical was the most amazing discovery I had ever made."

Socialism or not, young Wilshire was looking ahead to a Capitalist Paradise. At a time when most businessmen had lost faith in Los Angeles, a grubby town in the debris of its first burst boom; he could see a mighty city that was to extend infinitely "where then was but a sheep pasture." He set out to buy the sheep pasture, at bargain prices. Then, with the best engineering talent obtainable, "he planned and laid out from the city to the ocean the renowned Boulevard that now bears his name." Indeed, it does bear his name, which thus survives as illustriously as does that of President James Madison in a rival metropolis on Manhattan Island.

"Go where you will," cried Wilshire's biographer, twenty-odd years after the boulevard was laid, "go around the world, and from Shanghai to Leningrad, from Capetown to Calcutta, from London to Cairo, and you will hear of the Wilshire District and Wilshire Boulevard of Los Angeles. They are not only known but always referred to with admiration as among the finest examples of city planning and beautification in all the world."

Less widely known, yet an achievement which in almost any other man would be accounted of considerable note, was the founding of the city of Fullerton, California, which was soon "to enjoy the distinction of being the richest city per capita in the world." Wilshire was Fullerton's promoter and parent who "shouldered the responsibility of the town's development until his vision was justified."

One is not to think that in all this heady success with land and capital—and billboards—the former Socialist had forsworn the idealism in his character. In his promotion of Los Angeles and Fullerton real estate, one could still see "outcropping like a streak of gold in the mother lode, the essentially altruistic bent in the intellectual make-up of Gaylord Wilshire."

Now we come to Wilshire, the highbrow of life and letters, intimate of many of the great men of two continents in art, literature, science and politics, William Morris, Ambassador Bryce, G. W. Russell (A.E.), H. G. Wells, Havelock Ellis and—above all—George Bernard Shaw. Once we have come to Shaw, Wilshire's biography is so cluttered with Shavian references as to make one wonder if Wilshire or Shaw is the subject. "Indeed," says the biographer, "some think that Wilshire bears such a close physical resemblance to the greatest modern dramatist that one would almost take them for brothers."

So one would. Here from a page peer forth images of both great men, side by side, a double-headed vision of Mephistophelian aspect, as if prepared for sterescopic viewing. All the great boulevard promoter had to do, apparently, was to turn up his coat collar, ruffle his hair a bit, squint sideways, and there for all purposes of publicity squinted Bernard Shaw. An accompanying caption hammers home the resemblance for the weak-eyed or slow-witted.

The Wilshire biography proceeds to describe the correspondence between the two men which was carried on "with that camaraderie born of friendship, regard, and an obvious feeling of intellectual and social equality." But Shaw was "somewhat astonished," and probably nettled, when his friend apprised him that he had basked in the sunlight of a famous actress, "The Cleopatra of the English Stage," ten years before Shaw had come along with the idea of basking too.

After a too long diet of Shaw, Mr. Wilshire's biographer turns to science as represented by William C. Beebe, the naturalist and explorer who, among other things, had "recently solved the mystery of the Sargasso Sea." Wilshire didn't happen to be along on this expedition, but caught up with Beebe later in the jungles of British Guiana. Or perhaps it was the other way around—Beebe caught up with Wilshire, to find Wilshire right there in the jungle sitting on top of two gold mines, "one at Hoori, the other on the Little Aremu," and Mine Promoter Wilshire "put everything to the service of the Beebe expedition." Never unmindful of the exchange of courtesies, Explorer Beebe went out to capture and kill an immense serpent, which was to be used to make a fine picture for Wilshire's biography. It is an eye-stopper. The caption: "Wilshire and William C. Beebe Holding the Deadly Bushmaster Snake in the Jungles of British Guiana."

It is only with Shaw and Beebe out of the way, and the deadly bushmaster conquered, that Mr. Wilshire's biographer begins to ready his subject for Medicine. "He is in the full swing of the modern scientific movement," wrote Biographer Duraind, "abreast in the fields of biology, medicine, physics and electrical science." Long after midnight, this "keen, alert and vigorous mind is still absorbing some abstruse work of science." He is on familiar terms with the discoveries of Jacques Loeb, Dr. Otto Warburg, Dr. William Osler, and a virtual convention of other scientists.

Yet nowhere in the Wilshire biography is there mention of Dr. Albert Abrams. Possibly this was mere oversight. Abrams, the electronics man, the discoverer of E.R.A., was, as the reader is aware, two years in his grave when Gaylord Wilshire was ready to announce his own and even greater discovery, which he christened I-ON-A-CO. But it was amazing that Wilshire's achievement should have come so closely in the wake of Dr. Abrams, who had left an estate of approximately two million dollars.

Let us not, however, make the mistake of accusing Wilshire of appropriating Abrams's idea of using electronics to diagnose and cure disease in two simple operations. I-ON-A-CO borrowed less from Abrams than it did from old Dr. Hercules Sanche, who, as related, pioneered the wire and gaspipe field as early as 1890 and who now, in 1926, was largely forgotten, while his Oxydonors rusted in attics or disintegrated on city dumps. What Wilshire borrowed from Abrams was nothing more or less than the knowledge that Abrams had come by two million dollars in the brief period when some four thousand E.R.A. machines were working for him. To a man of Wilshire's temperament this was a challenge.

Wilshire's I-ON-A-CO was of course the reason for the Wilshire biography (Copyright 1926, The Iona Company), which referred to it as "a simple and effective method of using magnetism for the cure of human ailments." What it did was to attack the disease at its source in the cell tissues. No dieting was attached to the treatment. No gymnastics, no exercises, pills, powders; no purgative waters, no opiates, no drugs, "not even faith is required." Then, moving fast to place the device in its proper field of push-button therapy, one reads:

"All you have to do is to place over your shoulders the Wilshire Ring or I-ON-A-CO. That's all. You may then light a cigaret and read your newspaper for ten or fifteen minutes. Meanwhile its magnetic force is permeating your body, and effecting the cure. You see nothing, you feel nothing." [But listen, my friends—and here the pitch went into the crucial con.] "Often patients at the first treatment, like Lazarus, arise well and whole. . . . *IONACO cuts a new pathway to the cure of disease.*"

Except for its introduction of Lazarus, the I-ON-A-CO pitch was an accurate plagiarism from Dr. Hercules Sanche.

The American Medical Association was prompt to denounce I-ON-A-CO as comparable in therapeutic values to "the left hind foot of a rabbit caught in a churchyard in the dark of the moon." The Association took pains to alert the National Better Business Bureau. Local offices of the Bureau were quick to respond to the striking full-page advertisements that first appeared in West Coast newspapers. The bureaus of Portland and Seattle combined to have I-ON-A-CO investigated by a committee composed of physicians, X-ray technicians, and electrical engineers. By the time Wilshire's Iona Company had established sales offices in the two Northwest cities, the committee made its report.

"The IONACO," it said in part, "is a coil of insulated wire, worth about $3.50, 18 inches in diameter, with a plug that permits the coil to be attached to an electric light socket. With it is a smaller coil that performs no part in the alleged curative use of IONACO but plays an all-important part in the magical features of the scheme by impressing the purchaser with the marvelous potentialities of the larger coil."

(It was this smaller coil which, in the argot of con men, provided *the convincer.*)

"The small coil," the report continued, "has two free ends attached to a miniature light socket containing a flashlight globe. When the larger coil is plugged into an electric light socket where there is an alternating current, there is generated within the larger coil a weak fluctuating magnetic field. This would cause the flashlight globe in the small coil to light when the small coil is brought in close proximity to but not touching the large coil."

The Bureau's report here paused to stress the significance of the hookup: The phenomenon of a light globe coming alight though not plugged into an electric current supplies the element of magic, or at least of mystery, essential to productive quackery.

The Better Business Bureau's committee also made a detailed estimate of the total manufacturing cost of I-ON-A-CO. The figure was $5.75. The device was being sold for $58.50 cash, or could be had, with the usual easy payment plan, at $65. This information was given in their radio programs by the Seattle and Portland bureaus, which closed each broadcast with a slogan-type sign-off: "It Will Pay You To Investigate Before You Buy an IONACO."

Gaylord Wilshire's men had moved into the Pacific Northwest in a swarm, to open I-ON-A-CO offices almost simultaneously in Portland, Eugene, Oregon City, and Roseburg, Oregon; and in Seattle and Tacoma, Washington. Generous advertisements displayed Mr. Wilshire in full mustache and Vandyke, but something had been added: he was wearing heavy-rimmed spectacles, just then much favored by savants. In person he was lecturing from the platform and over the radio. "Delightful free treatments" were offered. So were free booklets, the cover of one of which presented a most effective likeness of the new scientist and the title *Gaylord Wilshire and His Amazing Discovery*. This was the extraordinary biography signed by George J. Duraind, as "reprinted from *San Francisco Chronicle*, July 18, 1926." No more entertaining booklet was ever offered to advance quackery.

At least one illustration in the booklet could have reminded survivors of Dr. Hercules Sanche's Oxydonor. This showed a "Charming Young Woman Enjoying Her IONACO." Like her spiritual mother of Oxydonor days, she reclines on a fashionable couch. Around her neck and body the Wilshire Ring—"Magic Horse Collar," said the American Medical Association—is plugged into a stylish standing lamp with fringe; while the caption declares "IONACO has not only given her hair a remarkable sheen, but also a natural permanent wave."

There could not possibly have been a finer picture and caption to show the almost incalculable progress made by quackery. Antique old Hercules Sanche's rig merely cured all disease; Wilshire's horse collar did as much, then went on to take the place of the beautician.

As was the case with Oxydonor in former times, imitators were not backward in riding Wilshire's discovery. Late in 1926 the Portland Better Business Bureau was investigating something called Mag-Kuro, to find a device promoted by one MacDonald, who "owns an apartment house," and one Johnson, "an electrician," who together planned to open "a clinic" in Tacoma to cash in on the Wilshire advertising and sell Mag-Kuro Belts.

Early in 1927 Oakland's Bureau was looking into a blind ad in Business Opportunities which said: "Partner Wanted to Take ⅓ interest in Magnetic-Electric Belt Co., Same as IONACO Belt. Just starting. Salary and ⅓ of Profits. Guarantee $300 to $550 a month. Must invest $1,500, money secured."

By May, 1927, the Portland Bureau received a request from the Indianapolis Bureau, asking for a report on Wilshire's I-ON-A-CO, in order to deal with a local physician who "is endeavoring to promote a similar device" in the Indiana city.

Wilshire's Oregon crew were aggressive fellows. They threatened Robert Mount and Lyle Janz of the Portland Bureau with all sorts of legal trouble, and protested that the Bureau's "unfair allegations" had resulted in barring I-ON-A-CO's advertising on local radio stations and in the newspapers.

Wilshire was still in the ring, and now appeared the *Ionaco News*, "Published in the Interests of Suffering Humanity." Its front page carried a powerful cartoon of a man struggling in a rough sea, while from a nearby ship a sailor is heaving a life preserver labeled "SS Ionaco, Magnetic Life Buoy." Below is the message of a New Hope of Health to Those Sinking in a Sea of Despair.

In the *Ionaco News*, too, Wilshire was bringing up his heavy guns in the form of testimonials. One was from Dr. Anna G. Lyle, family physician to Dr. David Starr Jordan, president emeritus of Stanford University. "I want to say I have fallen for the IONACO strongly," Dr. Lyle is slangily quoted: "It appeals to me because it brings the electro-magnetic force into the most convenient form for use in treating disease." Dr. Lyle is also credited, though not in direct quotes, as saying she "has examined Dr. Jordan since his treatments with IONACO and stated the other day that he was very much better."

Another prominent Californian offered probably the most telling testimonial of the scores printed. He was none other than Mr. E. K. Cassab, the "Pioneer fruit packer, who introduced the famous Cassaba melon to the world." He told Wilshire that "if I could not buy another, I would not part with my IONACO for $10,000!" Why? Listen, you sufferers, Mr. Cassab's back was broken in an automobile accident. He became paralyzed from the waist down. During the next several years he tried "sixty-seven doctors without relief. In trying to get cured he spent over $80,000." The implication was clear; the day of the conventional physician was done.

And then came what Wilshire called "The Vision of George Sterling." This was California's poet-laureate, "my dear old friend," who declared that "as I contemplate this recent invention of Gaylord Wilshire, I am not so sure that Man is not at least on the right road, if not to a cureall, at least to a means of alleviation of the greater part of the ills to which our ailing race is subjected. . . . I have seen, or been told, of the sudden and undeniable cure of indigestion, diabetes, goitre, varicose veins, gall stones, asthma, even of cancer."

What did it all *mean*? Well, said the noted poet: "In noting the number of cures, I can but have imaginings of a revolution in therapeutic methods, of a whole world renewed, rejuvenated, and freed from most of its ailments by the universal use of IONACO. A splendid and alluring vision!"

But the splendid vision was already beginning to fog up. Dr. Anna G. Lyle turned cobra-quick to strike at the inventor of I-ON-A-CO. In a letter to the press, and to the American Medical Association, the family physician of Dr. David Starr Jordan denied treating the famous man with I-ON-A-CO. "My name," said she, "has been used in advertisements without my knowledge and without my consent. I do not know Mr. Wilshire. I never made any of the statements ascribed to me in the advertisements."

The Cassaba melon man seems to have stood fast to his statement about I-ON-A-CO and $10,000; but a number of lesser testimonials washed out quickly. A Dr. Arbuthnot of Los Angeles General Hospital denied he had ever used I-ON-A-CO as alleged by Wilshire. H. A. Atwood, M.D., of Riverside, California, denied that he had even heard of a Mrs. Virginia Clements, much less that he had treated her for cancer, with I-ON-A-CO.

A favorite quote in I-ON-A-CO literature cited "W. F. Brady, M.D., Dean of the Faculty, School of Electro Therapy," of the University of Michigan. Inquiry brought reply that there was no Dr. Brady at the university; neither was there a "School of Electro Therapy."

Then, on November 18, 1926, Poet George Sterling, in the San Francisco club where he lived, shot himself to death, thus removing any danger that he might renege on his "splendid and alluring vision of IONACO."

Even the gorgeous façade of Gaylord Wilshire was crumbling. In the widely read *Hygeia*, for February, 1927, Dr. Arthur J. Cramp devoted four instructive and illuminating pages to a piece about Wilshire, telling of "The Metamorphosis of a Realtor into a Magician." The authoritative Dr. Cramp closed his indictment with an unusually kindly comment on what Mr. H. L. Mencken had recently called *boobus Americanus*. "The only reason that intelligent but technically ignorant people are deceived by a device such as IONACO," he wrote, "is because their credulity is born of lack of knowledge, not lack of brains."

Then the tough and respected Underwriters and Credit Bureau of New York City, which had been dogging the Portland, Oregon, Better Business group for more information about Wilshire, suddenly looked back into its own files, to come up with a sort of continued if long-forgotten story dealing with Gaylord Wilshire from 1907 to 1910. In the former year, the promoter was using *Wilshire's Magazine* to boom the Bishop Creek Gold Company, in Inyo County, California, which had just increased its stock from $5,000,-000 to $25,000,000 on the proposition of a Socialist mountain of gold.

How much of this stock was sold or how much gold came out of the Bishop Creek Company's diggings does not seem to be in the record. In any case, there was a hiatus of some three years before Wilshire got into the news again. This time, so Underwriters and Credit Bureau's 1910 files revealed, not only were Wilshire's Inyo County operations under investigation by the United States Post

Office, but also Wilshire's "gold and rubber enterprises" in the jungles of British Guiana, which he called the Aremu Company. ("Aremu"—that was the very place where Explorer Beebe and Promoter Wilshire held the "deadly bushmaster snake" for a picture.) Underwriters and Credit Bureau may not have heard of that celebrated serpent, but they did know that "some of Wilshire's anxious comrades had started an inquiry which resulted in charges of stock jobbing."

Nothing serious, however, seems to have come from the Post Office's investigation, which had nothing to do with I-ON-A-CO, except to show that Wilshire was indeed, as he often claimed to be, a go-getter, a do-er.

But something serious was happening to I-ON-A-CO during the summer of 1927. The combined barrages of the Better Business bureaus and the American Medical Association had begun to tell. The big advertisements of January and February had disappeared from the daily papers. I-ON-A-CO radio programs were losing out. Dissatisfied users of the Wilshire Ring were being heard from. One by one the Iona Company's offices were closing. And on September 7, Gaylord Wilshire, he who, as his biographer had recently said, was "standing on the frontiers of a new world," died, aged sixty-six.

In his reminiscences, Upton Sinclair, who liked Wilshire, mercifully ignored the I-ON-A-CO period. He thought Wilshire's Socialism was more of emotion than of intellect. "His greatest fault," Sinclair wrote, "was generosity which made it impossible for him to keep money." Of the gold-mine affair, Sinclair said Wilshire "bled himself and thousands of readers of his magazine who had been brought to share his rosy hopes." It failed in the end for lack of capital. Wilshire did everything "except to turn the mine over to some of the big capitalist groups who sought to buy it and freeze out the old stockholders." This, of course, would have been standard practice for capitalists.

Mr. Sinclair excused the mine-stock promotion on the grounds of belief the venture would support Wilshire's Socialist monthly. "But Socialists," he observed, "should never fool with money-making schemes in a capitalist society."

In Sinclair's gentle hands, Gaylord Wilshire comes through as a likable and improvident character, a man who had been rich and couldn't get used to being poor. I-ON-A-CO was his last-stand attempt to recoup. It is possible, I suppose, that he actually believed in the "Magic Horse Collar." Whether he did or not, the greatest disservice ever done his memory is the all but incredible biography written to his order by a hack. Out of *Gaylord Wilshire and His Amazing Discovery* steps one of the really superb con men of all time.

PART SEVEN

Notable Family Sagas

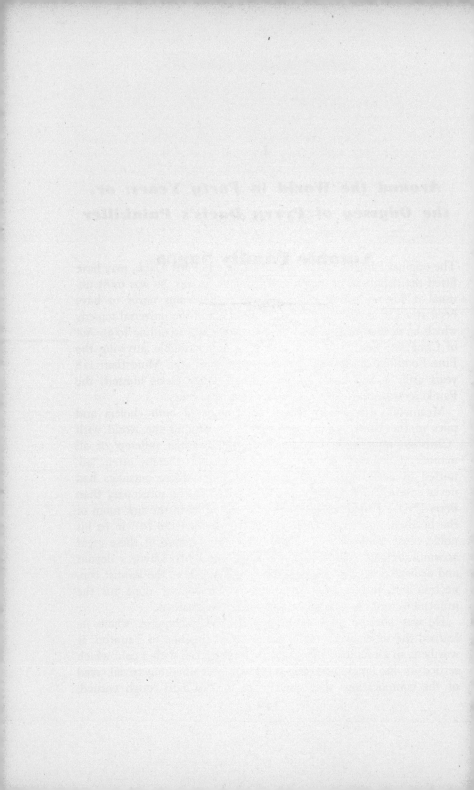

1

Around the World in Forty Years: or, the Odyssey of Perry Davis's Painkiller

The original Painkiller Man, whose name was Perry Davis, may have fitted the definition of quack. But if quack he was, he was most unusual if for no reason other than that he seems never to have been attacked as such by a medical society; and the universal remedy which he devised in 1840 and registered in 1845, according to an Act of Congress, appears to have had little or no trouble surviving the Pure Food and Drug restrictions of 1906 and later. More than 118 years after it had made a new man of Perry Davis himself, the Painkiller was still to be had in all its pristine potency.

Meanwhile, the famed compound conquered both cholera and piles in the United States, then went on around the world with "Christian missionaries who carried it to heathen sufferers of all manner of diseases" and who found themselves thereby often "admitted to sacred places in China and India where outsiders had never entered." Was anything better suited to the missionary than Perry Davis's Painkiller? "It gives him an entrée to the sick room of the heathen, and enables him by its wonderful cures to win to his noble cause the hearts of thankful patients." None of these great accomplishments could have astonished good Mr. Davis, a devout and dedicated man who not only gave generously to the Baptist connection but also credited the hand of Providence alone for the miraculous formula which he always "carefully guarded."

He was born in 1791 in Dartmouth, Massachusetts, where he learned the shoemakers' trade. Later, he set up shop in Taunton. It was here, in December, 1839, that he was stricken with a cold which settled on his lungs. Lest one think this was anything trivial, read of the complications that quickly set in. "A hard cough ensued, accompanied by pain in my sides," Mr. Davis remembered, when five years later he sat down to describe his condition at the moment of the Discovery. "My stomach became very sore. My digestive organs became weak. My appetite failed. Night sweats followed. Then my kidneys were affected. Piles in their worst form were preying upon me. The canker in my mouth turned very troublesome. Under all these circumstances, I thought I was a fit subject for the grave."

He tried many medicines without relief until one day he told his wife she must make up her mind to get along without him; he had done his last work at the bench. He must soon be numbered with the dead. He suffered a coughing spell of such intensity that "as I set in my chair, I exclaimed 'Is there no relief for the pain in my sides while I am dying?' I immediately commenced looking for something new."

It now happened suddenly. "I searched the globe in my imagination with eager anxiety," he recalled, "and selected the choicest gums and plants that I thought the world afforded. There and then, and directed as I believe by the hand of Providence," Perry Davis set about compounding the medicine thus revealed to him. He began using it at once, both internally and externally, "with no other hope than gently handing me to the grave."

But, mark you, the pain in his side was relieved. His cankered mouth began to heal. The night sweats ceased. His kidney complaints started to give way. The piles were cured. His appetite returned. His sleep was now refreshing. He went to his bench without further ado and started to work.

At this juncture, as Mr. Davis recalled the affair, his wife entered the room and made an observation in which there was neither joy nor astonishment, but which contained no little New England essence. "I thought," Mrs. Davis remarked—and all Yankees will be able to hear the tone of voice—"I thought," said she to her husband, who, bear in mind, had just crawled up out of the grave, "I thought you didn't expect to work no more?"

There are husbands who, in like circumstances, might have replied tartly to so calmly numbing an observation. Perry Davis did not do so. "I told her," he wrote in his engaging memoir, "that I had begun to feel like trying anyway." But Mrs. Davis refused to waste any silly talk about Mr. Davis's return from the dead. She was a direct woman. "*What*," she asked, "are you going to call the name of your medicine?"

"Here," said he, "was a nonplus, for I had never thought of a name for the composition." But in the face of an obviously determined female, there was no time to weigh the semantics of nomenclature. "I paused a moment," Mr. Davis remembered, "then replied I will call it Painkiller because it killed all my pains."

There it was, Painkiller—as unsubtle as an ulcerated tooth, as promising as untroubled sleep. Painkiller! The medicine may or may not have come from a miraculous formula, but it now had a name to take it to the ends of the earth. And Perry Davis knew it. "Relief for the Distressed!" he cried aloud, "Balm for the Wounded!" No proprietor of a nostrum ever cried to more purpose.

There is nothing in the record to indicate how Mr. Davis went about introducing his discovery in Taunton. That the Painkiller must have been well received is clear from the fact that by 1843 he had moved to Providence, Rhode Island, and listed himself in the City Directory as a physician. He was feeling fine and dandy, according to his own published statement, adding that "if there is a man in the world enjoys better health than I do, he has reason to be thankful." Nudged possibly by Mrs. Davis the realist, he invited skeptics to "call on me at 74 High Street, and examine my person and circulations," which would convince all "of the healing virtues of Perry Davis's Vegetable Painkiller."

Although from 1848 to his death fourteen years later, Davis was to list himself in the Providence Directory as a "Manufacturer of Painkiller," he had appeared earlier in that book as Physician. But he seems not to have referred to himself as Dr. Davis, and never used "M.D." with his name, which was odd enough in a period when "doctors" were almost as common as "professors" and "honorables." Still, he was not backward in offering medical advice. The treatment he prescribed for dyspepsia is surely worthy of attention in our day, when Spartan diets are in favor.

"The way I manage the dyspepsia or indigestion in my family," wrote Mr. Davis in 1845, "is to eat anything the appetite craves, say beefsteak broiled and buttered well, with a little cayenne pepper, and salt, with a Rhode-Island johnnycake, a boiled egg, and a good cup of gunpowder tea, made strong, and then reduced with sugar and cream. This is as light food as I should ask in any case of dyspepsia in my family." If, however, the gourmet should feel unease after this repast, then let him take the Painkiller, "say 25 or 30 drops in sugar and water." Mr. Davis warned, too, "to take the Painkiller every time you eat, even if it is six times a day. . . ."

In nearby Fall River, Massachusetts, where Enoch French & Company had already "sold some 500 dollars' worth of the Painkiller, made by Perry Davis," people had found it to be a truly protean remedy. One grateful customer wrote that its use by his family had "brought effectual cure of hard coughs" and had also given "great relief when applied to corns on the feet." The Reverend A. Bronson, pastor of the Second Baptist Church in Fall River, wanted "everybody to know what this invaluable medicine, through the blessing of God, has done for me."

Because Fall River was the home of the numerous Borden family, it might interest historians to know that a Mr. Leander Borden spoke highly of Painkiller. He did not mention its use in cases of dyspepsia, hence one may assume that table fare at the Leander Bordens differed from that of the Andrew J. Bordens who, years later, were to become widely known. Their servant, Bridget Sullivan, testified as to a Borden breakfast during extreme hot weather; it consisted of "mutton broth, cold mutton, johnnycake, and cookies."

Though Perry Davis jealously guarded the God-given formula of Painkiller, a sensational and spectacular accident on March 25, 1844, revealed at least one of the ingredients. On that nigh fatal day, as Mr. Davis was busily compounding a batch of his medicine, a "can of Alcohol exploded." His feet slipped, and "I fell upon my back into the flames, and had to turn over before I could extradite myself from them." In an instant his face "was burnt to a blister, and my hands and arms also burnt in a most shocking manner."

Mrs. Davis and daughter tore out of the room, but soon returned with help. As for Perry Davis, he knew just what to do: "While they were extinguishing the fire, I was putting Painkiller onto my burns, which gave immediate relief." And while he was applying the quick and sure remedy, he must also have been thinking of how best he could make capital of so dramatic an event. His terrible burns could hardly have healed when a local artist was engaged to depict Mr. Davis enveloped in flames, lying on his back, with wife and daughter fleeing the holocaust. The picture became a full-page illustration in *The People's Pamphlet* which Mr. Davis felt the urge to publish and distribute.

Neither the picture nor the text made any bones about *what* had blown up; the picture shows a whopping big can as the source of the explosion; the text refers to Alcohol with an upper-case A. If this was the first leak in the jealously guarded formula, it surely could have come as no surprise to the rising number of manufacturers of patent medicines. Some of these men already had "stooped so low," as Mr. Davis wrote, "as to steal the name of my medicine, and offer it for sale under the name of Herculean or Embrocation or some other Painkiller." He appealed to all persons using Perry Davis's Painkiller to "destroy the label on the bottle as soon as they have used the contents, as some people are base enough to procure the bottles and refill them with their own manufacture, and thus deceive the public."

Mr. Davis may have threatened or otherwise exerted pressure on these scoundrels, for among them was L. B. Allen of Providence who, wrote Mr. Davis, "has fled to parts unknown, and also Thomas Otis of New-Bedford." Henceforth, Mr. Davis announced, all his authorized agents were "to be supplied with a Certificate signed by Perry Davis, representing his residence, No. 74 High Street." This was of course the scene of the now famous explosion which had done something to blow Perry Davis into the public eye. Demand for the Painkiller was beginning to soar, and its inventor must have stocked up on its ingredients. These, according to an analysis made years later by *Western Druggist,* were as follows: Gum myrrh 2¼ lbs., Capsicum 10 oz., Gum opium 8 oz., Gum benzoin 6 oz., Gum fuiaic, 3 oz., and Alcohol 5 Gal.

No layman is competent to speak of the therapeutic value of this compound, but he may say with little danger of contradiction that in the hands of Perry Davis it was a compound to go far indeed.

The magnificent odyssey of Painkiller had its beginnings when Perry Davis, a basket on his arm, trudged from Providence to Boston, carrying the first lot of the medicine ever taken to that metropolis. The distance was a good fifty miles. Mr. Davis was fifty-three years of age, a well set-up man, with a distinguished countenance, smooth-shaven, wearing a double-breasted cutaway coat, and a beaver hat on his head of long iron-gray hair. He carried a cane, probably from habit, for he appears to have been the cane type of prominent man.

Prominent men, however, were not given to walking the high road while toting a basket; and Mr. Davis failed to make any impression upon the leading druggists of Boston on whom he called. They told him coldly that "they themselves made mixtures equally good for annihilating pain," and turned to other business. He was so mightily discouraged, when at last he came to the crowded streets around Quincy Market, that he made no effort to sell his wares. Instead, he "handed to each poor, sick or lame person he met a bottle of Painkiller, and directed him how to use it." Having done as much, one may suppose that he made his weary way back to Providence, to reflect that he had returned poorer than before, for "even his expenses to Boston and back were at that time a great item of consideration to him."

Better times were in store. Soon "the dreaded cholera" made its appearance in the United States, and "Painkiller was suddenly brought into general notice by the astonishing cures it effected of this terrible disease." Then, too, it was not long before Mr. Davis found that "each bottle given away in Boston had created a demand for many more." Before the year was out, "rising 6000 bottles were being sold monthly by the Proprietor." By that time Painkiller had invaded Philadelphia. It had got as far west as Owego, in Tioga County, New York, and eastward had "traveled through Maine to distant Norridgewock."

It wasn't long before "old sea captains, who happened to make Providence a port of call, sought out Perry Davis to thank him for his great discovery," then to stock up with full chests of Painkiller for their voyages to the Orient. In these vessels, too, went "Christian Missionaries whom no other class of men have done so much to facilitate the progress of Painkiller around the world." From Swatow, in China, the Reverend J. M. Johnson, missionary, wrote Mr. Davis to say that "our native preachers are never willing to go out on their excursions without a supply of Painkiller. It gives them favor in the eyes of the people, and access to the families and localities by whom otherwise they would be very indifferently received."

As early as 1852 one of Mr. Davis's old sea-captain friends left several cases of Painkiller with a merchant in distant Melbourne, Australia, where a gold rush was in progress, and the medicine was sold at auction "to the highest bidders among the miners and brought its weight in silver." In China, Japan, and India, Painkiller was "soon one of the few American manufactures seen by the traveler in his walk through the streets, standing prominently forth in nearly every shop window. . . . For these markets Painkiller is put up with directions printed in native languages."

The Hand of Providence was speeding the Gift to Man wherever Man lived. It was evident that something must be done about the foreign market, so what by then was the firm of Messrs. Perry Davis & Son opened a branch office in London, England. The sale of the remedy "increased more than a thousand-fold" and became "a household word in every part of the United Kingdom."

The aging Perry Davis continued to give generously of his money to the Baptists, and also contributed to the so-called Temperance Movement. He died in Providence on May 2, 1862, aged seventy-one, doubtless happy in the knowledge that his Painkiller "was a stimulant that will not destroy the soul by creating a taste for liquor," but on the contrary "has saved many from a drunkard's grave."

Son Edmund Davis, long associated with his father in the business, seems to have been an up-and-coming man of affairs, alert to the necessity of promotion and quick to call upon "the courts of many countries" to put down the scoundrels who sought to pirate the honorable name of Perry Davis's Painkiller. The younger Davis died in 1880, and the family business was sold to parties who continued its manufacture in Providence until 1895, when it was removed to New York City. In forty years the remedy had encircled the world.

In the years after World War I, Painkiller was continuing to work its wonders in far places. In 1920, on arrival in a remote logging camp in British Columbia, I discovered it to be a favorite item in the company store. It was much used by the loggers who considered it to have the great thaumaturgic properties claimed for it by its inventor; and by them was also especially indicated in light or grave cases of hangover.

In 1958 it was still on sale in Canada and in the United States; and though it had suffered semantic change by being labeled LINI-

MENT in large letters, its current proprietors had the grace to add in parenthesis "Painkiller Brand." Best of all, each bottle still carried the likeness of the venerable Dr. Davis, a man of distinguished mien, who peered forth from the steel engraving with a serene if somewhat austere countenance. Just the look of him gave me confidence.

Dr. Hostetter Was Here

Compared with Perry Davis's Celebrated Painkiller, which required forty years to make its healing way around the world, the fame of Hostetter's Celebrated Stomach Bitters was swift. The four years ending with Appomattox were sufficient to make this newer medicine the most popular "Anti-Bilious Alterative" in North America; in another four it was "known in the most remote regions of the habitable globe." During eight decades four generations of Hostetters stood ready to refund your money, if you were not satisfied in every respect, meanwhile wreaking disaster on the many imitators who sought vainly by formula and label to equal this veritable Balm in Gilead.

The formula was a prescription of Dr. Jacob Hostetter, a reputable physician of Lancaster County, Pennsylvania, who used it in cases of colic, constipation, and "the Intermittents," a type of fever especially prevalent in the American West during mid- and late nineteenth century. On his retirement from practice, in 1853, the old gentleman, so family legend had it, "gave consent to his son David to manufacture and sell the remedy."

Young David Hostetter was a bold and adventuresome fellow. He had gone to California in the Rush of Forty-nine, crossing the Isthmus of Panama on a mule, during which seven of his fever-stricken comrades died along the way. In San Francisco he set up a grocery store which was wiped out by fire within the month. He returned home to Pennsylvania, still seeking the fortune that eluded him in the West. The record does not say so, but it seems probable that so energetic and observant a young man had noticed the phenomenal rise in the number of patent medicines that accompanied the western migration and settlement. Right at home was the prescription his honored father had used successfully for many years. The idea of Hostetter's Bitters was born.

Important at this stage was a boyhood friend, George W. Smith, who in 1853 was a civil engineer engaged in driving a railroad through the Alleghenies. David Hostetter talked him into putting up $4,000 to make the family Bitters in Pittsburgh. It was enough to buy kettles and supplies, to lease modest quarters at $15 a month and, most important, to begin advertising.

The history of Hostetter's Bitters alone is convincing evidence of the relation of advertising to the success of a nostrum. During the first eight years of the Hostetter and Smith Company, the young proprietors put every cent they could spare into printer's ink and into paint to mark the name on billboards, fences, covered bridges, and large boulders in open fields and pastures. When war came in 1861, the name Hostetter so impressed the War Department that they were soon buying the Bitters in carload lots for the Union Army.

This enormous and sudden leap in business did not find Manager David Hostetter wholly unprepared. His career, both with the Bitters and later in other fields, showed him to be a far-seeing type not unlike his contemporaries, Andrew Carnegie, the rising young steel master, and Henry Clay Frick, soon to be known as the King of Coke. Young Hostetter met the demands of war, and in its second year issued the first "Hostetter's Illustrated United States Almanac."

At this period the Bitters contained modest amounts of cinchona bark, gentian root, orange peel, anise, and a less than modest dose of alcohol. Whether or not the alcoholic content was increased during the war is not clear, but for many years it ran to approximately 47 per cent by volume. This would seem to be enough "to hold in solution the extracted medicinal properties" of the formula. The nostrum was unquestionably of some service to the Union Army, as witness the postwar observation of a Pittsburgh historian. "Hostetter's vaunted remedial properties were sadly lacking," he wrote, "but many a frightened Yankee at Gettysburg knew he faced Pickett's Charge as bravely as he did because of the swig of Hostetter's under his belt."

It was not for nothing that the label on what was registered as Hostetter's Celebrated Stomach Bitters displayed Cavalryman St. George riding down and spearing The Dragon.

By war's end the Bitters was grossing $750,000 a year. The Almanac, in English and German editions, was circulating one million copies, heading for a peak of fifteen million copies printed in seventeen languages, with more than one thousand persons employed directly or otherwise in the business. Partner Smith died in 1874, and the firm's name became The Hostetter Company.

By that time David Hostetter was facing the competition of more brands of bitters than one would readily have believed possible. After all, almost any old crone or yarb woman had a bitters recipe that had come down through decades of folk medicine. The stuff might be concocted of dewberry, crane'sbill, wild cherry, gentian, yellow poplar, or sarsaparilla. It might be rectified with hard cider, whisky, brandy, or wine. It must, however, be very bitter, for in bitterness was potency—stuff to drive humors out of the body and purify the blood. In fact, the old reliable home remedy, long before the coming of patent medicines, was a bottle of bitters.

The quick and unqualified success of Hostetter's brought so many imitations there is no point in listing them. Mostly, they contained no little alcohol. But there were at least two brands of proprietary bitters which, to use a graphic phrase, worked the other side of the street. One of these was manufactured and sold as Old Dr. Kaufmann's Great Sulphur Bitters by A. R. Ordway & Company of Boston. Its advertising stressed a warning: "Never Use Cheap Rum Drinks Which Are Called Medicine."

Ordway & Company seem not to have stated the alcohol content of its Great Sulphur Bitters, yet they made a notable pitch for the Temperance trade, meaning the people who were Dry by conviction and who were often fanatical about it. In 1889 Ordway's advertising featured the likeness of Mrs. S. Louise Barton, "An Indefatigable and Life-Long Worker in the Temperance Cause." She was also and variously the Missionary of Morgan Chapel, Secretary of the Massachusetts State Reform Club, Grand Master Congress United Templars, and Deputy Supreme Councillor of the Royal Conclave Knights and Ladies. Said the *Boston Globe* of Mrs. Barton: "The friends of Temperance may well be proud to have one who can advocate with so much ability and eloquence."

Of Ordway's Sulphur Bitters Mrs. Barton spoke at some length, relating how dyspepsia had grievously troubled her for years, resisting the "remedies innumerable" she had tried, until Ordway's had given her what she believed was permanent relief. Then, as she had written on July 20, 1886, from Morgan Mission, Shawmut Avenue, Boston, "I do not think you realize how many a 'God Bless You' goes up from the lips and hearts of those whose bodies have been wonderfully helped by the Sulphur Bitters. He that giveth to the poor, lendeth to the Lord. Inasmuch as ye have done it unto the least of these ye have done it unto me."

I have no doubt that good Mrs. S. Louise Barton believed she was speaking up for a strictly Temperance or nonalcoholic medicine. Yet nowhere in Ordway's advertising could I find an unequivocal statement that Sulphur Bitters was nonalcoholic. The best they would do in this direction was to say "Never Use Cheap Rum Drinks Which Are Called Medicine," a sentence so full of holes as to have no meaning. What is "Cheap"? Does "Rum" here refer specifically to rum, or is it a generic word? And *who*, pray, would be calling cheap rum drinks a medicine?

No, Ordway isn't telling all. It is merely sitting quietly. And I fear that Mrs. Barton, the indefatigable worker for Temperance, was getting a moderate dose of a cheap rum drink with her Sulphur Bitters. Patent medicine formulas are not changed without good reason; and in 1916, when Ordway's Sulphur Bitters was hauled into court, to be convicted on a charge that the remedy was falsely and fraudulently claimed to be a cure for leprosy, and fined $100, the government printed the Ordway formula. All that is important to know here is that the alcohol content was 22.30 per cent. Two years later, Ordway was having the same trouble again, though this time the fine was only $25. The alcohol content was "more than 21 per cent."

Thus Ordway's was no more than a pseudo-Temperance medicine. This was not so of Hostetter's other competitor, which was the California Vinegar Bitters of Dr. Joseph Walker, advertised from coast to coast as "The Only Temperance Bitters Known." Dr. Walker was not, like Ordway's, working both sides of the street. His splendid almanac used large type to stress the fact his bitters were Free From Alcohol, while interlarded among his descriptions of many ailments were stout lectures against Alcohol, the Enemy.

Like the immortal Painkiller of Perry Davis, Walker's Vinegar Bitters was the result of self-doctoring. Like Davis, too, Walker had known hellish suffering before he hit upon the formula that made him as new. "In the year 1849," Dr. Walker recalled in 1874, "I went to California and while at the mines I contracted a combination of diseases from which I never expected to recover, and to which many a hardy fellow-miner had to succumb." Prospector Walker was suffering not only from Bronchitis, Consumption, and Palpitation of the Heart, but also from Piles and Rheumatism. "My physicians pronounced my case incurable, and die I thought I must."

Unlike Perry Davis who in a similar hideous condition had been directed by Deity to a sovereign formula, Walker came by *his* specific from "a tribe of Indians camping near me and gathering herbs." (It was the old Indian magic again.) The results in both cases were miraculous. As for the old Forty-niner, "many persons who knew my former condition were surprised when they saw how well and hearty I had become, and came to me for medicine for themselves and friends." So:

"I moved to San Francisco, and commenced putting up Walker's California Vinegar Bitters." The demand was so great that "I concluded to establish a depot in New York City." This was in 1867. And now—he was writing in 1874—his depot and manufactory had "a whole working capacity of forty-four thousand gallons." Never, he declared, had such an increase in popularity of a proprietary article been equaled as that accorded The Only Temperance Bitters Known.

I am reasonably certain, too, that no other patent-medicine pitch equaled Dr. Walker's in originality. Temperance organizations, said he, were fighting against terrible odds with the "nefarious business whose profits are almost beyond computation"; and thus it behooved all friends of this great Cause to stand shoulder to shoulder in "making war against the General Curse." One way to stand shoulder to shoulder was obvious; but lest the cynical chose to believe that the Temperance movement was "being used as a means of advancing the sale of Walker's Vinegar Bitters," the doctor swore that "a portion of the profits of this Temperance Medicine will be devoted to the promotion of the Temperance Movement."

With this statement of intent out of the way, Dr. Walker got busy with his message. This began with a purported timetable of "The Dead River Grand Trunk Railway, the Great Central Through Route," which listed the stations from Sobriety to Rumsellersville, on to Morning Dram, Loafersburg and Drunkardstown, still on to Gambler's Causeway, Guttersburg, and Paupertown, to Suicide's Cave, then to the end of the line—*Hell Gate!*

Dr. Walker went on to present a "Statement of Business of the Dead River Grand Trunk Railway," which included the carrying toward destruction of multitudes of the brave and noble young men in our army; the sending of 200,000 persons to the almshouse, and many more dreadful items. On another page Dr. Walker's Almanac printed a picture of Scene Two of Timothy Shay Arthur's famous novel *Ten Nights in a Bar-Room*, dramatized by William Pratt, showing the interior of the Sickle and Sheaf Tavern, with Little Mary singing "Come Home, Father," the plaintive lyrics of which were given below the picture.

Dr. Walker's Temperance Bitters was a noble and daring experiment. It is impossible to know what sort of reception was accorded the medicine. The Bitters have not survived. (I have been unable to find a druggist who ever heard of them.) It seems probable that they, like all the others, fell before the mighty campaign of David Hostetter.

As early as 1878 the alcoholic content of Hostetter's became of interest to the Internal Revenue Department, especially in relation to its career in Alaska Territory where the remedy was being sold by the drink in Sitka saloons. Only a little later, the Treasury Department wrote to the Collector of Customs in Sitka to say that in its opinion Hostetter's Bitters "should be excluded from Alaska under the executive order of Feb. 4, 1870, forbidding the importation of distilled spirits into that Territory." That did not end the business. Over the years, in the leisurely manner of government considerations, Hostetter's became a problem of muted conversations and gradually grew into something of an affair.

Was Hostetter's a medicine or an alcoholic beverage? David Hostetter could point out that the formula had been used for many years by his revered father, Dr. Jacob Hostetter, and that its content of alcohol was necessary, though at the time of the Alaska matter it had been reduced somewhat from its Gettysburg or wartime strength. The Commissioner of Internal Revenue found himself in an embarrassing position.

"Containing as it does," he wrote, "no deleterious drugs and only

4 per cent of anything like a drug, I should probably be entirely justified in deciding outright that one who sells it for any purpose was a liquor dealer." And yet the commissioner, a just man, admitted the case to be complicated by the fact that in the past the government had "classed the preparation as a proprietary medicine and collected the stamp tax on it." Was this not a question worthy of Solomon? Consider, wrote the commissioner:

> Should I hold it to be a medicine, I should do violence to an almost irresistible tendency of the mind to conclude that no genuine medicine needs so much whiskey and so few drugs in it, unless under very unusual circumstances. On the other hand, should I decide that it is no medicine at all, I would be confronted by the ten years' quasi recognition by this office to the contrary, as well as by the practice of many people who use it as such.

It was as pretty a statement of the problem as one could wish; and, having said as much, this remarkable Commissioner of Revenue settled it. "Let the use," he ruled, "give character to it. When Hostetter's is sold as a bona fide medicine, no action will be taken. When it is sold to be drunk as an intoxicating beverage, the seller will be taxed accordingly."

Thus did common sense settle, in a manner of speaking, the question of what Hostetter's Celebrated Stomach Bitters was. The commissioner wanted it understood, however, that he meant to keep an eye on the nostrum, and to the Hostetter Company he wrote as follows: "An article that contains so little of what is even nominally medicinal as yours ought and will be subject to very close scrutiny as to its use."

The Alaska case merely added to the legend that had been growing around the Hostetter name. Perhaps only that of Mrs. Pinkham could match it; and long before she went into balladry the name of Hostetter was said to stare at people from every barn, billboard, and boulder west of the Mississippi. It was told, by Westerners, in hoaxing tourists and other greenhorns, that when Jedediah Strong Smith, the paragon of Mountain Men and "the first Smith in California," walked down the west slope of the Sierras in 1826, he passed a monstrous cliff of lava labeled "Hostetter's Bitters"; and that owing to similar neolithic ads noted by John Charles Frémont, the Path-finder became a convert to Hostetter's.

The Hostetter legend operated also in local fields. I myself was not long in Oregon when I heard the incident of two young men, later to be famous in national politics and whose names were not Hayes and Johnson, who planned a Sunday's duck hunting. Saturday night passed before they thought to get the bottle of whisky which all duck hunters held to be as necessary as powder and shot. Oregon bars were closed on Sundays. So, when they were approaching the hunting grounds and came to Rickreall, a hamlet with a big general store, they went in and bought a bottle of Hostetter's, and drove on to the farm operated by young Hayes's father. Here they put their team in the barn, fed the horses and then, because the elder Hayes was known to like his toddy, carefully hid the Bitters in the hay-mow.

Late that afternoon they returned, chilled, wet, and duckless, but happy enough to contemplate the waiting Bitters. They went to the haymow. There, stretched on the floor and sound asleep, was the elder Hayes. The son woke him. As the old man yawned and slowly came to, he spoke. "Son," said he with some deliberation, "do you know what I'd do if I had one thousand dollars?"

"No, Father, what would you do?"

"I'd go right now to Rickreall and buy me one thousand dollars' worth of Hostetter's Bitters."

It was the same sort of folklore which much later grew up around Henry Ford's Model T. Money couldn't buy it.

In Pittsburgh it was said that the fame, fortune, and beard of David Hostetter grew with his Bitters. I do not know at what date Mr. Hostetter's portrait first came to grace the label. He was born in 1819. The portrait on my bottle displays a beard of major size, strikingly white, a beard to make sport of the comparatively dudish facial hair sported by Hostetter's colleagues named Doan, Sloan, Kilmer, and Pierce. I would guess Hostetter's picture to date from the early eighties, when he was in his sixties. I said his beard was a major work. It was more. In all the gallery of nostrum makers there is nothing else like it, nothing else fit to appear so near the fabled scene of St. George (Medicine) slaying the Dragon (Disease).

David Hostetter was also fit to meet the dragons of finance and business in whatever form they appeared. Henry Clay Frick was glad to pay him a reputed $20,000,000 for his Hostetter-Connellsville Coke Company. He held a quarter-interest in Pittsburgh's natural-gas monopoly. He founded banks. He financed the Smithfield Bridge across the Monongahela. He plunged heavily in oil and railroads. In 1874 he built the first oil pipeline from the Butler County field to Pittsburgh. He was even ready to tangle with the all-powerful Pennsylvania Railroad, which, so wrote a local observer, "wanted all oil shipped by rail, and was so infuriated by Hostetter's pipeline, it objected to his right-of-way at one point by hitching a locomotive to his pipe and bursting it."

Hostetter won the next battle and the war, but the Pennsy's churlish efforts rankled in the old man. He proceeded to build the Pittsburgh and Lake Erie Railroad as a gesture of defiance, and sat as its president until his death in 1888.

After David Hostetter's death, occasioned by kidney trouble which, incidentally, was an ailment the Bitters did *not* claim to cure, the Hostetter Company was headed by his son, D. Herbert Hostetter, who is remembered as "a friend of Theodore Roosevelt with whom he ranched in Dakota." He also built an immense home in California where he spent much of his time. He died in 1924, and his son, Frederick, also the absentee type, served as president until his death, in 1930, whereupon D. Herbert Hostetter, Jr., headed the fast-fading business until 1934, when he sold it.

The pattern of genetics of the Hostetters was characteristic of a majority of American big-business families. If you count old Dr. Jacob, the saga of the Bitters lasted into the fourth generation, but only because of the second-generation David, the bearded one, who gave it the impetus to last more than half a century after his death. One is ready to believe that neither David's son nor his grandson had any interest in the Bitters save for what it brought in income. They may or may not have belonged to the idle rich; certainly they were not of the Mogul breed.

The Pure Food and Drug Act brought a lowering of Hostetter's Bitters' alcohol content to 25 per cent by volume, and a change in the text of the label. Sales continued much as in the past. In 1920 the American Medical Association brought public and government attention to bear on the still generous amount of alcohol in Hostetter's, and more than intimated that its medicinal content was a fiction. The only noticeable reform in the company's policy was to change one word in the label—Stomach became Stomachic, a hair-splitting piece of semantics that could have had no effect on either content or sales.

When national Prohibition settled down for a long experiment noble in purpose, Hostetter's sales should have at least trebled. Instead, sales and prestige and profits went into eclipse. The heirs of the dynamic David, either through lack of interest or of complacency, did away with advertising. If anything were needed to demonstrate that the first concomitant of a patent medicine is advertising, Hostetter's fills the bill. During the first four years of Prohibition, sales dropped to less than half of what they had been in 1920. The decline accelerated until D. Herbert Hostetter, who lived in California and liked polo and yachting, was glad to sell it.

In 1935 a new concern, headed by Saunders Norvell, a former president of McKesson & Robbins, was incorporated with a capitalization of $300,000, and stock was issued to raise money for a special radio and newspaper campaign. Apparently the transfusion came too late, for in 1954 came another reorganization with a Charles G. Brown as president. The new outfit was "putting out but one product," which was "being distributed in small volume through wholesale druggists." Its name was Hostetter Tonic.

Hostetter Tonic, whatever its formula, was obviously nothing much to the taste of either the older or the younger generations seeking health. In 1958, in reply to a query, the Pure Food and Drug Administration wrote: "The Hostetter Corporation is definitely out of business, due to the death of the partners last fall. There is no plan to revive the business, although the formula and name may be sold at some later date, according to the firm's attorney."

Thus, after 105 years, the end. The wonderful vision of St. George slaying the Dragon had gone glimmering. Dragons are not to be slain by a tonic.

3

The Remarkable Doctors Pierce

During seventy-five years, beginning in 1867, the fortunate community of Buffalo, New York, was never without a Dr. Pierce engaged in the practice of medicine. Father and son, the two Pierces had distinguished themselves, according to Henry W. Hill's massive four-volume *History of Buffalo*, through the medium of the "institutions of healing" they founded, the "innumerable treatises and essays on medicine and health" they had written and published; and also by reason of "the proprietary medicines they have so widely distributed."

Because of these contributions, "the name of Pierce has been placed in the front rank of this city's most prominent citizens."

This is a statement overmodest to weakness. Historian Hill could well have boasted that the name of Pierce was no better known in Buffalo and in Erie County than it was in each and every one of forty-eight states. It was a poor county indeed that could not display a barn telling either of DR. PIERCE'S GOLDEN MEDICAL DISCOVERY or of DR. PIERCE'S FAVORITE PRESCRIPTION.

It was a bleak farm home, too, whose library did not have a copy of *The People's Common Sense Medical Adviser in Plain English; or, Medicine Simplified*. This was the crowning work of Dr. R. V. Pierce, described on the title page as "One of the staff of Consulting Physicians and Surgeons At the Invalids' Hotel and Surgical Institute, and President of the World's Dispensary Medical Association, Buffalo, New York, U.S.A." Although I shall return to this monument of health and medicine, this is the place to point out that it was first published in 1875, and thirty years later, when the sixty-sixth Edition appeared, no less than 2,140,000 copies had been sold, or at least distributed. It was no trifling pamphlet. It contained 1,008 pages. To say it was profusely illustrated is to make mockery of its several hundred pictures in black-and-white and four full-page plates of a leprous realism so vivid as to cause women to blanch, their children to cry aloud, and the menfolk to break out in sudden sweat.

The long saga of the Doctors Pierce began in 1862 when Ray Vaughn Pierce got his M.D. from the Eclectic Medical College of Cincinnati, then went to Titusville, Pennsylvania, where he was in practice four years before moving to Buffalo, which was to be his home ever after. Already married and the father of Valentine Mott Pierce, one of three sons who were to be associated with him in the family business, the senior Pierce almost at once set up a small laboratory in booming Buffalo and began to manufacture and sell proprietary medicines.

In 1867 the Eclectic school of medicine was growing rapidly. It discarded the powerful mineral remedies of the time and stressed the use of milder drugs derived from plants. Although the graduates of its recognized colleges were authentic M.D.'s, they were often called botanical doctors because of their reliance on the herbals or, as some liked to call them, the Remedies of Nature. Then or now, Nature is a powerful word, symbol of the acceptance of laws that are to be flouted only with dangerous consequences. From about 1850 to the end of the century, the close-to-nature doctors were in high favor.

So, young Eclectic Pierce, already familiar with all of the many botanical drugs in the United States Pharmacopeia, and familiar, too, with the many complaints and weaknesses of females, went to work in his little laboratory to compound an emmenagogue. It must have pleased him very much, for he registered it for copyright as Dr. Pierce's Favorite Prescription.

He must also have some sort of all-purpose tonic, or what medical men called an alterative, a remedy to cause "a favorable change in the disordered functions of the body." Young Pierce knew the answer, and into his mixer went the proper amounts of cinchona, columbo, guaiacum, licorice, opium, podophyllin, glycerine, and alcohol. Here, as he described it, was a compound to tone, sustain and regulate the body functions; and, "while increasing the discharge of noxious elements accumulated in the system, it promptly arrests the wastes arising from debility and the unusual breaking down of the cells incident to quick decline. It stimulates the liver to secrete, changes the sallow complexion, and transforms the listless invalid into a vigorous and healthy being."

Young Pierce not only knew what to put into it. He knew how to wrap it up for the trade; his all-purpose tonic went into the market as Dr. Pierce's Golden Medical Discovery.

Laymen are not competent to assess the therapeutic value of Pierce's compound; but the label on the bottle is something else. GOLDEN . . . DISCOVERY. Here are words to fire the dullest imagination. Either word by itself is potent. Put them together, insert the purpose of the discovery, and there were few listless, sallow-faced invalids still able to breathe immune to the promise of radiant health. Dr. Ray Vaughn Pierce was on the way.

Within a short time the two nostrums were doing so well as to call for a much larger laboratory. It is impossible to say whether the Pierce advertising at this period was confined to newspapers, or if a Pierce crew was already busy painting barns with the two Pierce messages of hope and cheer. It is known, however, that Dr. Pierce was engaged in writing the enormous treatise on health and medicine which, with the reminders on barns, was to produce an unbeatable combination. In July, 1875, he finished writing his *Common Sense Medical Adviser* which, though imitated times without number, never had a peer in the nostrum trade.

The immense labor of compiling the *Medical Adviser* in no manner exhausted Dr. Pierce's many energies. On Prospect Avenue, facing handsome Prospect Park, he built Pierce's Palace Hotel, an imposing hostelry, said a biographer, which was to number among its guests such eminent Americans as President U. S. Grant, President James A. Garfield, and Senator Roscoe Conkling. Dr. Pierce also felt the urge to serve his country, which he did when elected state senator in 1877 on the Republican ticket; and again as Representative in the Forty-sixth Congress.

In all these extracurricular activities, Dr. Pierce never for a moment lost sight of his towering ambition. This was patently a sort of cartel, a Standard Oil Company of medicine; or, to put it more happily, a vast headquarters of health staffed by the world's most eminent specialists, equipped as no single physician could hope for, with every known piece of scientific apparatus; a dispensary of the drugs of the world (doubtless including all the botanicals); a luxury hotel as hospital; in short, what we today might think of as a period Battle Creek and Mayo Clinic combined.

Dreams like this do not come full blown to fruition—a fact Dr. Pierce, the product of eight generations of Massachusetts Yankees, well appreciated. His first step was to found the Invalids' Hotel and Surgical Institute (Not a Hospital but a Pleasant Remedial Home) which took form, at 663 Main Street, Buffalo, as an immense four-story building of brick and sandstone. It was elegant in the meaning of that word in 1891 when it was finished, and by then patients were coming from afar. The main building had not been ready long before it was necessary to put up an Annex.

Among the physicians who joined the staff of the Invalids' Hotel and Surgical Institute was young Dr. Valentine Mott Pierce, A.B., Harvard, 1888, and M.D., University of Buffalo, 1891, who later became secretary-manager and, on the death of his father, president of the Institute. Other Pierces were coming along. Dr. Ray's second son, Ralph Waldo, was to enter the family business through the advertising and accounting departments, and was made treasurer; and a third son, Hugh, worked his way upward to the post of secretary. Still another member of the family, Dr. Franklin Duane Pierce, M.D., Syracuse University, 1904, a nephew of Dr. Ray's, joined the staff of the Invalids' Hotel.

Now that the first step in the elder Dr. Pierce's soaring ambition had been so successful, he moved ahead to incorporate the World's Dispensary Medical Association, a subsidiary of which was the World's Dispensary and Surgical Institute. The "Consulting Department" was merged with the Invalids' Hotel. The official seal of the Association shows a bearded figure leaning on a Staff of Aesculapius, a rod with only one serpent encircling it. (This is the correct symbol of the medical profession.) He is standing on the top of a world globe, rays of the sun blazing up from behind him. Below on the seal's margin are the names of two cities, Buffalo and London. (Dr. Pierce had announced that a European Branch of the Association had been opened at No. 3 New Oxford Street, London.)

Some of the most entertaining pages of Dr. Pierce's illuminating *Medical Adviser* are devoted to the Invalids' Hotel and Surgical Institute. Illustrations on every page lead the visitor to the Main Entrance, then take him, step by step, through every department. This is no hasty tour, for there is much to be seen and admired:

The magnificent main portals are breathtaking in their complicated elegance; that the invalids entering the premises are of high quality is clear from the conveyance waiting to disgorge more invalids; it is a fancy carriage driven by a coachman with a cockade on his silk hat. In the anteroom a Negro butler bows to accept the card of a patient; and so on to the Gentlemen's Reception Room and the Ladies' Parlor, the latter equipped with a grand piano; both open upon the Library and Reading Room, where magazines, newspapers, and books vie for attention with framed artistic prints and the busts of noted scholars. Then comes President Pierce's Office, with the neatly bearded Chief Physician in swivel chair at roll-top desk burdened with flowers, the walls an art gallery in themselves. Smaller but every bit as fine is one of the Private Consultation Rooms. In another consultation room a male patient is Undergoing Examination of the Lungs, and though even here the walls are crawling with art, an imposing array of scientific apparatus is to be seen.

It is when we come to a Patient's Room that we can appreciate the sumptuous quarters prepared for the Invalids. Neither the Waldorf in New York nor the Palmer House in Chicago could have offered more of elegance. The many operating rooms of necessity present scenes a little grim in comparison, but they are obviously equipped with "the most modern apparatus"; and the full-page view of "the Faculty in Session" immediately reminds one of "the Full Staff of Eighteen Physicians and Surgeons" ready to pool their knowledge for the benefit of Dr. Pierce's patients.

The conducted tour continues on into the Chemical Laboratory where, so one learns, there is a single boiler-shaped tank capable of storing ten thousand gallons of medicine, surely enough Golden Medical Discovery and Favorite Prescription to help, if not to cure at once, the one hundred thousand mail-order patients unquestionably dependent on Dr. Pierce's therapy. Handy to the great medical storage tank are the Bottling, Wrapping, and Mailing departments, alive with young women busy at long tables.

Because nothing is held back from visitors, one is shown the vast Printing Department where wrappers, labels, and literature are fed through the monstrous R. Hoe and Company's Web Press. This is the same machine, too, that uttered at least the Sixty-sixth Edition of *The People's Common Sense Medical Adviser in Plain English.*

One may be either delighted or appalled to contemplate the several million Americans who relied, over the decades, on the medical advice offered by this work; but there can be but one opinion of its value to Dr. Pierce's business. It was incomparable. Even a casual reading in it shows how the doctor's discussion of Biology, Physiological Anatomy, the Special Senses, the Human Temperaments, along with Marriage, Love, and Reproduction, leads, invariably, to mention of Remedies for Disease, and then, naturally enough, to mention of Dr. Pierce's specific recommendations, which were two in number.

Because some of his readers might be unfamiliar with technical terms employed by doctors, there were twelve pages of working vocabulary that must have left them at ease with everything from *Acacia Catechu* and the *Acetabulum* to *Vitreous Humors* and the *Volitive Temperament.* There is a General Index, and Index to Appendix, and a fine "Map of Central Portion of Buffalo" which shows not only the location of the five railroad depots, but also that of the Invalids' Hotel, 663 Main Street. Hardly noticeable in the book's 1,008 pages are the modest six pages of testimonials, captioned "As Others See Us," from more or less prominent male citizens of Buffalo; and another forty-four pages telling of the undying gratitude of women who had been patients in the Invalids' Hotel—or what we may properly term out-patients—cured by the Favorite Prescription. One way or the other, Dr. Pierce delivered the goods.

One should not forget that while generations of Americans were reading the *Common Sense Medical Adviser,* millions more of them were reading every day Dr. Pierce's brief yet potent messages on the barns of the United States. One is ready to believe that although Dr. Pierce's face, which appeared only in the frontispiece of his book, was unknown compared to the comforting likeness of Mrs. Pinkham, the same was not true of Dr. Pierce's medicines. They got around.

Dr. Pierce's income was such as to permit interests other than medicine. These included the Pierce Development Company and the Pierce Coal and Lumber Company, operating on 20,000 acres of pine timber and mineral deposits in Alabama; and 300 acres of farmland in the Berkshires of Massachusetts, once the home of the doctor's great-grandfather.

On the death of Dr. Ray Pierce in 1914, Dr. V. Mott Pierce took the helm, operating the Invalids' Hotel and Surgical Institute for another three decades, until its discontinuance in 1941, meanwhile serving as president of the World's Dispensary Medical Association. Despite the fact that he was a member of both the Erie County and New York State Medical societies, he was never shy about the Golden Medical Discovery or the Favorite Prescription. In 1900, and again in 1923, Dr. V. Mott Pierce was elected president of the Proprietary Association of America, the group of patent-medicine men who never turned the other cheek when attacked by organized medicine or the Pure Food and Drug Administration.

Samuel Hopkins Adams came to rate the younger Dr. Pierce as the most aggressive of the Proprietary Association's stalwarts in their war against state and Federal laws seeking to restrict patent-medicine advertising and labeling. He was a forward-looking man, too, undismayed either by the attacks on the patents generally or by those specifically on the Pierce remedies. To show his faith in the future be founded at Port Allegany, Pennsylvania, the Pierce Glass Company, whose product was bottles. Indeed, the future looked so inviting to this Dr. Pierce that in 1897 he bought the first horseless carriage in Buffalo, a Pope-Columbia, and three years later was one of the founders of the Buffalo Automobile Club.

By the time of the younger Pierce's passing, in 1942, the family's remaining medicine interests had been merged into Pierce's Proprietaries, Inc., which included the Favorite Prescription and the Golden Medical Discovery. Sixteen years later, in June, 1958, a rambling photographer laid eyes on a newly painted barn, a few miles from Chehalis, Washington, and came away with a really fine picture indicating that though the two Doctors Pierce had passed to their rewards, the old reliable twin remedies were as full of life as they had been when first made more than ninety years before. Barring an even more radical change in patent-medicine fashions than has yet occurred, Dr. Pierce's message of hope, which has outlived that of Dr. Hostetter and many another, may call for many more coats of paint in the years ahead.

4

The Giant Oxien

Undeviating Republicanism and dogged adherence to a Bone-Dry Law were for decades on end an indication that State-of-Mainers were no flighty people. They were not given to fads. During the golden age of quackery, only one patent medicine manufactured there achieved much of a national success, and it contained not a drop of alcohol. This was Oxien Tablets, sold by The Giant Oxie Company of Augusta, the Maine capital. These tablets were the original source of a sizable fortune represented by the Guy Gannett chain of newspapers and radio stations.

Oxien was dreamed up in the mid-eighties by William H. Gannett, the father of Guy, who operated both a variety store in Augusta and a soaring imagination. At a time when other Yankees were bottling potent mixtures under such names as Sarsaparilla or Celery Compound or Painkiller, and various Bitters, Gannett introduced Oxien as something which, among other things, "Cures Drunkards and Makes Weak Women Walk."

Merchant Gannett got into the patent-medicine business by way of the new soda fountain in his variety store. He noticed that by far the most popular soft drink was Moxie Nerve Food, a dark-colored liquid with a sort of rootbeer flavor, much like the later Coca-Cola. From a Boston chemist Gannett bought a formula which, though admittedly based on that of Moxie, had been "much improved" by the addition of other therapeutic agents, including extract of beef.

To advertise this plagiarized if improved Moxie Nerve Food, Gannett thought up a singularly revolting trade-mark, The Oxien Giant. No advertising agency of the time could have conceived so hideous a monster. Gannett's Giant was a muscular, thick-set creature with the body of a man and the head of an ox, maned and bearded, whose upraised hand held a huge, wicked-looking club. He seemed to be threatening Civilization. Beneath this bestial figure was the pitch: *Great Strength which all may share in if they but use the new and wonderful Oxien."*

This Oxien Giant was an appalling thing, when I was a child. And when, sixty years later, I saw him again, in the crumbling pages of *Comfort*, of which more presently, he was still appalling; and I was caused to wonder at the strange genius of William H. Gannett who, in a time when the hope of invalids lay in the hands of the kindly bearded doctors of the labels, conjured up this monster straight out of the visions of Daniel in the Old Testament. Yet there he *was*, and for half a century he *sold* Oxien Tablets beyond all count. It was too much to comprehend. I wonder what Dr. Freud would have made of him.

If the new and wonderful Oxien was an "improved Moxie," it also owed something of its original sales pitch to Moxie Nerve Food, which, according to the Moxie people, was "prepared from a plant, hitherto wholly unknown to botanists, discovered by a Lieutenant Moxie." Be that as it may, it was no mere lieutenant who discovered "the fruit of the Baobab tree" on which Oxien was based. It was a general. Gannett cooked up a pleasing little romance about this anonymous general who, "exhausted by the Rebellion and excesses," had gone to Africa for his health. "But the elephantine clime," said the Gannett Oxien copy, "did nothing for him until one day while lying on the ground, he happened to touch his lips to the fruit of the Baobab tree."

Gannett did not explain whether the general was "lying on the ground" because of his own excesses, or suffering sunstroke, but the officer opened his mouth and took a good big bite of the fruit. He was so soon restored to a condition bursting with health that he gathered a vast quantity of the fruit and hastened back to America where "it was found to be of great benefit to the Human Family."

Just possibly inspired by something in Mrs. Pinkham's excellent advertising, Gannett, an eclectic if ever there lived one, added a line to the effect that owing to the discovery of the Baobab fruit, and its presentation in the form of Oxien, there was "no longer danger of the extinction of our race."

Being a man who believed in utilizing an idea to its fullest extent, Gannett put Oxien on the market simultaneously as a medicine in the form of Oxien Health Tablets and as a soft drink. Buying a complete bottling outfit, he set it up in "the old Academy building on Cony Street, Augusta." He had the Oxien tablets made for him by a Boston house and shipped in barrels for packaging by The Giant Oxie (no "n") Company.

The tablets were "square, pale orange lozenges"; and at first Gannett planned to sell them chiefly through agents. He also began preparing a carnival-type ballyhoo for the soft drink. He bought a fine team and a covered wagon on which he had a local artist paint The Oxien Giant, then sent it with a couple of men to cover the state and county fairs. For the sake of the record, this soft drink, which sold at five cents a glass on the grounds, was a dilution of the essence of the magic Baobab tree, or *Adansonia digitata*."

Young Gannett's business career up to this time had been only as a merchant and a sawmill operator. He was, however, an observant fellow, and right there in Augusta he had seen the rise of two successful publishing concerns which by the 1880's were circulating tons of so-called story magazines named *Hearth and Home*, *The Literary Companion*, *Fireside Visitor*, *Good Stories*, and *Happy Hours*. The tone of this trash was highly moral. Its literary quality was a little less than zero. All of the periodicals carried patent-medicine advertisements. All were making money. *Hearth and Home* was said to be a mint.

Into this unfamiliar business young Gannett moved with one idea: a medium to promote Oxien products. With the luck that is said to accompany inexperienced gamblers, he chose a name that was to attract more than one million subscribers. It was *Comfort*. Just common comfort, it seemed, was "The Key to Happiness and Success"; and the cover of Gannett's pulp-paper *Comfort* displayed twenty-four scenes rubbing it in. There was the Comfort of Sailing, of simply Reclining in a Hammock, of Walking, Reading and, because Gannett was no reformer, the Comfort of Smoking. There was one scene indicating that comfort was to be had from Feeding Chickens. Indeed, comfort infiltrated the magazine throughout, beginning on Page 3 with the editor's "Comfortable Talks about Matters and Things."

The early issues of *Comfort* were printed on the press of the local daily, the *Kennebec Journal*. The first run, dated November, 1888, was thirteen thousand copies. Two years later, so surely did Lumber-man-Merchant-Editor Gannett gage his public, *Comfort* had a monthly run of one hundred thousand copies and had reached the ultimate capacity of the newspaper's press. Here, in the parlance of Maine, was a real corker. Gannett took over an old corset factory, purchased a $10,000 Hoe press, for which he gave his personal notes, and was prepared to print and fold one hundred thousand *Comforts* daily, if need be.

Now he had it. "Oxien and *Comfort*," as a Gannett biographer remarked, "made an unbeatable team."

The yearly subscription rate of *Comfort* was twenty-five cents. Although the new Hoe press was never called upon to print one hundred thousand *Comforts* a day, the magazine grew swiftly in circulation and size, but it never deviated from a literary quality of the lowest common denominator. By the end of the nineteenth century its logotype said it was The Key to Happiness and Success in Over a Million and a Quarter Homes. As an industry it had nudged Augusta's many sawmills into second place.

Barrels upon barrels of Oxien Health Tablets rolled into the little city, to be packaged locally, then shipped. (The soft drink seems to have petered out.) Those square, pale-orange tinted lozenges continued to cure an ever increasing number of ills, as evidenced by testimonials from grateful people in all parts of the United States and Canada. Mark you, among them were cases of dyspepsia, kidney complaint, malaria, colds, headache, and other such trifles; but also cases like insanity, alcoholism, and fading beauty. Nor did Gannett forget to remind his enormous if sickly public that "Oxien Makes Weak Women Walk."

If these far-reaching claims of cures should strike present-day Americans as obnoxiously crude, then they have remarkable loss of memory, or they were born too late to have seen patent-medicine advertising at its blatant best. Gannett's all-out pitch for The Giant Oxien was exactly right to fetch the customers he was after. In time he added Oxien Laxative Pills, Oxien Nazone Salve, Oxien Pile Treatment, Oxien Porous Plasters, and Oxien Special Back Plasters.

The Gannetts, father and son, were alert to the changing times. By 1910, or four years after the first Pure Food and Drug Act went into force, the claims of The Oxien Giant had been reduced to rhetorical questions. How Is Your Health? asked the advertisement;

then it went on to mention a whole slew of symptoms, and to inquire, "Wouldn't You Like to Feel Good Again?" If you read on,
you learned that Oxien Tablets were merely "a combination of
Pure Vegetable Tonics from Nature's Great Storehouse of Healing."

This was pretty weak stuff, compared to the God-given fruit of
the Baobab tree that raised fallen generals from the ground; but
Oxien was not alone in feeling the restrictions of government; the
nostrums that did not or could not conform were heading for
oblivion. Oxien might be worthless, as the American Medical Association said it was, but in itself it was harmless. It contained neither
narcotic nor alcohol. It was the nostrums containing opium deriv-
atives that were hardest hit by the new legislation and, after them,
the so-called Bracers, or substitutes for hard liquor.

In 1901, at the age of twenty, Guy P. Gannett, oldest son of the
founder of Oxien and *Comfort,* went to work in the company's home
office, and later to England on business connected with the Gannett
Trading Company of London, then returned to Augusta where
gradually he took over management of *Comfort*-Oxien from the
elder Gannett. But the son, so a long-time employee recalled, did his
work "without the cooperation of his heart." Apparently he just did
not care a great deal for either the medicine or the magazine. In 1921
he suddenly found what he wanted to do.

With both the means and the necessary credit, Guy Gannett
bought first the *Portland Press Herald,* then the *Waterville Morning Sentinel,* then the *Maine Farmer,* an eighty-year-old weekly.
The Gannett Publishing Company was formed; and it went on to
buy other Maine newspapers, and to buy or found radio stations, all
of which are beyond the province of this book.

Both Gannetts survived the long heyday of *Comfort* and Oxien,
which together were the original source of the Gannett fortune. As
of 1920, rural Americans were reading just as much trash as ever
before, as were urban Americans, too; but it was a slowly changing
trash. Thus, *Comfort* faded slowly. It was permitted to die quietly.
The Oxien business was sold to the Newbert family of Augusta.
The astute Newberts knew well enough that styles in patent medicines had radically changed; they changed the pitch of Oxien products.

"We soon dispensed with that monstrosity on the label known as

The Giant Oxien," Mr. John Newbert wrote to me. "We modernized the packaging to meet new standards. The demand for Oxien health tablets, which we advertised very modestly only as an appetizer, declined ever so slowly. Not until 1955, or thirty-five years after we bought out the Gannetts, did we decide the business was no longer worth the trouble of filling orders. We simply closed out all of the Oxien line."

The Giant Oxien was Maine's greatest and most durable pitch in the world of patent medicines. But nothing was safe or sacred any longer in a world where the State of Maine was ready to vote for a Democrat for President, and even to license the sale of what were admittedly intoxicating liquors.

5

Old Hinkley's Bone Liniment

It is probable that almost any well defined region of the United States had, at one time or another, a local nostrum of considerable popularity. Examples that come readily to mind were Fosgate's Anodyne Cordial, made at Auburn, New York, as early as the 1860's; Vermilyea's Oil of Life, of Grover, Pennsylvania; Dr. Leeson's Tiger Oil, long the pride of Cadillac, Michigan; and Lady Poor's Ointment, a New England favorite made in the hamlet of Bath, New Hampshire.

But neither these nor any of hundreds more could have achieved more luster and greater notoriety than Hinkley's Bone Liniment, which in 1959 was in its 103rd year and was still made, as it has been since 1856, in Saginaw, Michigan.

The story of Hinkley's is not technically a family saga, for its ownership changed hands several times over the decades; but unlike uncounted other "local patents" it is still on the market, made in the same place under the same brand, and is presumably performing the identical wonders that brought it fame when James Buchanan was President of the United States and Michigan was noted not for automobiles but for the excellence of its white pine lumber, lath, and shingles.

Saginaw was about to become the Sawmill Capital of the World, a concentration of manufacturing plants such as had never been seen before. At the same time the growing city was already the favorite place for loggers from camps all over Michigan, Ontario, and northern Wisconsin, to spend their winter's wages. When in the spring the drive came down, Saginaw's gaslights went on with full brilliance in the many saloons, fancy houses, and other dives that lined the riverfront.

The town was also the supply and outfitting center for camps and loggers. It was as logical as it was proper that James A. Hinkley should have selected Saginaw as the place to manufacture and distribute the sovereign remedy for all the ills that plagued the lads who cut the white pine into logs, then in the spring drove them down the Flint, the Shiawassee, Cass, and Tittabawassee rivers which united to form the Saginaw, and so on to the mills that whined and smoked day and night for decades on end.

Loggers were a race apart whose very occupation tended to eliminate the weaklings. One does not think of loggers as invalids. Nor were they invalids. Yet they were beset by occupational ills among which were several known generically as the rheumatics and which, under style of Muscular Pains, was significantly the first ill mentioned in the Directions for Use on the label of Hinkley's Bone Liniment. Hinkley's was no balm to trifle with; it penetrated right to and even through the bone.

Another dreaded ill, of acute rather than chronic variety, was simple hangover which Hinkley's label preferred to describe merely as Headache. But, lest victims of hangover missed reading the paragraph citing the many uses of the liniment, Hinkley's label had one line in larger boldface type to catch the jaundiced eye: Alcohol 47 Per Cent.

Who James A. Hinkley was, not even the liniment's present proprietor, Mr. Lynn R. Filbert, knows. Assuredly he was a man who recognized a need when he saw it and at Saginaw, in 1856, even then dusty and aromatic from sawdust, he compounded the first batch of his historic Bone Liniment. It is worth mention that Homeopathy seems never to have penetrated deeply into the timbered regions of the United States; and because lumberjacks favored heroic measures, Hinkley's then and for many years to come, until the government intervened, contained 86 per cent alcohol by volume.* Though success attended the remedy from the first, Hinkley sold the business and in the mid-eighties was serving his country as a deputy collector of Internal Revenue, among whose duties was the collection of taxes on intoxicants. The sequence of later proprietors of Hinkley's Bone Liniment is not exactly clear, but at one time or another they included

---

* In his *Secret Nostrums, a Book of Formulas,* Dr. Charles W. Oleson said the active ingredients of Hinkley's were: oil of wormword, oil of hemlock, oil of thyme, oil of turpentine, fluid extract of capsicum, and "alcohol to make."

D. F. Foster, D. E. Prall & Company, Mrs. Calvin Wadsworth, and the present owner, Lynn R. Filbert.

What is clear is that for over a century Hinkley's has been a philter of such legendary properties as to awe skeptics and demolish detractors. On the wangan (commissary) shelves of hundreds of logging camps it stood, as invariable a necessity as Peerless and Spearhead and, later, Copenhagen, which were favorite brands of smoking and chewing tobaccos. Patriarchs of the woods attributed what seem to have been miracles to Hinkley's. Internally or externally, as a carminative or a liniment, it got quickly down to business. And it was, to quote its myriad devotees, A Medicine Chest in Itself. In the gloom of night, on the wangan shelf, Hinkley's was said to glow through label and package with a luminous aura never seen to emanate from any other nostrum.

One of its several proprietors, D. F. Foster, could not always contain himself within common prose when he thought of the marvel of Hinkley's, but must sing in meter:

> Remember, then, this Pain's Great Master
> Is made alone by D. F. Foster,
> Who far and near spreads its renown
> From Jefferson Street, East Saginaw Town.

And when, in May, 1901, another proud proprietor of Hinkley's, Mr. Prall, noticed a libel in Saginaw's morning paper, he was quick to correct the canard and make a little hay, too. "This morning's *Courier Herald*," he wrote, "erroneously states that I have just been discharged from the Saginaw General Hospital. I have never been an inmate of this or any other hospital. I have not lost a day from illness for 30 years which, I hope, speaks well for the drugs I sell, Yours Truly, D. E. Prall, The Hinkley Bone Liniment Company."

No crossroads store in farthest Michigan, no great department store in Detroit or Grand Rapids, failed to stock Hinkley's; and though little or no effort seems to have been made to invade foreign parts, it is a standard item today (1959) not only in Michigan but in many drugstores of Ohio, Wisconsin and Minnesota.

Some time before January 1, 1918, the Pure Food and Drug Administration sought to tamper with Hinkley's formula, and the alcohol content was reduced from 86 per cent to its present pitiful 47 per cent. Again, the Federal authorities stepped in to forbid the use of "Bone" in the title, and it became Old Hinkley's Liniment. The venerable adjective had been well earned. Over the decades whole cords of crutches had been tossed away because of Hinkley's. Uncounted belches have been freed by its carminative powers. As for hangovers, it is not long since a veteran of the logging camps and river drives, now retired to Harbor Springs, Michigan, was heard to remark that "Hinkley's has always been superior in this field to the more widely known Hostetter's Bitters and the Painkiller of Perry Davis." Acclaim beyond that statement is hyperbole, and not to be trusted.

The present proprietor, Lynn R. Filbert, Saginaw pharmacist who bought Hinkley's in 1947, is as assured as he is modest in his claims. Besides relieving muscular soreness, he says, it can be recommended for minor throat irritations. Used externally, it is "non-greasy, very penetrating, and will not blister the skin. It is also impervious to changes in weather."

Mr. Filbert may well be proud that "five generations testify to Hinkley's usefulness when the physician is not within reach"; and I can imagine he is happy that, because the remedy no longer penetrates to and through the bone, the original trade-mark was long ago discarded. Its striking feature was a gruesomely dainty blue-tinted bone against a background of vermilion.

PART EIGHT

The World of Medicine Shows

1

The Queen of Pitch Doctors

The world of medicine shows comprised a few big outfits like Healy and Bigelow, to be discussed later, which operated the many Kickapoo troupes, and lone pitch doctors whose total equipment was a banjo-shaped benzine torch and a tripod and suitcase known in the trade as a tripes and keister. Healy and Bigelow were mass-production men. They had their own factory. The lone pitch doctor concocted his medicine daily as needed. In between these extremes were many practitioners who had the stuff made for them by a drug-manufacturing house.

When in the maturity of her years I came to know the late and remarkable Mrs. Violet Blossom, once the very Queen of Female Pitch Doctors, she recalled proudly that for a decade or more "the largest drug-mill in the United States" supplied her requirements. "My private formulas were on file with them," she said. "I could write or wire at any time for a barrel of this or that. It came in 110-pound drums. We bottled or packaged it ourselves, then affixed the labels."

It had not always been so simple. Mrs. Blossom recalled her early days in the business, around 1904, when she and her husband took to the road with two "original" medicines they had thought up. One was a salve called Tiger Fat, the other some pills they were pleased to call Vital Sparks. For many reasons these remedies were manufactured in whatever hotel or roominghouse the couple made their headquarters.

"Our Tiger Fat had a Vaseline* base," Mrs. Blossom remembered. "We melted the Vaseline in a large bucket over a gas jet, adding gum camphor, menthol crystals, oil of eucalyptus, turpentine, and oil of wintergreen. We shaved paraffin into the mixture to make it

* Vaseline is the registered brand name of a line of products including Petroleum jelly.

187

set, then stirred it briskly. While it was cooking, we'd spread out
several dozen small round tin boxes, their lids off, on the table. We
got the boxes from the same drugstore where we got the drugs.
Then, while the mixture was still hot, we poured it into the little
boxes.

"A label was important. Though we changed the directions-for-
use of the Tiger Fat from year to year, our policy was to be fairly
vague. Simply 'Tiger Fat, To Be Used as Needed,' or something
similar. Then we listed the things it was good for—eczema, ring-
worm, and so on, including rheumatism, old sores, burns, and what-
not."

Tiger Fat, boxed and labeled, cost about seven cents to make.
Vital Sparks, however, was much cheaper. It had to be, for this was
a sort of come-on. It was priced on each box at five dollars, then
given away free with every box of Tiger Fat purchased. Either that, or
it was sold for a token dime in connection with the salve, which
invariably cost one dollar.

In the manufacture of Vital Sparks, Violet, as I shall call her,
displayed considerable ingenuity, a faculty commonly developed in
the profession. "The first thing was to buy a great big bag of small
round hard black candy called buckshot candy," she said. "We
poured this into an empty bureau drawer, sprinkled water over it,
then shook the drawer back and forth until the candy was damp.
Next I threw over it a handful of powdered aloes, shook the drawer
again until the pellets were covered with a thin coating of the bitter
drug. The batch was ready to transfer the pellets into small paste-
board packages.

"Our label for this medicine was cryptic—'Vital Sparks, God's
Great Gift to MEN.' Use of the male plural made the medicine's
purpose fairly clear to all men over sixteen years old. But if it didn't,
our lecture attempted to make matters plain."

The pitches for both Tiger Fat and Vital Sparks had an Oriental
cast. Mrs. Blossom at this period was billed as Lotus Blossom, an
English-speaking Chinese of mandarin lineage. When I knew her,
Violet was in her sixties, and had developed a certain amount of
flesh. She might, indeed, have been termed comfortably stout. Yet
she retained a good deal of what must have been a dynamic personality. She had an excellent voice, used good English, and was highly
intelligent. A photograph of her as Lotus Blossom presented a charm-

ing picture of a short, slim, and very pretty Chinese girl. I began to understand how she had managed to survive three busy decades in a racket dominated by and composed almost wholly of men.

Her pitch, or lecture, for Tiger Fat was no more than good average med-show con. Into it she brought a visiting prince, taken on a hunt by some mandarin or other, and badly mauled by a tiger. His life was despaired of until an ancient Chinese physician had the tiger skinned and cut up, and then had the pieces put into a pot and rendered. Anointed with this fat and marrow the injured prince made a rapid and marvelous recovery.

But Violet's pitch for Vital Sparks was an outstanding lecture. I heard her give it "cold," once when I alone was the audience; and again in company of Robert Mahaffay, a newspaper reporter who was later to help Violet write a book. Mr. Mahaffay and I agreed that she could have had few if any male peers, and we regret to this day that we did not make a recording of her lecture. I hesitate to attempt to reproduce the finesse of her quiet eloquence in praise of Vital Sparks.

Violet as Lotus Blossom began her great pitch by relating a Chinese custom which I am sure was news to her audience; namely, that in China the secrets of medicine descended, over the centuries, through the female side of the houses of mandarins. This served to explain how this attractive young Chinese female was able to tell a group of men about Vital Sparks.

During the reign of the Whang Po Dynasty, a strange thing happened. All over the vast Empire the birth rate suddenly dropped to a fraction of its usual figure. Rich and poor alike were affected. Whereupon the Emperor publicly offered the enormous sum of millions of yen—which Lotus Blossom quickly translated, for her Occidental audience, into ten thousand dollars—for a remedy to restore normal vitality to several hundred million people. All efforts met with failure until a scientist, named He Tuck Chaw, came to the Emperor with a discovery which, within nine months or so, proved its worth. Little Lotus Blossom went into some detail.

"While exploring a volcanic region in Outer Mongolia," she explained, "He Tuck Chaw noticed untold numbers of small turtle-like animals. At first glance they all seemed identical in appearance. At rare intervals, however, he found one distinguished by beautiful golden stripes. This was of mild interest but at first did not impress him. Then, one day it occurred to him to wonder about the reason for the scarcity of the golden-striped turtles. Why?

"Although these little turtles were familiar to He Tuck Chaw, as of the Kup Ki See species, his curiosity was so aroused that he caught seven thousand of them and sat down, with the infinite patience of the Chinese, to investigate. It turned out that the brightly striped ones were males, and that the ratio of male to female was almost exactly one male to twelve hundred females."

(Here Lotus Blossom paused, ever so briefly, to permit the ratio of one to twelve hundred to sink in.)

"Sure now that he was on the brink of a discovery to shake the world, He Tuck Chaw pushed his studies forward with a new light in his eyes. Was not the fate of all China in the balance? He simply must determine the source of this incredible vitality possessed by the pitiably few but most potent males of these turtles."

Here, as Violet explained to me, it was Lotus Blossom's custom to pause again, and briefly to sweep her audience with one quick bold challenging look; and then, as if startled by so unladylike an action in herself, instantly to drop her eyes in a convincing try for girlish confusion. She herself came to believe that this piece of acting prompted the less sophisticated and slower witted of her audience to see in exactly what direction He Tuck Chaw's discovery was leading. Then she resumed:

"He Tuck Chaw found that the male differed from the female only in that it possessed a small pouch at the base of the brain. To this organ, for the sake of scholarly nomenclature, he gave the name of *Quali Quah pouch*. Then, working swiftly, he removed the pouches of the males he had captured, dried and powdered them, and hastened to the Emperor's court.

"Now, the Emperor, already desperate at the failure of his favorite physicians to do anything about the diminishing vitality of the Chinese people, told He Tuck Chaw he should at once be given several patients to experiment upon; and that if his Quali Quah powder was not effective immediately, then off came He Tuck Chaw's head. But if, on the other hand, the powder proved its worth, then he should not only receive the Emperor's prize, but other honors and emoluments should be his.

"My friends, do you know what sorry, hopeless victims of impotence the Emperor presented to He Tuck Chaw? All of them had passed seventy years of age; and one, the Emperor's own uncle, had passed fourscore and nine. Think of it! Mostly they were too weak to stand. These were the poor wretches brought forth to test the goodness of Quali Quah. . . . It was no laughing matter, I can assure you, when He Tuck Chaw looked upon these virtual—these virtual eunuchs and contemplated the chance of his own escape from the promised ax. . . ."

Here Lotus Blossom lowered her voice. The audience fairly stopped breathing to catch the words. The words came slowly, deliberately, with all the clarity of an unusual bell-like contralto voice:

"Gentlemen, in the space of four hours, those horrid examples of lost manhood were flexing muscles unused for decades, and were crying aloud, *Pong Wook-ee!* which as all of you know is the Chinese equivalent of Eureka!"

Whether or not they knew the Chinese equivalent, the youthful, the middle generation, and the aging males in the audience were ready, and Lotus Blossom finished her pitch.

"And, gentlemen, there is sufficient quantity of Quali Quah powder in these Vital Sparks, which I am now about to offer, to restore you to the identical condition of virility that has made China a marvel, as well as a problem, to the modern world. . . .

"I am not going to *sell* them tonight. I am going to *give* them away! Every one of you who buys a box of Tiger Fat at one dollar gets a five-dollar trial package of Vital Sparks. Think of it!"

They may not have exactly *thought*, but they put their dollars on the line, to go happily from the tent or opera house with the two miraculous medicines from Outer Mongolia in their pockets.

Men of Grand Rapids, men of Seattle, men of El Paso, and men of much of the intervening country saw and heard Lotus Blossom; and went away with one dollar's worth of hope in their pockets; and if in time the hope disappeared to leave nothing noticeable in its place, nevertheless they had heard one of the really great artists of the med-show world give what she privately called the Pong Wook-ee Lecture. It was worth one dollar.

In time Violet (Lotus) Blossom tired of the same old pitch. "I wanted to work herbs," is the way she described her next line of goods. Possibly she considered that medicinal herbs gave her a higher status in the trade than things like Vital Sparks and Tiger Fat. After all, status was not unknown in the pitch-doctor profession.

"I got my ingredients," she remembered, "from conventional wholesale drug concerns. Alexandria senna, cascara bark, Cape aloes, sassafras, sugar, baking soda, berberis root, and star aniseed. The herbs came finely ground, each in a separate bag.

"Our laboratory, for mixing the herbs according to my own formulas, was a hotel bathtub. I'd get one of our men to wash the tub with Lysol and water and dry it carefully. I'd give him the drugs to dump into the tub, then mix them with his hands. All of us, usually four or five, then filled regulation two-ounce spice tins, pasted on the various labels, and all was ready. We sold the stuff, which stood us about eight to ten cents, at one dollar a copy."

All labels on the two-ounce tins said they contained a "Pure Concentrate of Madame V. Pasteur's Herbs." And Vi refurbished her garb and personality to fit the new pitch. "From a theatrical costume house," she said, "I rented a college cap and gown. The get-up took so well with my first crowds that I had a ladies' tailor make me another that really fitted, of fine material. I never mentioned the name of Louis Pasteur, nor pretended I was of his family. I just left the matter up to the imagination and knowledge of the customers. They were never overburdened with knowledge, medical or otherwise, but it's possible that some of the boys had heard of Pasteur and drew their own conclusions. In any case, it was obvious my new character brought increased respect."

After a few weeks Madame Vi Pasteur thought best to add an item or two to her lecture. She had noted that Dr. Hartman, the Peruna man, was advertising his nostrum as a cure for all kinds of catarrh. He listed catarrh of the bowels, of the stomach, of the lungs, of the pelvic and all other regions Vi had ever heard of. So the new label of V. Pasteur's Herbs mentioned in blackface type that they cured "All Recognized kinds of Catarrh," then went down the line to cite the numerous catarrhs of Dr. Hartman, and a few which Vi added.

To give support to the claims of her new pitch, Vi Pasteur devised a new Convincer. On the sound theory of pitch doctors that seeing is believing, she added to her equipment a glass graduate, a glass drinking tube, some vinegar in a tiny vial, and a bottle of limewater. These things added up to a gimmick both scientific and impressive. In short, a fine Convincer.

After making her opening, which now was all Science, Vi lifted the bottle of limewater. "This," said she, "is pure water. To prove it is water, and nothing else, I am going to take a swallow." And she did, then poured some of the limewater into the glass graduate and stuck the drinking tube into it. "Now," she said, "I want someone in the audience, who is suffering from catarrh and may not know it, to step forward." There was always a native or "local" who thought he had catarrh. When he stepped up, Vi addressed the brave volunteer. "Take this graduate, if you will, and blow through the tube into the water. If you have catarrh the water will turn a milky color."

The local blew, the limewater bubbled and, as limewater always will, it turned the color of milk.

Madame Pasteur held aloft the graduate. "Hm-mm-mm"—the the sound had the right flavor of a warning, even of regret— "Hm-mm-mm, gentlemen, this—man—has—catarrh. You can see for yourselves." When this had sunk in, Vi told the now attentive audience she was going to show them, simply and clearly, how a pure concentrate of her herbs would sweep the vile disease from the most saturated system.

Still holding the graduate on high and shaking her head ever so slightly in contemplating the dangerously clouded water, Madame Pasteur demanded close attention. "Observe the reaction," said she, "when even a few drops of my herb concentrate are introduced." Into the graduate she poured a few drops of vinegar. Almost instantly the limewater turned as clear as if from a spring; and Madame closed her pitch: "You see, gentlemen, what happens to catarrh when it meets *scientific* attention?"

The limewater-and-catarrh demonstration was a pitch of classic simplicity. Vi never returned to Vital Sparks and her role of Lotus Blossom. As Madame Pasteur she wore out three or four black gowns and mortarboards. Just because she enjoyed it, and not because it was needed, she gradually built her lecture into a masterful tribute to Great Women, speaking well and easily of Elizabeth of England, Catherine of Russia, Isabella of Spain; then shifted to Helena Blavatsky and Annie Besant. She had good words for Sarah

Bernhardt, too. But Vi's greatest homage was for Madame—not Monsieur—Curie who, with her husband, as Vi felt constrained to mention, had made it possible for Madame V. Pasteur to complete the studies which led to the Concentrate of Herbs, and thus sealed the doom of Catarrh.

Looking back over the years, Vi traced the mounting restrictions on her profession. At first the only hampering things were the shakedown by local officials. These were of course a matter for private negotiation and "fix." But then came the Federal legislation. "When the Pure Food and Drug Act got around to the med shows," Vi remembered, "we saw we were flirting with Uncle. Hardly before we knew it, we dared no longer use 'cure' on our labels. By this time I was handling all affairs for my large business. I had to hire a lawyer to keep me posted on new legislation, both state and Federal —and local, too. I made my law-man write me a letter whenever any new law was passed, or even proposed. I kept the letters on file to show my honorable intent to operate within the law.

"Things got more complicated. We had to put the weight of the medicine on the label, and then the formula too. Next, we had to list the diseases for which the remedy was intended. I simplified matters by describing my herb concentrate as an 'Intestinal Eliminant.' I also added a line that said: 'In Case of Sudden Illness Call Your Doctor.'

"Next came a law stipulating that our medicines must be manufactured by a reputable drug firm. This was followed by another, something to the effect that all medicines must be packaged under the supervision of a registered pharmacist, and in sanitary quarters. We took this one in stride. It was always easy to get some drugstore clerk who was a registered pharmacist to come down to our hotel and relax with a beer while the herbs were being boxed. I'd show him the Lysol bottle to indicate our sanitary care with the bathtub. Then the clerk would sign the required statement testifying he had been present when Pasteur's Concentrate was being packaged under the most sanitary conditions imaginable."

Things worsened on another front. A pitch doctor's office came to be plastered with insurance policies. One protected him if anybody suffered ill effects from the medicine. Another policy guaranteed the medicine to be harmless. Still another protected the locals, just in case they fell down or suffered bodily injury while on the pitchman's premises.

These and other harassments, plus increasing years and a happy marriage to a nonprofessional, at last induced Violet Blossom-Pasteur to leave the business. In her thirty years, in addition to making and selling medicine, she had worked in at least two so-called Medical Institutes; conducted a free Museum of Anatomy and, just for the excitement of it, made a tour of country fairs as a Painless Dentist, having learned the gimmicks from the protean Hal the Healer, a man of practically unlimited talents.

I recall her saying there were two rules she early made for herself, and never violated: "Never doctor a sick man, and never, never doctor a woman, sick or well." She made it clear that she adhered to the rule about women because she respected them on two counts—they were much harder to fool than men, and they were not backward to "kick up a fuss if they figure they've been gypped."

"All sold out, Doctor!"

Until changing conditions slowly brought about the virtual dis-
appearance of the old-style medicine shows, one of the most entertaining pages of *The Billboard,* a weekly trade journal, was a
column signed by Gasoline Bill Baker and headed "Pipes for
Pitchmen." This had to do with itinerant peddlers of many kinds,
roughly divided into two general types. Those described profession-
ally as High-Pitch worked from a platform, often from a stage in a
tent or an opera house; those called Low-Pitch worked on street
corners or vacant lots from an open suitcase set upon a tripod,
lighted at night by gasoline burning in a banjo torch.

Pitchmen sold almost everything from glue to alleged diamonds,
from razor strops to patent apple parers. They also unloaded an immense tonnage and gallonage of dry and liquid medicines. These
men might be operators of sizable medicine shows, or lone workers
selling to passers-by from a satchel. All were covered by the general
term of "pitch doctors."

At least two celebrated literary characters, Eugene Field and James
Whitcomb Riley, admitted in their later years to having been members of medicine shows. Riley took to the road with Dr. C. M. Townsend, proprietor of the Wizard Oil Company, then of Lima, Ohio,
whose outfit traveled overland throughout the Midwest. During the
winter Doc Townsend prepared and packaged or bottled his Cholera Balm and King of Coughs which, together with Wizard Oil,
offered relief and probable cure for practically all ills. Come spring,
Townsend's professional talent gathered at Lima and the company
began its tour in a caravan of wagons.

On approaching a village, which an advance man had prepared for
the coming, Townsend's chief musician let go a stout blast on a
coaching horn; then all the bandsmen got down from the wagons,

formed ranks, and led the procession into the town. Young Riley played bass drum, and at the night show gave readings and performed chalk talks.

Whether as a troupe or singly, pitch doctors provided some sort of entertainment to attract and hold an audience. But at carefully calculated intervals the audience had to listen to the Lecture, as they were to do later when medicine shows moved into radio, and then into television, and the Lecture became a Commercial.

In the tent and opera-house days, the Lecture ended when the Doctor announced that his young men would now pass through the audience to sell Wizard Oil or whatever the product was. Shouting, setting up an exciting din, the young med-show interns moved about with baskets of bottles; and every little while this or that one would cry, "All sold out, Doctor!" This message became legendary in the trade. If the outfit was headed by an alleged Quaker, the Doc, usually called a Healer, responded to the all-sold-out cry by shouting, "Bless you, my friends!"

The pseudo-Quakers almost invariably dressed in gray or fawn-colored clothes and wore wide-brimmed, low-crowned hats. Their trousers were the "barn-door" type, which buttoned up the sides instead of the front. When dealing with the public these fellows automatically thee-ed and thou-ed everybody, and were careful that no profanity passed their lips. Among the nationally known Quaker medicine shows were three operated separately by three men, the Messrs. Beason, Ferdon, and Anderson, all of whom were said to have been born in the same lucky town of Litchfield, Illinois. Hal the Healer was a "Coast Defender," his operating region being the Pacific Coast states where, depending on conditions, he toured with troupes of six to a dozen members; or he worked alone, even to setting up his tripes and keister in isolated logging and construction camps.

More numerous than Quakers were the Indian medicine shows, with which I shall deal later. And next to the Indian outfits were individual pitch doctors who assumed the form and manner of a straight Western-type character. The get-up of these fellows varied, and ranged from gaudy to downright startling. Most of them wore shiny boots with silver-capped toes. When fully accoutered, Joaquin Miller, the medicine man of poets, was a perfect ringer for a prosperous pitch doctor.

One of this type was Doc McBride who billed himself as the Great King of Pain, and toured much of the West after the end of the Civil War. A reporter on the *Republican* of Stillwater, Minnesota, saw him "arrayed in a black coat, a wide-brimmed hat and such hair! For many years he has been letting it grow, and now it falls gracefully down his back in saponaceous curls, each individual ringlet consisting of over 13 hairs. . . . All gazed and admired and wondered. . . . His handbills announced that Doc McBride had brought a new era; that all sorrow and tears and pain had disappeared forever." He made a pitch on the street, apparently to a group of loggers on a visit to Stillwater's bright lights, and offered to cure any aches or pains instantly. "Fortunately," said the reporter, "several men ached more or less from last night's potations and came manfully forward. The puissant King of Pain proceeded to shower and shampoo the apex of the pericranium with some fiery liquid, till the smarting so much exceeded the pain that the patients were glad to escape by acknowledging that they didn't ache any more."

But the mayor appeared to inform the doctor that he would have to pay three dollars a day for the privilege of curing Stillwater citizens, whereupon Doc McBride "departed in a huff, paid his bill at the Sawyer House, and left town with a great flourish of trumpets so to speak."

A little later the King of Pain showed up in Central City, Colorado, where he was arrested for lack of a license, "his divine right as king being disregarded by the rude mountaineers." He left town, and dropped out of sight, until late in 1871, when the Stillwater paper, which seems to have kept an eye on this character, published a brief item: "Doc McBride, the noted King of Pain, who travelled through the West, selling large quantities of his quack cure-all, is dead. He led a dissipated life, lost several fortunes by gambling, and made several by Faro and quackery. He was a man of generous impulses, but lacked judgment." One would look far to find a capsule obituary so near perfection.

It was almost standard practice with the big medicine shows to have a genuine M.D. in the troupe, just in case some town official or disgruntled "patient" should bring charges of illegal practice. These physician-fronts may have been the last professional men in the United States to dress for business in frock coats, white vests, and silk hats. They paid some attention, too, to the arrangement of their whiskers. They might or might not lecture at the performances, this depending on their eloquence; but they were on the premises, their certificate to practice displayed prominently.

The medicine-show physicians were pitiable figures, usually far gone in drink, who had, as the phrase has it, seen better days. They had come from Harvard, from Dartmouth, and from almost any other medical school you could name. Some were the victims of narcotics, yet liquor had been the downfall of so many that the physician with a med show was often referred to merely as The Boozer.

The nonmedical pitch doctors were a raffish crowd composed in large part of remarkable individualists. There was Big Foot Bill Wallace who worked electric belts and invariably opened his pitch with the cynical statement that "I'm Big Foot Bill from over the Hill/ I never worked and I never will." His electric belts sold from twenty-five cents to two dollars each, according to his calculations of the tip (audience), and were noted for their flash, being covered with what he called *Imperial* Purple Satin. The belt was studded with small areas of zinc, dosed with vinegar, and produced a temporary tingle when placed next to the skin. ("See, mister, it's begun to work already!") As long as he kept moving, Big Foot did extremely well with his belts. He had learned that it did not do to remain overlong in one place, for his customers often developed sores on their backs or stomachs, and went seeking their benefactor.

On the road many years with a tapeworm remedy, Doc Arthur Hammer, who always appeared in frock coat and silk hat, appears to have had little trouble with his customers, but developed so great a thirst as to cause him to drink even the alcohol in which were preserved the standard display that accompanied his lecture. Doc Will Cooper, who worked Tanlac, buttoned his coat with twenty-dollar gold pieces, his vest with ten-dollar coins, meanwhile delivering a lecture that touched on a host of human ills which might be *relieved* —he never said *cured*—by the constant internal application of Tanlac, a remedy then earmarked with the legend "17 per cent Alcohol." Doc Cooper stressed the exotic sources of Tanlac, whose essences came "from the remote regions of the Globe," but did not, apparently, include Dayton, Ohio, where the remedy was made.

Doc Wirt Robe, for whose pioneering parents the town of Robe, Washington, was named, traveled for several seasons as a banjo and trombone player with an Old Wa-Hoo Bitters medicine show, and came to believe this fine tonic had greater possibilities if properly marketed. Thus, when Snohomish County surprisingly voted dry in a local option contest, he opened in Granite Falls a store he called Wirt Robe's Second-Class Emporium, over the counter or bar of which he sold Old Wa-Hoo Bitters at two bits a glass, declaring it to be as fine a Temperance drink as any man could want. For the next two years Wirt never blew trombone or picked banjo, save for pleasure, and the men of Granite Falls were never without a tonic drink of astonishing powers.

When I knew Wirt Robe, then all of eighty, he had long since retired from the road, yet, in a way, he was still in the medicine business. Having retired to the homestead he had staked in the 1880's, he spent part of his time gathering cascara bark from the shrub that grew in profusion beneath the towering hemlock on his claim. The tall gaunt old man was wonderful company. Perfectly cynical about medicine shows, and about most medicine, too, he liked to recall the days when he toured the country and when "All sold out, Doctor" meant that business was good.

One season in the nineties Wirt went out with a Doc Ennis who was selling his own Universal Balm. "The stuff was of course good for almost everything," Wirt remembered, "but because Doc Ennis was basically a kidney man, he bore down strong on kidney troubles. Ennis wasn't a good lecturer. He lacked the old-time eloquence, and just didn't know how to talk to a crowd. Now, you take Ennis alone, why, he could scare all hell out of a man—one single man, just telling him quietly how his innards were haywire, pointing out symptom after symptom, using fine medical terms, until the guy was feeling terrible all over, especially in his kidneys.

"But with a crowd—no, Ennis could neither get their undivided attention, nor hold such as he did get. We'd been out a couple of weeks working small towns and little settlements around Puget Sound, and doing just fair. Then, Ennis booked us for three nights in Stanwood. I knew Stanwood was a right wild and tough place, a center for loggers from surrounding camps in the virgin Douglas fir timber. The boys there had run more than one show troupe out of town, and I knew they had a reputation to live up to. I was uneasy.

"But we had a pretty good show, much better than average, and though Doc Ennis sure was less than average as a lecturer, I figured we'd get by with our musicians, dancers, and singers. So, we set up shop in Stanwood. Come evening and the place was crawling with loggers. A couple of saloons were doing business, but at that time there were no recognized fancy houses in town. No regulars. Maybe a few part-time workers. The saloons, plus our show, were enough to bring a big crowd of the boys to town.

"For two nights we played to packed houses. Free, of course. But Doc Ennis just could not get them to buying Universal Balm. If we were going to make expenses, we'd have to do it on the third night, which a Saturday. Well, sir, Stanwood that night was a hulla-baloo. The hall was packed. Every bench filled. Five rows deep standing in the rear. We give 'em our overture, then Doc came on-stage to make the Lecture. He hadn't more than got under way when a big feller down front started to get to his feet.

"Right then and there I thought to myself, This is it. We're going to have to fight to get out of here at all. This big fellow was a famous bullpuncher who drove bulls—oxen to you—on a skidroad near town. He must have been seven feet tall. Why, when he started up from his bench I thought he never would stop standing up, he was that tall. And when he did stand up, he let go a most un-Christly yell.

"'Hold on, hold on!' this big guy roared. I naturally figured he was going to tell Doc Ennis that his medicine was no good, and then proceed to break up the show and take the hall apart. Things like that had happened right here, and we had noticed the unhealed wounds of past troubles in broken windows and broken benches.

"But no, not this time. 'Hold on!' the big guy yelled again. He got plenty of attention from the audience. And from Doc, too. Poor Ennis stood there on the stage, his face white. I could see he was shaking like a poplar. The big feller went right ahead. 'Lissen,' he cried. 'All of you here knows me. You know I been sick for two months. Well, day before yesterday I bought a bottle of Doc's Universal Balm. And now I'm cured, cured, cured! A well man, cured, I tell you, and I go back to work Monday. Wonderful, won-derful!' Then he sat down.

"We sold every last bottle we had of the medicine that night. The best of it was, that big bullpuncher was no plant, no shill we hired. He honestly believed Doc Ennis's Balm had cured him. Further, I don't doubt for a minute it had cured him. Nobody can tell *me* that a patent medicine won't cure some people just as well as some New York specialist with a degree from Columbia College and a goatee in the right style."

I wish I might have heard Doc Ray Black lecture. Here was a pitch doctor who, judging from the admiration in which he was held by most of his fellows, was a true master, unique in his pitch, and possibly the most eloquent in the trade.

Doc Black was a lone worker, with neither band nor banjo player to attract a crowd. He set up his tripes and keister on a vacant lot, then displayed his ballyhoo on a second table. This consisted only of a human skull, a big black Bible, and a short length of hemp rope. What these objects were supposed to mean was never known, for Black never once mentioned them. He merely stood there, his back to the sidewalk, moving first the skull, then the Bible, then the rope, rearranging them ever so little, as passers-by stopped to see what he was up to. He was most patient. He would stand there making no sound for half an hour or longer, moving the oddly assorted objects, frowning, moving them again, until a sidelong glance told him enough yokels had gathered to start his lecture. Then he would suddenly whirl to face the crowd, and instantly go into his pitch.

Unquestionably many had stopped only to see what this man was going to do with rope, Bible, and skull. Doc told professional friends that his assortment of objects was perfect, that it was practically impossible for curious locals to resist them. Anyway, he never changed them, and once he had a crowd he began to talk, and few ever left until he was done. Doc Black was noted among pitch doctors for the longest lecture in the business. It was reported that on occasion he spoke for five hours without stopping to sell anything. Though this must be a mild exaggeration to emphasize Doc's ability to hold a crowd, he was doubtless a magnetic speaker; and it is likely he did speak longer than most pitchmen for reasons he was ready to impart to his fellow workers.

"I am a kidney man," he liked to say, "and if the crowd stays with me to the end of my lecture they're going *to buy*. By then their heels are round. After standing stock still in one place for an hour or two, most men have aching backs. Meanwhile, I've been working on them, gently suggesting that backache is merely the first sign of kidney trouble, and kidney trouble is the surest and quickest way to the grave."

Abjuring mention of all other ills, save to list them as the excuses of incompetent physicians for the deaths of patients who actually had kidney trouble, Doc Black wound up for his terrific finale:

"Kidney trouble, my good friends, sneaks up on you like a viper in the grass, like a thief at night. It spares neither rich nor poor, neither the famous nor the unknown. The poor little waif, existing in the slums, the little princeling, surrounded by every elegance, attended by the finest physicians, even these innocents, infants though they be, are not immune to the dread infection that masquerades in many disguises.

"Why, my friends, all of you will recall that not long since, as the noble Archbishop of Canterbury was descending the steps of that magnificent English cathedral, he fell down like an ox smitten in the shambles—stone dead! An autopsy was held by the greatest lords-medical of the Empire. And what did they find? There was nothing wrong with the stomach of that man of God; nothing wrong with his heart, nothing wrong with his lungs.

"But, gentlemen, listen to me." Doc Black's voice dropped to a tone that brought a complete hush over the crowd. "Gentlemen, when they turned that man of God over and looked at his kidneys, those parts looked exactly like a rotten and squashed tomato. . . ."

And then, though he had no helpers, old Doc Black must have heard in imagination the classic cry of good news in medicine shows time out of mind. Almost never, it was said, did he fail to sell the last bottle in his keister on the spot.

3

A Splendid Tonic—KA-TON-KA

So far as is known, the Oregon Indian Medicine Company of Corry, Pennsylvania, never operated anywhere near Oregon, though among its several fine products were remedies named for, and thus a libel on, the fierce Modocs and the basically peaceful and intelligent Nez Percés, both tribes native to the far Northwest.

This remote connection between manufacturing plant and alleged tribal sources was something of a convention. From the older and much larger Kickapoo Indian Medicine Company, down to the smallest pitch doctor working Indian herbs, the factory and operating headquarters were all east of the Mississippi and commonly east of the Hudson; but the ingredients must of necessity be credited to some region or other in what was still thought of as genuine Indian country. The tendency of Americans to favor exotics in medicines, added to the myth that the noble red man possessed healing secrets more potent than anything conventional physicians could offer, combined to favor the Wild West as a reservoir of magic drugs.

Exactly when the Oregon Indian Medicine Company came into being is not known; but by the late eighties it was a going concern in Corry, Erie County, Pennsylvania, and one of its best-selling numbers was labeled Donald McKay's Indian Worm Eradicator, thus honoring him who may well have been the only Oregonian in the outfit but who in any case was one of the boys who had come up through the ranks of med-shows to achieve the celebrity of his picture on a label. Young McKay, reared in Oregon's Umatilla County, was a lively character. His letters to his brother William at home make a tantalizing picture of what a medicine show was like during the twelve years he was on the road in the eastern United States. Spelling was not Donald's strong point, but for narrative sense he is hard to beat. From what he said was Terra Haute (*sic*), Indiana, in October, 1880, he wrote to Brother William:

"Your letter went to Pittsburg. I left thear one week before the Expo closed. I cam to Chicago and thear I met Kit Carson and a man name of Red Fin with long hair and pases himself for an Indian Doctor. Him and Carson made lots of money this fall. But you know what kind of doctor he is. He is a humbug. But they are the ones that makes the money. They made me an offer of $25 a week and I tuck them up."

Trouble was brewing. It blew up on October 23rd:

"We bin here for ten days and was doing well, but you know how some men is they cant precheate a good thing. Last night our long hair Doc had to git drunk and raze hell and some fellow gave him a belt on the nose and laid the Indian doc flat on the floor with his long hair all over his face and this morning thare was a long peas in the paper. . . ."

The show's boss, one of the many Kit Carsons trading on the name of the celebrated Western character who had died in 1868, told Donald not to worry, that he would not be idle for long. Kit was going to get a new Indian doctor. As a class they were unreliable:

"Kit has had bad luck with his Indian doctors. He had a man name of Dr. Yalla Stone and he run away with Carson's dimond pin that cost five-hundred-and-fifty dollar." They had been doing a big business, too, "making four thousand dollars in three weeks."

And Donald regretted that he himself could not fill the bill, for he had discovered he did not have the nerve to "lie to people when they git close to me." Out on the streets, however, or in the tent, "I can tell more lise than patch hell a mile." What Kit wanted most of all was a fellow to "go to Boston and open an Indin labatre [laboratory] or Indin erb store." Donald knew he wasn't equal to such a task. If Kit closed the show, Don thought he would go to Chicago. Meanwhile, "I am a litel excited. Our Indian doctor has chalang his man to fait a dul and I might go and see it." In any case Don told his brother: "You ned not write. I will let you know soon as we get straitin up."

Whether the duel was fought in Terre Haute, or what happened to Kit Carson and his show, or even what Donald McKay did next is lost to history. Yet somebody must have written to Colonel William

F. Cody, the famous Buffalo Bill, for there is a reply dated Dec. 7, 1880, from Boston, in which the great Wild West showman says: "I never like to give advice to anyone. Kit Carson is a sincere fellow, but how responsible I won't say. But if I was a regular doctor I would not give it up and take chances in an outside speculation. That's my opinion, W. F. Cody."

Mist closes over the career of Donald McKay for almost twelve years. Yet he must have been doing mighty well, for in April, 1890, he writes to Oregon from Corry, Pennsylvania, on stationery of "Office of The Oregon Indian Medicine Co., Col. T. A. Edwards, Manager."

His spelling shows little improvement, but his narrative sense is still splendid:

"Dear William, I am here as you cin see that. I got here last Tuesday all safe. Col Edwards was glad to see me. The furst thing he dun was to dress me up with a $40 dollars soot and a $16 dollars hat. I have only bean here two days and thar was over two thousand dollars orders was sent from difrent druges stores from difrint parts of this state so you cin see how the Ka-Ton-Ka is selling."

In short, the Oregon Indian Medicine Company is rolling high. Donald is elated:

"Col Edwards has a large place to manufacter the medicine. He has two men and four lades at work all the time. I tell you he will be a rich man in a few years. But you dont know [how] much it takes [to] *advertise*." As for Donald, he is about to take to the road again in that $40 soot and $16 hat:

"Thare putting up a large tent in Eary [Erie]. They got it up yesterday and I will go over thare next tusday to stay thare a while. . . ."

What Donald, who is obviously now the firm's Lecturer, is going to sell in that big tent shows how far he has come from his days with Kit Carson. His assured pitch now is that all his medicines come from Oregon, where the old Indian women of the Modoc and the Nez Percé tribes "gather the ruts and dry them" for processing and packaging or bottling by nobody except the Oregon Indian Medicine Company of Corry, Pennsylvania.

It has grown to be an imposing line of remedies. There is the popular leader, KA-TON-KA, the Great Indian Medicine, which the label declares in so many words to contain 20 per cent alcohol, and which is described as "A Splendid Tonic, Improves the Appetite and Aids Digestion." It is also "Guaranteed to be In Every Respect as Represented." No less splendid is the gorgeous figure that occupies much of the space of label and carton of this generous eleven-ounce bottle. It can be none other than Donald McKay. He is not named here, but who else, pray, of the Oregon Indian Medicine Company is so fit?

There he stands, this bold Frontiersman of the far Nez Percé and Modoc country, perfect from the top of his turned-back Stetson on down the long magnificent buckskin shirt and pants, both fringed and beaded, to the tip of his decorative moccasins. It can be no one else than the man whose name appears on every bottle of Donald McKay's Indian Worm Eradicator.

Other remedies prepared from "the ruts" shipped from Oregon to Corry included Nez Percé Catarrh Snuff, Modoc Oil, Indian Cough Syrup, War Paint Ointment, and Warm Spring Consumption Cure. The herbs for the last-named nostrum must have been rare indeed; it sold for five dollars a bottle, or fifty dollars a dozen. The other remedies ran from twenty-five cents to a dollar each.

Success attended the Oregon Indian Medicine Company. Four years later, or in 1892, Donald McKay wrote his brother to say that "Colonel Edwards is thinking strong of going to Oregon to put a labatory thare," and that the only thing holding him back is that he fears "we cant git bottels bload in that country and it will cost so much to ship bottls you have no idea how much bottal are. . . ."

Apparently the move to Oregon was never made, for twenty years later KA-TON-KA was still flowing from Corry, and though we do not know if Donald McKay and Colonel Edwards were still in the concern, the Oregon Indian Medicine Company got into the news early in April, 1918, when Federal busybodies laid hands on a shipment of KA-TON-KA to declare it was "Falsely and Fraudulently Advertised." A court upheld the allegation, and the company was fined $200 and costs.

It is interesting to learn exactly what "ruts" gathered in Oregon by the old women of the Modoc and Nez Percé tribes went into "The Great Indian Medicine." The Federal chemists said it was "a mixture of alcohol, sugar, aloes and baking soda."

4

Kickapoo: King of the Road

The Barnum and Bailey of the medicine-show business was operated under style of the Kickapoo Indian Agency. Its founders were John E. Healy, sometimes known as Doc Healy, again as Colonel Healy, and Charles H. Bigelow, or Texas Charlie, who seems not to have acquired either a medical or a military title. For many years their headquarters occupied an immense four-story building on Grand Avenue, New Haven, Connecticut, to which the partners liked to refer as the Principal Wigwam and from which, in season, went forth as many as twenty-five complete shows to provide entertainment and therapy, not only to village and hamlet but to many cities of some size both in the United States and abroad.

The origin of this king of all med-show outfits is misty, a thing of legends. Many years after the dissolution of the partnership and sale of its properties, old Doc Oliver, known also as Nevada Ned, gave a reporter the following account. "In the fall of 1881," he said, "I got a telegram from John Healy asking me to meet him and Texas Charlie Bigelow in a Philadelphia hotel. I did. And it was there and then that the Kickapoo Indian Medicine Company was born."

Nevada Ned went on to say that the first Kickapoo show was staged in Providence, Rhode Island. "We had Chief Thunder Cloud," he recalled without effort, "and seven braves of the Caughnawagas, an Iroquois sub-division from the South bank of the St. Lawrence river above Montreal."

Another legend has it that Healy and Bigelow formed their partnership in Worcester, Massachusetts, in 1875; and that some five years later they selected New Haven to be their permanent operating base, and still later built a factory in suburban Clintonville. Both men were veteran troupers. In the partnership, however, Healy seems

208

to have taken care of engaging the Indians and the white performers and of staging the shows; while Bigelow managed the medicine and general business, which included advertising. (Nevada Ned recalled that in his later years Bigelow "looked a great deal like the elder J. Pierpont Morgan.")

Legends continue: Before he teamed up with Bigelow, Healy had been on the road with his delightfully named Healy's Liver Pad Concert Company, touring the eastern United States in a big wagon, brightly painted, which served as a stage for the company's three performers and from which Doc Healy dispensed liver pads of sterling quality. Healy's pitch was a dandy: "These pads, ladies and gentlemen, contain no harmful chemicals, but a potent, carefully proportioned mixture of roots, barks, gums, leaves, oils and berries. When the pad is applied to an aching spot, the warmth of the body releases the medicinal qualities of the herbs which penetrate directly to the ailing spot, affording almost instant relief."

"Be careful," Doc Healy warned, "to place the red spot on the pad exactly over the seat of disorder. This will guarantee even distribution and penetration."

It may have been a libelous canard perpetrated by other pitch doctors envious of Healy's success, but it was told that his liver pads were stuffed with sawdust that had been treated "to smell like a drugstore." The "red spot" was red pepper and glue. When warmed by body heat, as Doc spieled it, a "gentle soothing warmth begins to act on the ailing part due to release of the powerful medicinal qualities of the herbs." Doc's pads came in two sizes, $1.00 and $1.50. The larger contained more sawdust, more red pepper, and more glue than the smaller size.

Healy did an enormous business before he and Bigelow joined forces to think up immortal Sagwa, then to select the Kickapoos, the remnants of a subtribe of former Lake States Indians, for the honor of allegedly making Sagwa and other nostrums put out by the Kickapoo Indian Medicine Company. The name Sagwa was sheer inspiration. And no matter the actual tribal sources of Healy and Bigelow's Indians, which included Mohawks, Iroquois, Crees, Sioux, and Blackfeet, no other tribe possessed the semantic properties of Kickapoo. Nobody could forget it.

With superb showmanship, Healy and Bigelow announced that they were bringing to New Haven, "from their home in Indian

Territory," a group of pure-blooded Kickapoos, men, women and children, "the most noted of all Indian medical men," and would house them in the Principal Wigwam being built at 521 Grand Avenue. This would be their home. From here, their botanical scouts would go forth to search the woods, from the Green Mountains to the Rockies, for "blood root, feverwort, sassafras, slippery elm, white oak bark, wintergreen, yellow birch bark, dock root, sarsaparilla, and other simples," from which were compounded the marvelous remedies for which the Kickapoos were famous.

When the Principal Wigwam was ready, into New Haven came the Indians, making a grand show as they paraded from the station; and with them, too, came a sizable consignment of what the press was told were mustangs. At least they were horses, and within a day or two Kickapoo braves were out riding along the streetcar tracks, to the great wonder of citizens. The whole business of arrival and getting settled must have been one of New Haven's most exciting periods of all time.

There seems to be no record of how many Indians came to live in the Principal Wigwam or how long they stayed. Legend places the number as high as three hundred, including women and children. It is known that many of them remained in New Haven for at least ten years, and another fourteen years in suburban Clintonville. One thing about them seems agreed; they were almost invariably peaceful, minded their own affairs, and had little or none of the trouble with alcohol usually associated with the Red Man.

The number of tribesmen probably fluctuated. On one occasion, when the medicine company was short of personnel, Colonel Healy "raided Buffalo Bill's Wild West Show and came away with a dozen fine looking Sioux," who, of course, at once became Kickapoos. Again, an item reported that "Gordon Lillie (Pawnee Bill) has arrived in the East with a band of 200 Pawnees he has engaged for Healy & Bigelow."

Much of the success of the Kickapoo Indian Medicine Company over thirty years was due to fine organization, superior showmanship, and what amounted to ethical standards in a business notorious for cynical con men and fly-by-night troupes. It was the boast of Healy and Bigelow shows, called Kickapoo Camps, each designated by a number, that they could always play return engagements. Year after year they toured the same villages and cities, never playing less than one-week stands, often staying three or more weeks in the larger centers.

In quick time the Healy and Bigelow shows gained such a reputation for all-around reliability that the owners were besieged to sell rights to use the Kickapoo name and remedies in specific territories. It seems likely that the partners agreed, if only to prevent low-class imitations. They let contracts to such producers as agreed to the rather strict stipulations laid down by the partners. The arrangement seems to have been one of rental fee plus royalty on the volume of medicines sold. There had been nothing like it in the med-show business, and from it each of the two partners amassed fortunes that permitted them to build imposing mansions in New Haven.

Several of the chartered or licensed Kickapoo shows equaled small circuses in size, and went abroad to Europe and Australia. A photograph dated "Rome, Italy, March 6, 1890," shows a Kickapoo troupe of twenty-eight Indians and palefaces, many of them mounted, in an immense arena.

As far as the United States was concerned, the Kickapoo outfits played, during summer months, under their own canvas. In winter they booked into town halls, lodge halls, and opera houses. Mostly they moved by railroad. The smallest Kickapoo Camp or show mustered at least three Indians and three professional entertainers, and of course the Professor who managed the company and made the pitch or Lecture. The troupe I personally recall was larger.

The time was the winter of 1907-1908. The place was Colebrook, New Hampshire, population some two thousand. The Kickapoo unit arrived by the Maine Central Railroad. It comprised the manager, an imposing figure, in yellow buckskin with long hair and big hat; plus five white performers and half a dozen alleged Kickapoo Indians. They showed six nights in the Town Hall. On Monday all seats were free. On other nights the fee was ten cents.

The company stayed at the Monadnock House, Colebrook's best hotel, in the fine style of traveling repertoire people, like Price Webber, and Klark-Urban, and the Guy Brothers' Minstrels. The Kickapoos did not stage a street parade in Colebrook. They didn't need a parade. The Indians presented a magnificent spectacle simply by walking, single file, down Main Street to pose briefly in front of each of the two drugstores, then move on to the Town Hall to ready the place for the night show.

Many of us youngsters at Colebrook Academy had already seen Buffalo Bill's Wild West when it came to White River Junction, Vermont, but the sight of real Indians right on Main Street in our town was most impressive. Decked out in full regalia, the Kickapoo chief and braves, together with a pretty young squaw, and at least one matron with papoose on her back, made a picture against the glittering snowbanks. *Here* was the Wild West on Main Street.

I recall seeing a couple of the braves drop into Harry Legro's store to buy cigars. One of the Kickapoo squaws stopped at Jennie Walker's Notions to purchase something or other. Chief Red Bear, along with the Professor, was to be seen during the day conferring with one or the other village druggist. This was a fine piece of Healy and Bigelow's public relations: Kickapoo remedies were not sold exclusively at the show. They could be bought from the local druggists where the complete Kickapoo line was placed on consignment, thus making friends with the merchants who otherwise might protest, as they invariably did, against pitchmen who "had no interest in our village except what money they can take away with them."

The Kickapoo line of remedies was long. Sagwa was the leader, but there were also the wonder-working Kickapoo Indian Prairie Plant (Female Complaints) and Kickapoo Indian Oil, Salve, Cough Cure, Pills, and Worm Killer, all compounded from ancient tribal formulas, and "as safe as they are efficacious." Kickapoo remedies were the miracle drugs of the horse-and-buggy era.

What the Kickapoo troupe gave us at the Colebrook Town Hall for ten cents was, by village standards of the period, a remarkably good show, interrupted no more than four times during an hour and a half by the Professor's Lecture followed closely by sale in the audience of the remedies. These old-style commercials were not hard to endure. The least talented of Healy and Bigelow's Professors was a master of eloquence under perfect control. His salient points were stressed less by vehemence and gestures than by the soft-spoken bedside manner of a physician. The pause, then the whispered diagnosis—*Kidney Trouble*, or *Cruel Dyspepsia*, or *Consumption the Killer*—must have carried conviction; for suddenly, at the end of a lecture, war whoops shook the house and down the aisles came the chief and his braves, each toting a basket stacked with bottles that were quickly purchased. "All sold out, Doctor!" shouted the redskin salesmen in pretty fair English, and the entertainment was resumed.

The show consisted of singing, dancing, acrobatics, a chalk talk, a fire-eater, and skits known in the trade as afterpieces. But the particular feature of this particular Kickapoo troupe in 1907 was a moving picture. Set up on the main floor of the Town Hall, as we entered, was a machine only a little smaller than a J. I. Case Traction Engine. It was surrounded by a wooden fence within which was an empty flour barrel, the significance of which became clear only when the hall lights went down and the huge apparatus started to groan, grind, and click, and what seemed like miles of film unwound into the waiting barrel. (The Professor had warned against smoking or lighting matches, as well he might.)

In 1907 there were few movie houses in northern New England, and none in Colebrook. True, we had seen moving pictures, but nothing like the featured article of the Kickapoo show. It was called "The Dream of the Rarebit Fiend," a fantasy that ran some fifteen minutes, and was as wildly funny as it was wildly improbable. Half a century later I can recall the dreadful nightmares that possessed the Fiend, as he sailed into clouds, was stymied in vast underground caverns, and attacked by demons, giants, and fierce little men like ants.

Then came the final lecture of the evening, another round of the whooping salesmen, and a comical afterpiece, "Over the River, Charlie."

Colebrook was no more immune than Lancaster, Berlin, St. Johnsbury, and other larger towns in the region to the magic of Healy and Bigelow's entertainment and therapy. For another half-dozen years, or until the spread of the automobile and movies, Kickapoo was a welcome attraction in villages and small cities.

How "good" or "bad" were the Kickapoo medicines I would rather not guess. The record indicates they were not made from those "native herbs familiar to Indian doctors," or at least not in the form of "barks, berries and roots," but were compounded in the Kickapoo factory at Clintonville, Connecticut, by Healy and Bigelow's chief chemist, a Mr. Ford who, as one who was there remembers, used to "stand on a ladder and stir the huge vats with a long paddle." The vats contained drugs received from reputable manufacturing houses.

In 1958 Mrs. Ethel R. Blakeslee, a native of Clintonville, who worked for several years in the Kickapoo factory office, recalled that the ingredients of Kickapoo Cough Syrup included Jamaica rum and New Orleans molasses; and that Kickapoo Oil, for external use only, had a heavy content of camphor, which came in large sheets. My own cherished bottle of Kickapoo Oil was made during or after 1919, as indicated by the label, which mentions "J. Revision of Formula 1919," and states the ingredients to be "camphor, ether, capsicum, oil of cloves, oil of sassafras, and myrrh." The label states also that the medicine is "For the Relief of Aches and Pains" (which is a notable comedown from the label of pre-1906, which called the oil "A Quick Cure for All Kinds of Pain. Good For Man or Beast"). The label on my bottle was the product of Kickapoo Indian Medicine Company, Incorporated, with offices in New York and St. Louis, and it adds, "Formerly of Clintonville, Conn."

Mrs. Blakeslee could not remember what went into Sagwa, nor did Dr. Oleson, author of *Secret Nostrums,* discuss this formula, though he printed the formula for Kickapoo Oil. The American Medical Association refers only once to Kickapoo in the indices of its three big volumes of *Nostrums and Quackery,* to report that government chemists declared a shipment of Kickapoo Cough Syrup to be misbranded in that it "did not possess properties recognized by the medical profession as necessary for the proper treatment of the lungs." Kickapoo was hailed into court, where "a fine of $25 and costs was imposed."

Mrs. Blakeslee says that the United States Post Office at Clintonville was in the same building as the Kickapoo mailing department, a cozy arrangement in view of the tons of circulars and other matter incident to supplying as many as threescore Kickapoo touring shows with proper advertising.

In the top floor of the Kickapoo factory and storehouse, said Mrs. Blakeslee, were dozens of big trunks packed with Indian regalia, including headdresses or war bonnets, buckskin garments, and weapons such as tomahawks and scalping knives.

The site of the factory, now a vacant lot with no sign of the former building, is on Connecticut Route 22, not far from where Pond Hill Road meets the highway. Near the site are still to be seen the grass-grown tracks of the Airline Railway, New Haven to Willimantic, over which, in the great days, came the hogsheads of rum and molasses for the Kickapoo Cough Syrup. The community today is properly described as the Clintonville district of North Haven.

The dissolution of the firm of Healy and Bigelow is as misty as its beginnings. It is strange that in the collections of the Connecticut Historical Society, the New Haven Colony Historical Society, Yale's Medical Library, the Connecticut Medical Society, and the Connecticut Pharmaceutical Society there is little or nothing about this giant of the medicine-show business which permitted Mr. Healy and Mr. Bigelow to retire with fortunes, which for thirty years employed an average of some three hundred people, and which in 1912, when it was sold to a new corporation, brought no less than $250,000. It was not big business compared to the Winchester Repeating Arms Company or to Yale University, but in size and influence it was without equal in the world of entertainment and therapy combined.

Champions in any line of endeavor deserve better of history than New Haven and Connecticut have accorded Healy and Bigelow. They created an enduring legend in small-town United States. No medicine I know of can be more widely memorialized than the "Kickapoo Joy Juice" featured in a popular comic strip drawn by Mr. Al Capp.

PART NINE

Back-Country Healers

1

A Wilderness Paracelsus

More than a hundred years ago a philosophical M.D., then practicing in the Midwest, observed that although there were still many Americans who believed in supernatural cures of diseases, the most successful forms of quackery were those that blended some measure of natural means with their sorceries. For example, a profitable combination could be a Seventh Son who dispensed amulets, and also prescribed certain medicinal herbs.

To eradicate these favored healers—wrote the physician-philosopher—would be "more difficult than to root out the sour dock and Canada thistle of our fields." Planted in ignorance, he went on, and cherished by their natural authors, the "impostures are fixed upon us as the poison oak encircles the trunk of the noble tree whose name it has prostituted."

Reflecting that if every dog has its day, so has every nostrum, the observant M.D. noted that when one of these quackeries is inoculated into a community, "nothing can arrest its spread." Like smallpox it prevails until all of the susceptible are infected. Why is this so? Well, sir, it is so because the propensity to be cheated is not confined to men or women, to the young or old, the poor or rich, the unlearned or the learned, but "displays its workings in the weakminded and the credulous in all walks and stations of life."

Except for a few minor qualifications and an intervening sixty-odd years, this astute physician of 1840 could have been writing specifically about Healer John Till and his thousands of patients, a phenomenon of thaumaturgy that came into view in 1905 and lasted almost two decades.

In 1905 John Till was a woodsman, a good man with ax or cant dog, employed in a logging camp near Turtle Lake amid the tall pines of Barron County, Wisconsin. He was a handy man to have around on several counts. He could make a sled from bunk to runners. He could shoe a horse and mend a chain. And on Sundays, when need arose, he dispensed without charge a healing salve that seemed to be pretty good stuff.

In that time and region, which was the valley of the St. Croix River, the Wisconsin-Minnesota boundary, there was no place where one could hear of more and greater marvels and true wonders than the deacon seat of a logging camp. This was the classic bench that ran the full length of the bunkhouse; and on it, of an evening and on the Sabbath, there operated a forum to deal with any and all problems meriting discussion. Between, say, the first of September and the first of April, a habitué of the deacon seat got a complete education in woods technology, in general history, sociology, and science, including therapy. And it was unquestionably here, on the deacon seat of a camp near Turtle Lake, that John Till's nigh magic way with medicine got the airing that started him on the path to becoming Dr. Paracelsus of the Midwest pineries.

Word of Till's quick cures of his fellow lumberjacks soon reached Turtle Lake village, then spread, in the manner of marvels, up and down and across the St. Croix River Valley. One day in 1905 there came to camp a Mr. Octave Cloutier, an ex-logger who had gone to farming near Somerset, in adjoining St. Croix County. His wife, Meline, was suffering from an infected cheek. No doctor, no medicine had had the least effect. The genial Till accompanied Cloutier to his farm, treated Meline with a "plaster salve"—and lo, she was cured, quickly and manifestly.

So miraculous a recovery needed no advertisement in the papers. John Till was scarcely back at work in camp before relatives and friends of other invalids were demanding that he do for them what he had done for Mrs. Cloutier. Till was willing enough, and when Octave Cloutier invited him to use his farm home as headquarters, Till rode the cars from Turtle Lake to Somerset to spend Sunday treating the dozen or so patients waiting at the farm. The cures continued.

John Till's sole biographer, Mr. James Taylor Dunn, says that the man was born in 1870 in "the poor mountain village of Einsiedel, Austria." While still a lad both of his legs were crushed and broken in a hay wagon accident; and his cobbler father, too poor to afford a doctor, took him for treatment to a *Kurschmied*, or healing blacksmith. The boy survived both the accident and the blacksmith, but was left with one deformed leg. As he grew older Till became interested in the ancient folk cures used by the smithy-healer who had learned them from a hermit monk. Among these were the notions that sour red wine boiled with nettles was a specific for hemorrhage of the lungs, and that if you were bitten by a snake the thing to do was to kill the snake and eat its skin.

At the age of twenty-eight, Till left home for the United States, which he entered from Canada. The next half-dozen years are shadowy, but were probably spent in the logging division of the still-booming lumber industry of the Lake States. By 1905, when he emerged at Turtle Lake from obscurity, Till had either by revelation or by some sort of eclectism arrived at a point where he was using two, and only two, remedies. One was a "burning plaster" composed largely of Croton oil and kerosene; the other was a "secret plaster salve." The latter, which had wrought the marvelous cure of Meline Cloutier, was said by Till to contain a mysterious agent he called 4X. This salve was applied to open wounds and sores. The Croton oil-kerosene mixture took care of all other afflictions.

No matter his many talents, John Till was to prove again and again that he needed a manager. He was vain, careless, and as credulous as any of his patients. One is prepared to believe that his faith in the two nostrums was unbounded. Whether or not he had fooled himself, other men found him an easy mark for their promotions. He was opinionated, not only in matters of therapy, but in everything else. Both friends and close relatives found him most difficult to live or work with. Mr. Dunn, his biographer, seems to believe that without a capable manager, which Octave Cloutier turned out to be, Till would never have been heard of beyond the bounds of Turtle Lake village.

During the three weeks when Till commuted between the logging camp and Somerset, the number of his patients increased notably. Cloutier proposed that Till move to and make his home with the Cloutiers at their farm, a mile or so from Somerset. He did so. Now began a period of prosperity for Till, for his manager and technical assistant Cloutier, and also for people and services in the towns roundabout.

In little more than a year after Meline Cloutier's remarkable recovery, as many as 150 patients were coming daily to the farmhouse. From six in the morning until ten at night Till treated all who came. The place was a confused hubbub until Cloutier, or Clootsie as he was known, installed a sort of system, and set twelve as the number to be admitted at one time to the operating room.

When the dozen patients were seated in as many backless chairs, Doc Till, as he was careful never to call himself, walked down the row, feeling the jugular veins of each, with unwashed hands. This was the diagnosis, and by it Till could spot, instantly, active or incipient palsy, paralysis, rheumatism, locomotor ataxia, cancer, appendicitis, dyspepsia, blindness, varicose veins, and all other non-contagious diseases.

Diagnosis required but a minute, or less. Then the treatment. Only a few required the 4X plaster salve. All the rest got the burning plaster. These run-of-the-mill patients bared their backs; and Doc Till came down the line again, this time toting a pail of the kerosene mix which he smeared from shoulders to the base of the spine, using one and the same sponge for all. The plaster came in three strengths—mild, strong, and what Till called Horse Treatment. This was for the gravest cases which he considered on the brink of dissolution.

As soon as Doc Till started down the line, Clootsie followed, sewing cotton batting on the undergarments of those in the habit of wearing undergarments, to keep the clothes from chafing the flesh, which soon enough felt the first blistering effects of the concoction. The patients meanwhile got a brief warning from Till: Under no circumstances were they to expose themselves to cold or rain; and they were to wash their hands only in warm water. If these directions were violated, extreme suffering, even death, might well result.

The fortunate twelve were dismissed, and another dozen came in to sit on the backless chairs. Over and over, the line refilled as fast as Till and Clootsie could swab and sew. No fee was charged, but Clootsie did not fail to remind his patients that "contributions" were welcome, suggesting they might leave whatever sum they cared to. A newspaper reporter who was permitted to watch a batch go through the plaster mill observed that "none contributed less than one dollar, which sums were carelessly thrown into the treasury box to the rear of the thrifty and industrious operator who appeared not to give it a thought."

Doc Till in professional action must have been something to see. Only on infrequent state occasions did he wear shoes, and his feet appeared not to have been washed in a long time, perhaps years. Oil-stained galluses held up trousers so caked with dirt that "a coal heaver would have blushed in them." He wore neither beard nor mustache, as though he disdained the cliché of the pointed Vandyke of the specialist, or the general practitioner's moderate growth on upper lip. Doc Till's facial trademark was a singularly unbecoming three-day growth of whisker. No brush ever touched his yellowed teeth.

Yet every man has some small ostentation; in each of Doc Till's grimy ears was pierced a small gold ring.

It is of course possible that Till's studied indifference to appearance indicated a careful attention to the value of public relations: A man from the *Stillwater Gazette* in Minnesota once heard him gently admonish a patient: "Remember, Christ who owns the whole world was dressed poorly."

On and on came the halt, the lame, the distressed, mostly under their own power, yet no few carried by devoted friends to the Wonder Healer of Somerset. In a little while the pressure became so great that Cloutier, the ever watchful manager, issued numbered tickets; and these, in time, became items for barter, even for sale to those in a tear for plaster attention. Clootsie was alert, looking to the future. He ordered lumber, hired a crew of carpenters, and soon a staunch wing almost doubled the floor space of the farmhouse. Hotels in nearby Hudson and Stillwater were booked solid for rooms weeks in advance. In Somerset itself sixteen carriages, each seating six persons, continuously plied the four miles between the Cloutier farm and the Wisconsin Central Railroad depot. Hank Farmer, the livery-stable magnate of Stillwater, across the river, doubled the number of hacks he needed to carry what he called the Plastertown traffic. One up-and-coming farmer on the road to Cloutier's spread clean hay on the floor of his big barn where, without blankets furnished, you could stay the night for thirty-five cents.

The whole economy of Somerset and environs felt the effects of Doc Till's boom. Many arrivals found reason to patronize local stores for underwear. Clootsie was buying cotton batting by the bale. It took a lot of kerosene to keep Till busy. The town's single restaurant could not begin to handle from 500 to 1,300 new cus-

tomers daily. Half a dozen quick-lunch places were opened. The
local saloons, however, long conditioned to meet the periodic if
brief visits of woods- and river-driving crews, managed to supply
sufficient service to steady the nerves of patients against the ordeal of
Doc Till's operating line. One amateur professor of economics estimated that at five cents for beer and fifteen cents for whisky, each
of the Somerset bars was grossing $100 a day.

I like to wonder if, during the early weeks of these almost incredible happenings, Clootsie did not conjure up a vision. He was
obviously a man of some imagination. Did he, as the crowds continued coming—fifty, a hundred, five hundred, then a thousand
people—did he reflect on what the Doctors Mayo had accomplished
in and for the flourishing city of Rochester, Minnesota, where people from the far corners of the nation, people from foreign lands, the
well-to-do, the wealthy, millionaires, were coming for no other
reason than to consult the Mayos, father and sons? True, they were
"regular" doctors, and yet . . . yet were not these lowly and suffering one-dollar patients being benefited by the administrations of
John Till? Who could say they had not been cured? Might it not
come to pass, here in this hamlet of Somerset, that John Till the
Healer had lighted a lamp whose light, given a little time, would
shine as far as the light of the Doctors Mayo? . . . The Till Lamp
shone from the farm of Octave Cloutier. Would this not be the
right place to smooth the furrows of the fields and on the fields erect
the Till Sanatorium—a huge edifice dedicated to the suffering of the
world?

Dimmer-witted men than Octave Cloutier have dreamed such
dreams. We do know that he was already dreaming a moderate-sized
dream, a Cloutier Hotel for little Somerset. Then, if all went
well . . .

The stigmata of commercial success soon appeared, when a Dr.
Johnson set up as a plaster expert right in Somerset town; and in
Dassel, Minnesota, a cigar maker announced himself ready to treat
all comers with plaster medicine. In Knapp, Wisconsin, Samuel
Tufts, the village bard, composed and published a come-all-ye type
of song entitled *John Till of Somerset*. All that was needed now was
a John Till Cigar.

The two plaster imitators of Till did so poorly that they soon quit business. The ballad seems never to have become popular. It mattered little to Till. His days, and much of his nights, were filled with activity. There was no need even to spend money for advertising. People paid *him*. They bought postcards with his picture captioned The Plaster Healer, five cents each, which boys hawked on the street. These were doubtless the idea of Cloutier, a man quick to recognize the carnival spirit, who also rented the soda-pop and chewing-gum concession at the farm to an experienced carnie worker from St. Paul. There were long waits to see Doc Till and, if pop and gum were a weak substitute for the goods sold in Somerset saloons, they may have helped to pass the tedious hours.

What all this business meant to Doc Till and Manager Cloutier was clear to the bank at nearby New Richmond where, according to Mrs. Grace Thomas, every two weeks a wagon came from the farm, the cash bags were unloaded, and the bank clerks counted for deposit an average of $3,000, mostly in silver dollars and dollar bills. It was generally understood that Cloutier's share of the take was a straight fifty cents per patient. During the first season, the Till-Cloutier deposits totaled $80,000.

Till's first of several arrests on the charge of practicing medicine without a license soon occurred. But no jury would convict him. After one of these trials, held at Hudson, the county seat, Till on his return to the farm was met by the Somerset Cornet Band who escorted the Doc to his office where, during the evening, an enormous crowd of well-wishers, including more than 1,300 patients, staged a joyful celebration.

Twice during this Somerset period (1906-1908) Till visited his native Austria. With him the second time he took Mr. and Mrs. Cloutier. As the time approached for their return in September, Somerset tradespeople began planning a monster welcome-home affair. After all, the merchants, restaurants, livery stables and even the Soo and the Wisconsin Central railroads had noticed the quick drop in business when Doc Till departed. Several tradesmen had gone into debt to improve their establishments, and counted on Till's return to set the glorious wheels of commerce rolling again. It was said, too, that Octave Cloutier himself had invested $3,000 in a new hotel.

As plans congealed for the homecoming, it was decided that the returning travelers should be met at the railroad depot by the town band plus a splendid coach pulled by eight white horses, and conveyed to the fine home of Merchant Henry A. La Grandeur for a reception. There would also be "feasting and dancing in the streets."

The event never came off. "Exactly what happened," wrote Till's Biographer Dunn, "is not clear, but a rift between Till and the Cloutiers was the outcome. On arriving at Ellis Island, Till, who had never been naturalized, was temporarily detained because of his crippled leg. Many felt the Cloutier family to have been responsible, and said that they deserted their benefactor in his hour of need." Instead of returning to Somerset with the Cloutiers, Doc Till went to the home of his sister in Almena, near Turtle Lake. Despite the pleadings of Somerset people, Till never returned.

In Almena, Till and his sister, Mrs. Bertha Stoeberl, combined their talents to form a sort of plaster doctor clinic. They quickly fell into disagreement about splitting the take and parted company. Bertha seems to have been prepared for such a contingency; she induced two of her brother's interns, or assistants, to join her in a clinic of their own. Doc Till simply packed up and moved to New Richmond where, with happy memories of the bank in which he used to deposit as much as $6,000 a month, he set up shop. He still had the right touch. Within weeks he had patients coming from points all over the Midwest, and found need to visit the New Richmond bank daily to make a deposit.

While operating at the new stand, Till made another trip to the Old Country where he married Hedwig Steiner of Freudenthal, Austria, bringing her to New Richmond where a son was born in 1913. Money continued to flow; and Doc Till, like many another budding capitalist, began to seek opportunity to invest some of his surplus. As a speculator, Till was no Jay Gould type. One of his several projects, the Till Bus Line Company, which sounds like a sort of complement to his plaster shop, caused him no end of trouble. For years he was fighting his bus-line associates, in the courts and, at least once, in an unseemly brawl. Meanwhile he constantly had to defend himself against suits charging malpractice brought by ex-patients, in some cases by the heirs of ex-patients. The state medical society and the American Medical Association did not lessen their efforts to bag him.

There appears to have been no falling off in Till's business, yet he

was not content in New Richmond. His extracurricular affairs were
costing too much time and money. In one of the many suits about
the bus line, Till was haled into court by a private detective for
alleged nonpayment of wages. Another suit was brought against the
Doc by something named the Honduras Development Company,
to collect notes Till had given to pay for stock in this concern. (He
had yet to learn that "Honduras" had long since earned in specu-
lative circles the reputation of being questionable; professional con
men had worn it to a frazzle; he had also to learn that *any* company
with "Development" in its corporate title could be less than gilt
edged.) Whatever the cause, in 1916 Doc Till was looking around. In
May the papers reported he would move, of all places, back to Turtle
Lake, and so he did. He built a home there, and also the John Till
Hotel which he operated in connection with his plaster clinic. Within
a year he was arrested and charged with practicing without a license.
This time a jury found him guilty. Said the *Barron County News*:

> Heretofore, Till has escaped because he did not pose as a doc-
> tor and did not charge for prescriptions. The law has been
> changed, and now provides that no person may prescribe or
> give away drugs for any purpose, without a license. Till will
> appeal to the Supreme Court. District Attorney Soderberg says
> a number of complaints are now on file against Till and they
> will be prosecuted one after the other. Severals deaths in Barron
> County within the past year are charged directly to the treat-
> ment received at Till's plaster shop.

As the appeal from Till's first conviction began its three years of
slow motion in the courts, the John Till Hotel at Turtle Lake was
destroyed by a fire many believed to have been the work of Till's
enemies. Doc Till again began looking around. This time he pulled
up stakes and moved to North Hudson, only a few miles from New
Richmond in St. Croix County. That he was planning great things
was indicated by his purchase, for cash, of the rather imposing if
then vacant Galahad School for Boys, a private school founded by
a Mrs. Jean Jefferson Penfield. With him, too, Till brought to North
Hudson what he hoped would be adequate protection from the
devilish harassments of the Wisconsin Medical Association. This was
Dr. W. A. Synon, a "regular" physician, who was to be Medical
Director of the new plaster shop. Even the shop was to take on a new

tone as the John Till Institute. The treatments here were not to be dependent on the free-will offerings of patients. They were to cost $2 each.

It tells something of Till's financial condition that when a man from the Hudson bank responsible for selling the school property to him went to Turtle Lake to finish the business, Till took him into a room where stood an old couch. "Without further ado," recalled the banker many years later, "Doc Till stripped from the couch a thick covering of old newspapers, revealing an even thicker layer of green currency. The bills were fives and tens with a scattering of twenties. Till counted out sixteen thousand dollars. The deal was consummated. I toted the cash in a suitcase back to Hudson and put it in the bank."

The Tills moved to the Galahad School property, which comprised six buildings, to make their home in the structure named "Sarras," which may have meant no more to Till than "Galahad" did, unless he were better acquainted with the Arthurian legends than the average plaster doctor of the time. The five other buildings became the John Till Institute, in one of which was the office of Dr. Synon.

The Institute opened to brisk business at $2 per treatment. And though Dr. Synon was occasionally under the weather owing to what was described as bottle trouble—an affliction common to many medical men engaged for legal-protective purposes—there were no complaints. All went well until late in 1920 when a sheriff came to take Doc Till to the county jail in Barron. It was that old conviction at Turtle Lake. It had been almost three years coming. The courts had been as adamant as they were slow. Nothing remained now but to lay it out in Barron jail.

Quack or no, John Till had many friends, among them no few who appreciated the economic value to North Hudson of the Till Institute, and others who swore Till had cured them after conventional physicians had given up. Within a short time Doc Till in jail was a first-class and most troublesome martyr. One local paper observed that the governor of Wisconsin had been "deluged with letters and telegrams begging him to turn Till loose. An amazing number came from Barron County and from Hudson and vicinity, others from scores of towns in Northern Wisconsin and Minnesota. . . . Business men and poor people said they had been cured of all manner of diseases by Till, while others now under treatment said they would die if the treatments were stopped. . . ."

The protests were in the familiar pattern of martyrdoms beyond memory. The Wisconsin Board of Pardons, however, refused to act, saying that Till "does not benefit patients, his treatment is harmful."

Far from quieting, the noise increased. George Skogmo of River Falls, a state senator, and Spencer Haven of Hudson, a former attorney general of the state, appeared in person before the governor to ask pardon for Till. The waves of pleadings and demands from "poor common people" rose, then fell, then rose again, in the manner of organized efforts connected with martyrs. But old Doc Till remained in jail. After ten months and a few days he was pardoned by Governor John J. Blaine, his stated reason being that Till's health had broken.

Back again at the Institute, Till told a reporter that "two hundred and fifty new patients" were calling every day; Till was so busy he did not have time to look out the window on the fair scene of Lake St. Croix. He had enjoyed himself in jail. Got plenty of rest. Did him good. He planned now to improve the Institute's buildings. And "all future professional activity will fully conform to law."

Yet there was something else, for soon after Till's return the local Star-Observer published an unconfirmed report to the effect that "Till has promised to leave the country," and added, "This is something to be grateful for." Apparently the report was authentic. On March 22, 1922, the Tills sailed for Europe "unwept and completely unnoticed by all the St. Croix valley newspapers that had given him so much free advertising during the years of his plaster doctoring."

Back in Austria the Tills settled down "on a sizable estate" at Ditersdorf which he had bought long before on one of his several visits. His son recalled that Farmer Till raised fine cattle and horses for which he was given "a gold watch and another prize" at whatever they call fairs in Austria.

Twenty-four years later, or in February, 1946, the Times-Broadcaster of Turtle Lake, Wisconsin, electrified old residents with an item: "John Till is back in this community after an absense of many years." He was in the best of health. Said he might "start the healing art again." Apparently he made no attempt do so, but died of a heart attack on July 14, 1957, while visiting friends in Kiel, Wisconsin.

Till had lost most of his Old Country possessions, first to the Germans when they overran Austria, then to the Communists during and after World War II. In the United States, not even the Galahad or Institute property, which he had left in charge of a Minneapolis man, remained to him.

Octave Cloutier died in 1950, aged eighty-nine. His widow, Meline, was living in St. Paul in 1955, where now and then she stirred up a batch of the old plaster salve—the 4X formula—at the request of old-timers in Somerset who still used it. In Somerset and other towns of the St. Croix River valley, Till is still a legend, though a controversial one. To some he was everything from a harmless, ignorant quack to a dangerous man guilty of murderous nostrums. An editorialist in the Hudson paper said a good deal about therapy in one sentence: "The independent American invalid will have his way in spite of all arbitrary and futile prosecution."

In an attempt to account for Till's success Dr. Justus Ohage, a former Commissioner of Public Health at St. Paul, indicated, at one of the plaster healer's many court trials, the man's shrewd understanding of psychological processes. "If a patient were suffering from stomach trouble," said Dr. Ohage, "he soon became absorbed in the condition of his blistered back and so forgot about his stomach disturbance. . . . When people go to Till, as so many thousands do, they can't *all* be fools! . . . When Till afflicts them with sore backs, they can't think of anything else for two months. They are so happy when their backs heal, they never think of their stomachs."

As recently as 1958, when I asked a former Wisconsin resident about John Till, he thought for a moment, then cried almost as if a specter had appeared: "Till! Till, the plaster healer! I hadn't heard his name in more than forty years." He went on to say that Till was "the hill-billy doc who either cured or killed every other rheumatic old lumberjack in Wisconsin and half of Minnesota, around 1908, when I was a schoolboy back there."

2

The Blessed Handkerchiefs

Placing John Himself Braun in the ranks of back-country healers is an arbitrary thing. Both he and his wife Kate Herself Braun were gifted people who could, without injustice, be classed in almost any number of healing schools. Indeed, one of the many charms of this couple was the ease with which they changed front and personality. It is only because they first came to attention in small Red Bud, Illinois, and went on to accomplish some of their most noted miracles in places with names like Nokomis and Peru and Goshen that I have thought it fair to put them in the Small Time, or what was known early in this century as the Kerosene Circuit, which has reference to municipal lighting. That, and because one of their numerous profitable methods was based on Blessed Handkerchiefs that came as high as ten dollars each. This kind of pitch, surely, has the full-bodied flavor of back-country operations.

At the time of the Spanish-American War, John F. Braun was the village photographer in little Red Bud, Randolph County, Illinois. He was an ambitious young fellow; and because Red Bud, even in the boom times of 1898, did not appear to offer much of a future for photography, Braun, already married and with an infant daughter, signed up for a mail-order course in Magnetic Healing. It is unfortunate that which one of the several colleges of magnetic therapy then in operation granted a degree to young Braun is not known; for here was a graduate destined for no little celebrity.

The lure or pitch of these mail-order colleges was practically sure-fire. *Don't Be a Wage Slave!* said their advertisements. *Earn from $3,000 to 5,000 a Year!* In six months, by applying your spare time industriously, right at home, you could earn a Diploma certifying your graduation as a Professor of Magnetic Healing. Young John Braun sailed through the course without the least difficulty, and with honors. His first difficulty appeared in 1900 when the Illinois Board of Health ordered his prosecution on the charge that he was practicing medicine without a license. But on his promise to cease and desist, the charge against him was dropped.

The Brauns disappeared from Red Bud, but Professor Braun neither ceased nor desisted. Moving first to Sparks, then to Nashville, both in Illinois, the Brauns became a team or sort of clinic of magnetic medicine, and practiced under the unusual style of Prof. John F. Braun Himself and Prof. Kate A. Braun Herself. The entry of Mrs. Braun into the profession may have come about because of the prevailing mores of many American women who thought it indecent to consult a male doctor in regard to Female Weakness. A man-and-wife team was the Brauns' answer to the problem.

In the Brauns' case, at least, there may well have been a second contributing factor. Prof. Kate A. Braun Herself was both a good-looking woman of charming personality, and a most fruitful mother who, first and last, was to bring no less than ten Braun children into the world. The increasing number of mouths to feed may have had something to do with prompting her medical career.

But the Illinois State Board of Health was a troublesome and determined crowd. In 1903 they hailed Professor John Braun into court at Nashville where he was fined $100 and costs for practicing without a license and, on failure to pay, was thrown into jail. He appealed, then paid his fine before the case came to the higher court. Within a year he was in worse trouble when Federal authorities arrested him on the nonmedical charge of sending obscene matter through the mails. Lodged in St. Clair County jail at Belleville, he was fined $500 and costs, and was either unable or unwilling to pay, and was sentenced to six months' imprisonment.

The fussy State Board of Health was keeping an eye on the Brauns, for late in 1905 Prof. John Braun was arrested for illegal practice in Nokomis and Hillsboro, and again sent to jail, this time for a mere thirty days.

Nothing daunted, the resilient Brauns moved north to Bloomington, and began to advertise generously in newspapers. How little they feared state or Federal authorities was indicated by the use in the ads not only of their names but their pictures. Here was Prof. Kate A. Braun Herself, the Renounced (*sic*) Specialist in Diseases of Women and Children; and here, too, was Prof. John F. Braun Himself, The Expert Diagnostician and Drugless Healer.

Prof. Kate presented a handsome face framed above by a stylish Gibson-girl hairdo, and framed below with a dashingly bold stock-tie of snowy white. Prof. John is shown in semiprofile wearing the almost standard Vandyke affected both by eminent physicians and by eminent quacks.

The Brauns, who started in business as straight magnetic healers, had, by about 1906, added notably to their field. They were now, said the new advertising matter, not only able to cure all diseases without drugs or surgery, but cure them sight unseen. They had added telepathy to their therapy. Telepathic-magnetic healing was distinctly a double-headed threat to illness; and it could be had by mail from "Our Permanent Address, 601 Washington Street, Bloomington, Illinois."

Leaving a clerk at the Permanent Address, and probably a woman to care for their increasing brood, the Brauns went east to open branches in Indianapolis and Greenfield, Indiana. And then, lest the ailing be slow to write, the Brauns began touring in what one can describe only as full-gospel pitch-doctor style.

Employing an advance man, who "papered" their one-night stands, the two Brauns used slightly modified medicine-show bills and placards headed COMING . . . FOR ONE DAY ONLY, then stressed the fact they would appear, Rain or Shine, and warned of the need for making up one's mind promptly. The Brauns offered Free Treatment to all, stating that their cures were accomplished with No Drugs . . . No Rubbing . . . No Knife. Full across the placard, beneath the pictures of the two Brauns, was an invitation: *The People You Hear So Much About. Meet Them Face to Face.*

The placard strikes one as being virtually a challenge to the state and Federal authorities. Perhaps it was; and it is possible that the seeming delay in punitive action was occupied by the necessity of getting complaints against the Brauns that would stand up in court. The couple carried on their telepathic-magnetic business without hindrance for some three years. But then the Post Office Department struck a hard blow. In October, 1909, charges were brought of using the mails to defraud by a scheme "devised and operated for the sole purpose of defrauding the sick and afflicted." At the same time the

Brauns were indicted on criminal charges. John Himself was sentenced to one year and a day in the Federal penitentiary at Leavenworth, Kansas. Because of the large number of dependent children, the charge against Kate Herself was not pressed.

How fared the many Brauns while John Himself was in prison is not of record, though I fancy that with so able a mother they did not suffer want. Nor was John Himself wholly idle. A year and a day were time enough for him to reflect upon his career to date and to plan his future along new and what he doubtless believed to be safer lines. Let us now, for the sake of clarity, drop the name Braun temporarily and substitute for it the name of Schiller.

Shortly after the release from prison of Prof. Braun Himself, there came to Rockford, Illinois, the Rev. D. R. Schiller, his wife, and their several children. Though the denomination he served was a little vague, the Rev. Dr. Schiller was a healer whose method appears to have been a laying on of hands, plus the application of what he called a Blessed Handkerchief. His charges for treatment fluctuated from time to time, but there was one ex-patient who in court testified that Schiller had demanded $10 "for treatment and one Blessed Handkerchief."

At some time in 1911 Schiller set up a headquarters at 519 Toner Avenue in Rockford from which he ranged widely over the Midwest. In January, 1913, a newspaper reported he had sold "more than one hundred Blessed Hankerchiefs in Elgin"; but in the same month he was reported "mobbed" at Jerseyville, Illinois, because, after advertising that his treatments were free, he refused to treat two patients who had no money.

This was to be a most active period for him who now billed himself, with a touch of nostalgia for the old days, as the Rev. D. R. Schiller Himself. In March (1913) he was arrested in Marion, Iowa, charged with violating the State Medical Practice Act. The disposition of the case is not known. In June he was in Indiana, where a Greencastle paper reported he had been doing a thriving business until his arrest, followed by a fine and "being forced to refund all of the money he had taken from people in this community." In November he had moved to Michigan; and there at Ionia was arrested for practicing without a license, then placed on probation for two years after he had "promised to give up quackery and return to his home in Rockford, Illinois."

It was now Mrs. Schiller's turn. Not as Mrs. Schiller, but as Delia Deimling, described in advertisements as "The Noted Healer," she had opened a Divine-Healing Institute in Rockford, at the very address on Toner Avenue where the Rev. Dr. Schiller had his headquarters. Delia's picture appeared in the ads, and she looked enough like the former Prof. Kate A. Braun Herself to have been an identical twin. Delia had worked up an especially fetching testimonial: "Throws Away Her Old, Crooked Cane," said a portion of the ad, and "One Ministration by Delia Deimling Does the Work." This referred to an old lady of Route 2, Galena, Illinois, who for fifteen years had bravely withstood the pangs of sciatica until "she could not walk across an ordinary room without her cane." Then came Delia Deimling. But no, the poor old woman would have none of her healing. No, sir! Yet, the kindly Delia persevered and, sure enough, the patient after one treatment threw her old, crooked cane away.

Not right away. "She presented it to Delia Deimling, and the cane, photo, testimonial, etc., may be seen at the Deimling Divine-Healing Institute, Rockford."

This remarkable cane and testimonial were simultaneously to be seen in Beloit, Wisconsin, where a Hulda De Muth, also a Noted Healer, had opened the Psychological Healing Institute. Hulda's advertisements had the same Old, Crooked Cane Delia's did; and Hulda was a spitting image of Delia and, for that matter, of Prof. Kate A. Braun Herself.

The very same cane and picture were simultaneously on view in the advertisements of the Mary A. Rose Healing Institute, Milwaukee, Wisconsin.

Of the triple healers, Delia Deimling was the first to get into trouble, and it was none other than the Rev. D. R. Schiller who came forward in her defense. Delia had been arrested in January, 1914, at Greenville, Ohio, for violation of the Medical Practice Act. Unable to raise $300 bond, she was sent to the local jail, carrying in her arms her six-month-old infant.

Back in Rockford, the Rev. Dr. Schiller, writing on stationery which indicated him to be Secretary-Manager of the Psychological

Healing Institute, sent letters to those newspapers which had been running Delia Deimling's advertising:

> Sir: Delia Deimling and six-months-old babe are now languishing in Greenville, Ohio, jail, because she will not pay $35 fine for alleged Practicing Medicine without a License. If this interests you, use it. Your brother in the work of love and truth, Rev. D. R. Schiller.

How long Delia and babe wasted away in Greenville's jail is not known. In any case, they were back in Rockford by June, 1914, when the United States Post Office issued an extension to its fraud order of 1909 against the Brauns, this time adding the names of Rev. D. R. Schiller Himself, Hulda De Muth, Delia Deimling, Mary A. Rose, the Psychological Healing Institute, *and* Madame De Muth Deimling. I do not know how Madame got into the act.

It was now Schiller's turn at bat. Whether he had become discouraged over the way things were going, or whatever else may have driven him to drink, he returned to Rockford, on the night of November 3, 1914, from a trip to nearby Janesville, Wisconsin, sunk in liquor and looking for trouble.

Armed with a revolver and several bricks, the Rev. Schiller started to demolish and clean out, as the term has it, the premises of a Rockford barber against whom he had long nursed a grudge. The police came to take him in action, and so to jail. He was still there, on various charges growing out of the barbershop raid, when he and his wife, whom now we may again consider as the Brauns, were arrested by Post Office agents on new charges of fraud. The trial of Braun or Rev. D. R. Schiller Himself, held before Judge Kenesaw Mountain Landis, served to bring out what I consider the positive character of the man who, despite his faults, was no weakling.

When a witness for the prosecution related how he had paid Braun $10 for a treatment and a Blessed Handkerchief, then demanded return of his money, Braun gave him a short lesson in the proper ethics toward suckers in any and all forms. "Dear sir," he wrote to his disgruntled ex-patient, "If I should return your money, every cheap screw [extortionist] in the country would demand a refund."

There was another incident to show that even in the pietistic role of the Rev. Dr. Schiller, Braun knew what he wanted. Introduced by the prosecution was a letter from Schiller-Braun to a young rustic who hoped to get into the healing business and who had applied to the Reverend for a job. Braun-Schiller's reply:

Yes, by all means, raise that Van Dyke, for I would not think of placing you in office without it. It will make you look ten years older, and that counts for much in this business. Never mind what your best girl says about it; you must choose between her and the Van Dyke and the job. The more you force it, the sooner the position will be open to you. Mioz [a former assistant] wants to come back but I will stick to the proposition I made to you, provided your physiognomy will be in proper shape to look patients in the eye and see how much money they have in their pockets, Yours, Rev. Dr. Schiller Himself.

There was nothing of the mealy-mouth about Schiller-Braun.

But his time was running out. On November 12, 1914, Judge Landis sent him to the Federal pen for four years. Kate A. Braun Herself was acquitted on the grounds that she had been influenced and coerced by her husband, and because, as by now the reader will have guessed, of ten dependent children.

The brave mother did her best to provide for them. For almost two years none of her several professional names got into the papers; but then, in October, 1916, Mary A. Rose was arrested in Peru, Indiana, for practicing medicine without a license. It was, of course, durable Prof. Kate A. Braun. She pleaded not guilty, posted $100 bail, and disappeared.

More than a year later Braun was released from the by then only too familiar confines of Leavenworth. He had been away almost four years. The children had been growing—and learning a good deal, too, as soon became apparent. It was time the young people contributed something. In early March—it was now 1918—newspapers in Wabash, Elkhart, Miami, and Fulton counties, Indiana, broke out with a rash of advertisements announcing the coming-soon of Miss Bonita Rose, the Healer of Peru, and her brother Oliver Rose. About the advertisements was something of the fine rich flavor of the Rev. Doc Schiller:

Bonita, a noble, beautiful character, was born of poor parents in an obscure American village. This sweet and unpolluted flower of love and kindness has sympathies as wide as the world. She is a perpetual surprise, even to those who know her best. And there is something about her no one has even been able to explain, not even herself.

The *News-Times* of Goshen presently carried an editorial saying it had only the week before refused an advertisement announcing the tour of Miss Bonita Rose and her brother. A few days later the same paper printed a news story from Rochester to the effect that Bonita had been arrested on the same old charge that had so often troubled her father and mother over the years. She had violated the Medical Practice Act. What was more, in Rochester the fascinating Bonita had been "enjoying a few days of fine business . . . and it is believed she extracted about $500 from local people."

Brother Oliver Rose apparently was not held. Bonita was tried before a jury in Fulton Circuit Court, found guilty, and on June 5, 1918, was fined $25 and costs. One may wonder if this event, occurring so early in her career, may have discouraged the talented girl from carrying on the profession of her parents. As the daughter of her for whom the cripple of Galena threw away her old, crooked cane, she might have gone far.

PART TEN

Testimonials

1

Old Resident Given Up by Doctors

The late Dr. Arthur J. Cramp, long-time director of the American Medical Association's Bureau of Investigation, pondered much on the commercial value of testimonials for nostrums. "They have always been, and probably always will be," he wrote, "the sheet anchor of the quack." The perfect testimonial, he believed, must have the appearance of truth and must be acceptable to those who, from lack of special knowledge, are unable to recognize any fallacy that may be present. Thus the bulk of such testimony that is commercially valuable in the medical field is also scientifically worthless. "It comes from those whose testimony is incompetent."

Dr. Cramp added that contrary to the belief held by most physicians, that testimonials were either faked or purchased, the majority of them were documentarily genuine. They were given in the best of faith. If they were edited before publication, as many of them were, it was chiefly to "render less obvious the ignorance and illiteracy of those who wrote them."

What a really versatile editor could accomplish with a simple testimonial was perhaps never more graphically demonstrated than by Dr. George Coutant, a talented quack, when—during his Deafness Cure Period—he used two pictures of one Henry Farrar to promote the nostrum. In Northern newspapers Henry was shown wearing the honored hat and medal of the Grand Army of the Republic, and the accompanying text called him a Civil War veteran whose bugle had led Union troops to many a victory over the Rebels.

But age had impaired the old hero's hearing until "he could no longer hear his beloved bugle." This was where Dr. Coutant came in; with the Coutant Home Treatment and Nasal Douche, Veteran

Farrar's ears had responded marvelously, and now he could sit on the porch to blow sweetly on his battered bugle and hear the notes as clearly as the brave Boys in Blue heard them at Antietam.

In Southern newspapers, however, the same Mr. Farrar, divested of his GAR hat and insignia, and dressed in civvies, becomes a "Veteran Musician" who, until Dr. Coutant came along, could not hear his "Beloved Cornet." Almost everybody knew the difference between bugle and cornet.

During his historic tour of American quackery, Samuel Hopkins Adams was particularly taken with the testimonial system used by the Peruna Company. Doc Hartman, head of the firm, was generally conceded to be the champion testimonial getter of them all. In addition to his stable of congressmen and Army and Navy brass, he published fair words for Peruna undersigned by five regular physicians whom he described as prominent. Other Peruna addicts included a batch of United States senators, a whole slew of gentlemen of the cloth, a state superintendent of the Missouri Christian Endeavor Society, the rabbi of a synagogue in Albany, New York, and the Honorable I. S. Smithmeyer, "Architect of the New Congressional Library, Washington, D.C."

But what interested Mr. Adams was not so much the high caliber of these givers of testimony as the manner in which the Peruna Company kept in line the great common herd of "its allegedly unsolicited beneficiaries." These were the John Does and Jane Roes whose names and faces were unknown except locally. Mr. Adams investigated.

Doc Hartman's outfit left as little as possible to chance. Once each testimonial had been printed, Peruna began periodically to remind its correspondent that "as you are aware, we have your testimonial as to our remedy," then went on politely to inquire as to "your present state of health" and to ask "whether you still occasionally make use of Peruna"; but above all to make sure "you are giving favorable answers to such letters of inquiry which your testimonial may occasion." The correspondent was asked to bear in mind that "we allow 25 cents for each letter of inquiry." All he needed to do was to send on the letters he received, together with copies of his replies, and Peruna would "promptly forward 25 cents for each pair of letters." Peruna thoughtfully enclosed a stamped addressed envelope for reply.

Mr. Adams was in no way astonished to discover that, aside from Peruna, there was a brisk market for the sale of testimonials and lists of people who were inveterate users of nostrums, or what in the trade were and are known as sucker lists. A glutton for punishment, Reporter Adams purchased several bundles of testimonials, and names of prospective testimonial givers, from firms whose business was the collection of these names and addresses. You could buy what you wanted in specific categories *by diseases*—tuberculosis, cancer, heart trouble, "men's secret," or whatever.

Mr. Adams did a great deal of reading of testimonials. His conclusions were singularly unflattering to a few well defined regions. "Is it only a coincidence," he asked in *Collier's,* "that the mountain districts of Kentucky, West Virginia and Tennessee, which are recognized as being the least civilized parts of the country, should furnish a number of testimonials, not only to Peruna, but to Pierce's Golden Medical Discovery, Paine's Celery Compound and other brands, out of all proportion to their population?"

I have spent many happy hours reading patent-medicine almanacs, along with the several cookbooks which a few of the more up-and-coming nostrum vendors issued to keep their customers in interesting reading matter between the annual booklets. It is best, I have found, to skip the jokes interlarded among the testimonials, for humor is a fragile thing. It ages rapidly. Topical allusions are meaningless. Puns become rancid.

It is the letters from grateful men and women that are often immensely absorbing. There is the obvious pleasure these people take in relating what desperate condition they were in before starting a régime of this or that nostrum. ("After twenty years of doctoring, the physicians had given me up as a hopeless case.") Then comes use of a long archaic term for an illness, or a phrase of period elegance, or even of once up-to-date slang like "a corker" or "wheel" (bicycle); one and all, they set the time as no calendar can set it. And so, often enough, do the very given names of the letter writers, especially the men. Almanacs of the 1840's and later show that many a Josiah or Silas was dosing for "the intermittents" (fever).

Fifty years later Josiah and Silas had pretty much disappeared. So had their intermittents. In their places were U. S. Smiths and Robert E. Joneses, all now suffering from catarrh or consumption, but doing better with every bottle.

There seemed to be less change among the women, though time had removed the fine Deborahs and Hesters, and brought a Ramona and a Genevieve who needed a specific for *prolapsus uteri*.

No less entertaining are many of the names of the places where lived the simple people who were grateful for what this or that nostrum had done for them. I still want to visit Oatmeal, Texas, and Pocahontas, Oklahoma; but I actually did visit Remote, Oregon, where a man named Henry Johnson was once cured of some dread ailment by a steady diet of Perry Davis's Celebrated Painkiller.

Given a clearly printed and well preserved stack of patent-medicine almanacs, plus only a little imagination, a man has before him a pleasant evening filled with drama, changing scenes, preposterous statements, together with enough unintentional comedy relief to offset the tragedies. And *always* a happy ending, with Peruna or Vegetable Compound or Centaur Liniment triumphant.

On the inside front cover of "Bristol's Free Almanac" for 1846, dealing chiefly with C. C. Bristol's Sarsaparilla, is a fine testimonial from the noted Horace Greeley. The great editor of the *New York Tribune* opened by pointing out that "the virtues of Sarsaparilla as a restorer of purity of the blood" were well known; so, when the young child of a friend became dangerously diseased with tumors which had long defied medical skill, "we urged that a bottle of Bristol's Sarsaparilla be tried" because "we knew Mr. Bristol and had faith in his statements." Well, sir, that was two years since, and "now the little fellow is in excellent health."

Dr. David Jaynes's "Medical Almanac & Guide to Health" (1854) had many letters from most sections of the United States, but made a special feature of "Certificates of Cures" in foreign parts. Headed "News from the Sandwich Islands," came a notable report postmarked 1848 at Kohala, from the Reverend Elias Bond, to say that Jaynes's medicines "have accomplished for our family, under God, what all other medicines utterly failed to effect." He then goes on to blast "the vile system of fraud practiced by the thousand-and-one other patent nostrums of the day." Another was from the Reverend D. Baldwin, dated 1851 at Lahaina, to say that a box of Jaynes's Expectorant, and Carminative, and Sanative Pills, received the year before, "was incomparable. We shall not feel reconciled to be destitute of your Articles." The Reverend Lorenzo Lyons, at Waimea, wrote that he used Jaynes's remedies for his own family and the natives too.

The Kingdom of Siam was being made more healthful by the God-given medical supplies from Dr. Jaynes, according to letters dated at Bangkok by reverend gentlemen named Goddard and Chandler. And under the head "Important News from Asia," one could read letters from American missionaries, all in praise of Jaynes, at Moulmein, Sandoway, Akyab, Arakan, and Rangoon. Indeed, the Word was being taken around the world; and right here at home, the Reverend Rufus Babcock, former president of Waterville College, Maine, but in 1854 agent for the American Bible Society, came through with wonderful words for Dr. Jaynes's Carminative.

That Dr. Jaynes was doing well, not only for the Lord but materially, could be seen by the picture of the immense "New Eight-Story Granite Building, No. 84 Chestnut Street, Philadelphia," into which he had just moved; and where, it is worth noting, he was prepared to furnish "Paints, Oils, Varnishes, Fancy Articles, Window Glass, and Pure Medicinal Wines, Brandies, etc., etc."

Sixty-seven years later, in 1921, the Jaynes "Almanac & Guide to Health" still advertised the Expectorant, the Carminative, and the Sanative Pills, but it did not contain a single testimonial.

Dr. Jaynes did not operate alone with the implied sanction of the Lord. The firm of Dr. L. R. Herrick & Bro. not only put out a fine almanac but were proprietors of Perrin's Fumigator, invented by the Reverend John Perrin, "a clergyman of Western New York, who cured himself of Catarrh with it," a device which, for reasons not immediately clear, was "Especially Recommended to Ministers of the Gospel." Dr. Herrick & Bro. seem not to have been favorites with foreign missionaries; they preferred doing good nearer home. In their splendid "Almanac For the Year of Our Lord 1875," they printed a fine warm letter from Mrs. L. Salsbury, Matron of The Home of the Friendless, Albany, New York, thanking Dr. Herrick "in behalf of the Inmates of this institution for the bountiful supply of your SUGAR-COATED PILLS and KID PLASTERS received this morning." Matron Salsbury went on to say, most gracefully, that "your annual

donation to the unfortunate ones under my charge comes with all
the regularity of the seasons, and awakens thoughts of thankfulness
in those you have so often benefitted."

Another letter to Dr. Herrick from Volney Foster, Keeper of the
Almshouse, Jefferson, Wisconsin, is a heartwarming short story:
"Dear Dr. Herrick, I write for G. H. Marble, a pauper, who is sadly
troubled with Catarrh. A friend presented him with a 25-cent box
of Perrin's Fumigator, from which he has experienced such relief that
he has managed to come by one dollar, which I enclose for a Large
Size box. You have the name of being most charitable to the poor
and the friendless. Please send as much Fumigator as the spirit of
love and charity will dictate." Yet, Herrick & Bro. had a host of customers like Mr. Jesse Uher, Fowlerville, Michigan, who, on July 20,
1874, took pen in hand: "Dear Dr. Herrick: I have walked twenty
miles today to get a box of your Sugar-Coated Pills." He was obviously
worn out, but cheerful, and inquired why Herrick did not "make
an agency here for your Pills, Plasters, and Horse Powders." Jesse
Uher was the right kind of customer.

(Though L. R. Herrick was an M.D., he could print a joke about
Rabelais lying on his deathbed and listening to a consultation of
physicians. "Pray," said he to the doctors, "pray, let me die a natural
death.")

Competing with Herrick and Jaynes in the field of Family
Remedies was the Graefenberg Company, whose "Almanac & Life
Preserver" printed no jokes but was well filled with marvels of therapy, such as reported by Mr. R. B. Jasquith, East Wallingford, Vermont: "I must tell you of a case or two of your Green Mountain
Ointment. My mother-in-law was not able to shut one of her
hands for twenty-three years. She got a box of your Ointment and
put it on a few times and now she can shut her hand with ease.
She also suffered from Gout in the feet. Your Ointment was used a
few times and now she can run a mile." Away out in Iowa, even
greater ills were falling before the power of Graefenberg's Catholicon, according to a letter from Harrison Noble, dated at Yankee
Settlement, who reported complete cures of St. Vitus Dance and
even of "female troubles" among the pioneers.

Dr. Radway at this period did not bother with an almanac, but
relied on his "Hope for The Sick" pamphlet to advertise his Ready
Relief and other items. Because he "could not begin to find space

for the Certificates which have come flowing in to us," he was content to list the "benefits and cures achieved" by name, address, date,
and disease. This he did in two pages of closely printed matter,
starting with Affections of the Heart and ending with Whooping
Cough. The distribution of his Ready Relief was remarkable, including not only Boston, New York and Philadelphia, but Widder
Station, Ontario; Toms Brook, Fores Store, and Rice's Depot, Virginia; Holstein, Iowa; Motor, and Sauce, Kansas; and Button, Nebraska.

Dr. O. Phelps Brown's annual pitch was a "Shakespearian Almanac" illustrated by scenes and excerpts from the Bard's plays, and
devoted in large part to praise of Brown's Male Fern Vermifuge,
Renovating Pills, and Woodland Balm. He seems to have concen-
trated on Pennsylvania where some of the most remarkable cures
were reported in letters from Speedwell Mills, North Cornwall Furnaces, Blue Ball, and Gap.

On every other page of Dewey & Company's (1888) Almanac,
children cried for Pitcher's Castoria. The alternating space was devoted to Centaur Liniment. The Centaur pitch was powerful
enough, but general. It seems that the TURKS used it for Sabre
Wounds, so did the ARMENIANS and the TARTARS; the CHINESE and the
JAPANESE found it good for Opium Dizziness; as for AMERICANS they
used it for almost everything—for instance, Mr. Patrick Power, 419
Court Street, Brooklyn, who fell three stories to land fair on his
head against an Iron Fence. He was soon "rehabilitated" by Centaur. Meanwhile: " 'Tis a jolly day from East to West/for Children
thrive, and mothers rest/The Darling girls all named Victoria/And
with the boys, they have Castoria. . . ."

One of the earliest Cooking Receipt books appeared in 1871, in
the combined interests of Jeremiah Curtis, proprietor of the famous
Mrs. Winslow's Soothing Syrup, and John I. Brown of Brown's
Bronchial Troches. Curtis and Brown wanted none of the herd to
testify until eminent men had had their say. So here is the Reverend
Henry Ward Beecher saying carefully he has never "changed my
mind about Brown's Troches from the first, excepting to think better of that which I began thinking well of." And here is N. P. Willis,
noted editor, writer, and dramatist; "They are an elegant combination for Coughs." In regard to the Soothing Syrup, the Reverend
Sylvanus Cobb, noted clergyman, though already five years dead, was

quoted as saying that Mrs. Winslow's product was "an article which works to perfection and is harmless."

Hood's Sarsaparilla often brought out a cookbook between almanacs, and in its edition for 1880 seems to be an overheavy load of testimonials collected right there in Lowell, where the Hood medicines were made. If these tended to give the booklet a parochial tone, compared to the continental spread of Herrick and the international flavor of Jaynes, Hood nevertheless could brag of an eloquent convert. He was Geo. W. Bosworth, of Amherst, N.H., who wrote that for many years he had been an "avowed enemy to all patent medicines"; he had been outspoken in his opposition until his wife took ill; no doctor could do anything to help her; then, in a day of desperation when all seemed lost, he had been given by a friend a bottle of Hood's Sarsaparilla. "Try it!" pleaded the friend. And now —well, she was cured, and Hood had a new friend who henceforth would at every opportunity recommend this incomparable specific.

Although since mid-century no nostrum had been more widely advertised than Dr. Jacob Hostetter's Celebrated Stomach Bitters, the family had, by 1900, come to put their faith, as far as testimonials were concerned, almost solely in physicians. Hostetter's sober, pale-green Almanac for 1902 carried the familiar St. George and the Dragon on its cover, and inside had the usual run of jokes and dialect humor. But almost all the testimonials were signed by M.D.'s who, one is to suppose, were "regular physicians." To a man they were friends of Hostetter's. "I could not," wrote Dr. S. W. Kellens, Medical Springs, Indiana, "practice medicine without your Bitters at my command." Similar eulogies came from doctors in eight other states.

In the almanacs and cookbooks put out by Healy and Bigelow, who liked to describe themselves as "Indian Agents for the Kickapoo Medicine Company, New Haven, Conn.," I was not able to find a single letter from a physician. Nor am I in the least astonished that this is so, for the Kickapoo line, led by its famous Sagwa, performed wonders beyond the ken of conventional doctors. A single letter in the "Kickapoo Family Cook Book," issued in 1901, should suffice to give one the full flavor of what Healy and Bigelow considered a really favorable testimonial. It was written by Silas Harcourt, Midland, Michigan, a man who in the realm of tapeworms must stand with the more famous Alexis St. Martin whose visible stomach permitted Dr. William Beaumont to study the action of gastric juices. Wrote the devoutly grateful Silas Harcourt to Healy and Bigelow:

"I have been troubled for the past year and a half with a disease which baffled the doctors, and not one of the many who treated me could bring relief. I finally bought and took one 25-cent box of Kickapoo Indian Worm Killer; and soon enough, to my great astonishment, I passed a tape-worm of some size, it measuring, head and all, a full fifty-five feet. . . ."

I like to think that Silas Harcourt's tapeworm was among the frightening exhibits I saw years later in one of the two drug-stores in Colebrook, New Hampshire, when a Kickapoo Indian Medicine show, headed by Chief Red Bear, played a one-week stand. Surely, it must have been the Leviathan of tapeworms.

2

Glad Tidings Sounded Clear

On the bright, clear first day of January, 1898, there went into the
United States mails, at New York City, many thousands of copies of
a thirty-two-page, small-format pamphlet. On its cover of delicate
gray appeared the chaste winged figure of a sculptured Victory, one
arm holding a long trumpet to Victory's lips, the other grasping a
wreath of flowers that look like roses. Victory stands on one foot, as
if dancing atop a pedestal which is labeled Civiale Remedial Agency.
Above the statue is the pamphlet's title, as cryptic as it is arresting:
Glad Tidings for Men.

Glad tidings indeed! This was "The New Edition of Our Brochure
on the Diseases of Men," distributed by Civiale Remedial Agency,
Private Address, Mr. W. M. Clark, 115 West 43rd Street, New York."
The Private Address is obviously to complement the Civiale people's
genteel practice of mailing their remedies in Plain Sealed Wrapper.
(One should note there is no M.D. attached to Mr. Clark's name,
the absence of the title being a protective measure.)

The very nature of "the diseases of men," often described as
"secret," virtually proscribed signed testimonials of a public nature.
Grateful men who had been cured preferred to remain anonymous,
no matter how grateful. Thus there were no conventional testimonials in the Civiale Remedial Agency's *Glad Tidings.* There was,
however, an insert of "Scientific Information" neatly folded with the
main brochure. Captioned "One of our Endorsements," the folder
quoted *The American Journal of Health* as speaking highly of the
Civiale Agency's "Crayon Method of treatment," and offered to
send a reprint of the article to all who should write for it. (The
periodical quoted was a notorious fake.) The folder contained many
letters allegedly from grateful but unidentified males living in
Greenville, Tennessee; Hoboken, New Jersey; Thetford Center,

Vermont; Gibralter, Pennsylvania; Pocahontas, Arkansas; and other centers of population. Each letter had a boldface heading of its own: More Than He Hoped For . . . Our Treatment All Right . . . Another Permanent Cure . . . Gain Every Day . . . Gratitude . . . and such cheery items.

Yet, in spite of these special dressings, the testimonials were unsubstantial. They were unsigned. What confidence, pray, did it give an ailing man to read that ". . . after 10 days of your treatment I could feel the gain in power," if the letter ended with a couple of blank dashes below "Very truly yours?"

No, these were hollow fellows to a man—faceless, nameless. Let them remain so, if they would, it was still no way to sell Civiale's Treatment for Disorders of the Generative System. Contrast this futility with the frankness of the grateful men who had been cured by dealing with The Globe Company, Consolidated Block, Denver, Colorado, Proprietors of the World's Greatest Scientific Inventions and Appliances, Progress Our Motto, Satisfaction Guaranteed.

Among these inventions and discoveries none was more important to mankind, meaning males, than the Scientific Appliance patented Jan. 9, 1900 (No. 32,102), by Professor Bartholomew—no first name, no degree—called simply "A Boon to Men," simply because it was "Nature's Cure for Loss of Manly Power Without Drugs."

Professor Bartholomew, who may well have *been* The Globe Company of Denver, as well as The Appliance Company of Detroit, both of which used identical literature, was coy about his first name and qualifications, but he was clear and direct in regard to The Appliance. "It stands alone," he wrote with blunt assurance, in a sort of introduction to "Glowing Words of Truth," which were his magnificent testimonials. "It excels all other treatments. It is only a matter of time when the Appliance will be universally used for the relief of Impotency." As a clincher he pointed out that "the United States Government has unhesitatingly granted a patent for it, which speaks for itself." Then he got down to business.

To the Globe people, from J. A. Blaydes, M.D., Hot Springs, Arkansas, came a letter dated October 2, 1901: "Gentlemen: Enclosed find check for which send me one dozen of the Appliances. Having fully tested merits of same, I have concluded to use them in my practice. Divide the sizes—one-half Small, one-half Large. They are a good thing. Respectfully yours . . ."

There spoke no mealy-mouthed hypocrite. A year later Dr. Blaydes was at it again: "Gentlemen: Please send me by express C.O.D. one-half dozen Medium, one-half dozen Small. As to using my name as to the efficiency of the patent, you may do so and make it as strong as you wish. I am known in every state of this Union, favorably, I hope, amongst the 20,000 patients on my register since 1876. I can speak in no uncertain terms of your Appliance; it is the Acme of Perfection, and will do all you claim for it. Respectfully, John A. Blaydes, M.D."

Between those two dates, so the Globe people remarked in an aside between testimonials, Dr. Blaydes "has sold several thousand Appliances."

The glad tidings had already spread into Texas, and at Fay, in the Lone Star State, Mr. C. G. Tubb sat down to pen his enthusiasm to The Globe Company: "Dear sirs: Your Appliance came in due time, and of course the first thing to do was to try it. It worked like Magic. They are the proper thing. I am 50 years old, and would not take $50 for it if I could not get another one."

Up in Ashland, Maine, which pine and potatoes were making into a busy and prosperous shipping center of Aroostook County, there lived one Bill Thistle, a daring fellow who, on April 3, 1901, decided to take a chance and send $2 away to The Globe Company. "I have made up my mind," he wrote, "to test your appliance. Please send me a Medium size, for which I inclose cash, Yours truly, Bill Thistle."

It must have given satisfaction, for within a week he writes again to Globe, not so much to express gratefulness, for he is obviously keen to cash in on his daring; he wants to talk biz. "I tried it personally," he writes, "and it works O.K. Now I am willing to act as agent if you will allow me a reasonable commission. Kindly send me best price of dozen and half-dozen lots. Better ship right off two Mediums by American Express C.O.D. if you wish, providing you will allow me commission. After this I will pay cash in half-dozen lots."

In Bill Thistle we have a real hustler for fair. Within days he writes again, this time for "five Appliances Medium size." Another brief stretch and: "Send two Mediums and four Smalls," adding, "I am buying so many Appliances I think you could afford to pay express charges." Apparently The Globe Company thought so too, for here is Bill again: "Appliances all sold. Please rush me one-half dozen Medium, one-half dozen Small. Ship C.O.D. as before."

Did Bill Thistle go onward and upward to become the Appliance King of Maine, or at least of Aroostook County? There is no record, yet it may be of interest to know that decades later, Bernarr Macfadden was working to improve the same or a similar appliance which—according to Emile Gauvreau, his biographer (with Mrs. Macfadden)—was intended to "eliminate the kind of distress that literary commentators blamed for the frustrated marriage of Thomas Carlyle and his wife Jane."

But the art of the testimonials touched perhaps its highest point in the hands of those promoting Dr. Wilson's Restorative Remedies, the sole proprietors of which were L. F. Page & Company, Marshall, Michigan. No testimonials appeared in Dr. Wilson's literature. This was a startling folder, properly entitled "Startling Disclosures," which went into the serious matter of "50,000 Young Men Going to Premature Graves . . . Due to Constitutions Impaired by Excesses." It was frightening enough with its before-treatment pictures of the "victims of indiscretion"; and the accompanying text bore down hard on the absolute necessity for prompt action "if the grave is to scowl with disappointment to know that Death" had been cheated by Dr. Wilson.

There is circumstantial and convincing evidence that, having read one of the folders, many of those 50,000 doomed young men wrote to L. F. Page & Company to learn how much it would cost to be properly fixed up by Dr. Wilson's Restorative. Having addressed his inquiry to the Page Company, 201 State Street, Marshall, Michigan, one of these fellows may have been somewhat surprised to receive a prompt reply, not on Page stationery but on the really elegant letterhead of the Michigan Musical Supply House, Importers and Retail Dealers in Musical Instruments, Strings, Sheet Music and All Kinds of Musical Instruments, L. S. Franklin, Prop., 58 Main Street, Marshall, Michigan.

If the young man wondered how his query, addressed to a drug house at 201 State Street, had come to be answered by a musical house at 68 Main Street, he soon forgot the oddity in the fine flowing prose, in a clever imitation of handwriting, of Mr. L. S. Franklin, the musical man who, it quickly appeared, had himself been snatched from the ranks of the lost 50,000 by the efficacy of Dr.

Wilson's Restorative. Long since restored to complete health and manhood, Franklin now made it "a sort of hobby" to tell others that salvation could be had for only $3 COD plus express charges. What was more, continued Mr. Franklin in fine Spencerian script, he had just that moment put a package in the express company's hands— billed as merchandise—addressed to his correspondent. Whereupon he closed on a note of hope:

> My afflicted Friend, do not despair. You *can* be cured. Try these remedies I beg of you and you will ever give thanks to your friend L. B. Franklin.

It must have been as convincing a testimonial as ever a man received. Surely it was one of the most astonishing. Was ever such indirection displayed? Possibly it was unique in the trade. It showed you, too, how Orpheus and Mercury could work in harmonious, and just possibly, therapeutic conjunction.

On the Rise and Decline of Status

Of late years social historians have been giving some attention to newspaper and magazine advertisements over the decades. Nothing else shows more graphically the material changes that have come into our lives, and when. For example, the long period between Improved Spermaceti Candles and the Mazda Electric Lamp was marked by many an innovation in lighting, including the kerosene lamp, the Rochester Burner, and innumerable gadgets to burn illuminating gas.

Advertisements for something actually or allegedly new are usually aimed at the more sophisticated, or at least those prone to be "fashionable." They want the latest thing, often regardless of its usefulness. They set the styles in clothes, in foods and entertainment, in home architecture and decoration. It is they who ride in the first rubber-tired buggies. They chew the rubber-gum with the new Tutti-Frutti Flavor. They sing the latest songs, read the newest novels, and are privy to the newest jokes. By the time these leaders in cultural advance and material progress have accepted this or that notion or fad, the ads are shooting, shotgun style, at the masses.

The social historian, in his study of advertisements, will do well to pay some attention to the testimonials, especially those in which prominent and even eminent men and women speak with everything from guarded satisfaction to wild enthusiasm for this or that newest thing on the market, observing not *how* they testify but *who* they are. They may not be fashionable in the generally accepted meaning of the term, but they are likely to be those who, at a given period, are members of some profession or occupation currently commanding respect, even veneration. The rise and decline of popular heroes can be read in the testimonials.

During the first half of the nineteenth century, a purveyor of almost any commodity could have no more effective testimony than that of gentlemen of the cloth. By the 1840's no gentlemen of the cloth were more highly regarded in the United States than our missionaries in foreign parts aggressively engaged in efforts to Christianize much of the known world. This regard was due to their calling as holy men and also because they were explorers in benighted places with romantic names. For well over a decade they were dedicated heroes. To judge from patent-medicine almanacs, and religious papers too, they were making the most of their day in the limelight.

The foreign missionary as hero began to lose status just before the Civil War; but our local preachers of the gospel held on much longer, even while the devastating theories of Charles Darwin were permeating—"and poisoning!" cried many a reverend gentleman—the American people. Almost coincident with Darwin came the laissez-faire doctrine of Herbert Spencer's economics, to make a true religion of Business. Taken together the influence of Darwin and Spencer tended to reduce the status of the clergy and to enhance that of industrialists and businessmen generally.

Even so, and though the foreign missionaries were gradually dropped as givers of testimonials, our preachers of the gospel retained no little of their ancient status. A few of the most eminent, like Henry Ward Beecher, continued to speak good words for parlor stoves, improved lamps, good books, and many another thing. Mr. Beecher spoke in praise, too, of Dr. Townsend's Remedy for Catarrh, for Brown's Bronchial Troches, and other nostrums. Scores of lesser divines meanwhile were dictating testimonials for a variety of patent medicines, except of course those having to do with the awful Secret Diseases of Men.

With the end of the Civil War, its veterans did not as a class immediately achieve a hero status; there were too many of them. The few who got into the patent-medicine almanacs were mostly wounded or ill ex-soldiers confined to military hospitals where, oddly enough, they seem to have absorbed a goodly quantity of patent medicines apparently supplied free by the manufacturers. But veterans were to have their day later.

Meanwhile railroad men were becoming popular contributors of nostrum testimonials. One finds, in the almanacs, almost all ranks from "Station Agent, Lafayette, Indiana," and "Switchman, Chicago & Alton," to half a dozen vice presidents one and all "improved" or "cured" by Swamp Root, Peruna, St. Jacob's Oil and lesser known remedies.

This new status of railroad men stemmed from several sources. Railways were still a rather new and wonderful thing, and the men who operated them were romantic characters. Horatio Alger, Jr., the author of boys' books, contributed something, too, by translating the philosophy of Spencer to make heroes of industrial workers and industrialists and, almost unbelievably, of bankers.

By the eighties the ex-soldiers returned to the limelight owing in no small part in the North, to the organization and political power of the Grand Army of the Republic, and in the South to the formidable Daughters of the Confederacy. The patent-medicine advertisements swarmed with pictures and letters from the aging Boys in Blue and Gray.

Ordway & Company, proprietors of Sulphur Bitters, came out in 1889 with a gorgeous cookbook, a "Collection of Valuable and Reliable Receipts Compiled by Ladies of the Grand Army, Post No. 68," which contained testimonials from veterans: "I think Sulphur Bitters saved my life"; "The best investment I ever made was a bottle of your Sulphur Bitters."

For Dr. Hartman's Peruna, Mrs. Colonel E. J. Gresham, Fairfax County, Virginia, Treasurer, Daughters of the Confederacy, wrote a fine letter, to say she was "a true believer in the worth of Peruna as a sure cure of Catarrh."

It was now time for the people of the stage; and many actresses— and a few actors—came to hold enormous status toward the end of the century. Lillian Russell must surely have been the champion testimonialist of these beautiful creatures, with Sarah Bernhardt, a Frenchwoman, as a close runner-up. In the mid-eighties Miss Russell's portrait began to appear, and before long it was being used in advertisements for practically everything, and so were her eloquent words. She had a long run with "Carboline for the Hair," which she said contained just the right "elements required for the hair to feed upon." Paine's Celery Compound captured Madame Bernhardt, who thought it was by far "the most powerful nerve strengthener" that could be found.

Peruna's Almanac carried pictures of handsome Julia Marlowe, of pretty Anna Held, and of the imposing Mrs. McKee Rankin and

Mrs. Leslie Carter, the latter noted for her *Zaza* and *Du Barry*. Among these and other beauties was a mere actor, Mr. Ralph Kellard, a member of the Viola Allen Company playing *In the Palace of the King*. Mr. Kellard wrote that he was "often in such a condition that I could hardly work, until Peruna came to my relief."

The Electro-Chemical Ring Company, Toledo, Ohio, seems not to have gone in for almanacs, but for almost a quarter of a century its active genius, W. G. Brownson, who signed himself "Medical Electrician," periodically issued a fetching booklet which carried signed testimonials from bank presidents, commercial travelers, presiding elders, postmasters, veterinary surgeons, and those persons weakly described only as "Ladies."

But, as Mr. Brownson sternly pointed out, there were two classes of people who were *not* represented in his "roster of cures." These were "Jewelers and Druggists." Why? "Jewelers," explained Mr. Brownson, "have sold so many FAKE rings they have injured the business and we cannot afford to put our Ring in that trade." As for the druggists, "They cannot afford to sell our Electro-Chemical Ring because it cures too many diseases for which they have medicines to sell."

Which showed you the low ethics in the drug and jewelry trades.

Brownson's original and genuine Electro-Chemical Ring retailed at $2. It was made of iron, worn like any other ring on a finger, and it was "Warranted to Cure" twenty-one ailments, among them Diabetes, Cancer, Psoriasis, and Epilepsy. Little wonder if druggists and jewelers yearned to add it to their lines. They yearned in vain for twenty-three years, or until October 1, 1914, when a fraud order by the Post Office denied Brownson use of the mails.

There was at least one medical almanac that seems never to have displayed any interest whatever in the changing status of givers of testimonials. This remarkable booklet was put together for the Shaker Herbal Medicines by a Mr. A. J. White, New York City, and was issued from 54 Warren Street. Apparently White, whether or not he was a member of the sect, was, like the Shakers, a nonbeliever in the mouthings of worldly figures of no matter what eminence. There are few testimonials of any sort in the Shaker almanac, but the one featured contains the essence of the devout practicality of the Shakers.

It is a letter from a Benj. Barber, Greenwood P.O., North Carolina. It is rather long for a testimonial, but it is as specific as one
could wish. Mr. Barber begins by saying that for thirty years he has
suffered from "what some said was heart disease, while others called
it dyspepsia." In any case he had endured, all this time, most terrible pains in stomach, kidneys, urinary organs, and around the heart.
Then, one day, he had tried a bottle of Shaker Extract of Roots, then
one more bottle, and:

"I feel greatly benefitted. I am about 60 years of age and attend-
ing to a mill. Today I can tote and handle a three-bushel sack
of corn or meal with more ease than I could one bushel before using the medicine."

Although the honest and modest Shakers may have regretted the
necessity of advertising their herbs in much the same manner used
by Hostetter's Bitters, Swamp Root, and Peruna, the letter of plain
Benj. Barber must have warmed their hearts. Here was a man who
took genuine pride in an honest day's labor; and who else, at sixty,
could tote three bushels of corn with the ease of a biblical Samson?

PART ELEVEN

Diploma Mills

1

"... Medicorium, Chirurgorium et Specialium ..."

Because there is no mind more sensitive to the needs or even the fancies of society than that of the truly gifted con man, it is likely that the first granting of diplomas by a legitimate medical school was followed rather closely by the first fictitious college of medicine, complete with faculty for instruction in all branches and specialties, an allied hospital and, most importantly, a fine diploma in black script and Latin.

There does not seem, however, to be any documented historical record of the continuous production of quacks by this method. By late nineteenth century the diploma-mill industry was flourishing in the United States, especially in the Midwest where it centered in and near Chicago. One of the most notorious of counterfeit medical colleges was operated as St. Luke's Hospital, Niles, Michigan, brief mention of which was made in an earlier chapter referring to Samuel Hopkins Adams. The crusading reporter had noticed its diploma hanging on the walls of many of the quack doctors he called upon; and he learned from the American Medical Association that St. Luke's had closed up shop in 1900.

So it had, yet St. Luke's had been a busy place during its less than four years of life and had issued nobody knows how many of its imposingly "authentic" and beautiful certificates. These were not too expensive even for the most poverty-stricken quack. For $5 the document came on "Heavy Royal Linen Paper"; $7.50 bought one on "Imitation Parchment"; the Genuine Sheepskin job cost $10. Every certificate came "with your name handsomely engrossed in an old round hand style of letters, with two pieces of dark blue ribbon and a large corporate gold seal affixed thereto." St. Luke's promotional literature thoughtfully added, in an aside, that the document gave "the general appearance of a regular Hospital Medical Diploma." The implications of the adjective "regular" were probably clear enough, without italics, to prospective members of St. Luke's Hospital Staff.

The fog that surrounded St. Luke's affairs was almost opaque, yet in spite of its imperfect records the place was generally believed to be doing a land-office business when the Michigan State Board of Health became actively interested. Investigation showed it had been incorporated in 1898 under state laws with a capital stock of $100,-000. The founders and incorporators were Dr. Charles H. B. Granville and Annabelle Granville, both of Niles, and Dr. Arthur C. Probert of Washburn, Wisconsin. The Board of Health also discovered to its profound dismay that in selling fraudulent diplomas, St. Luke's was engaged in a perfectly legal enterprise. It mattered not that "the hospital has never had a patient." There was no Michigan law compelling it to do so, nor to prevent it from selling diplomas.

The lack in Michigan statutes was remedied in 1899 when the Legislature passed an act entitled "An act to specify the sources of authority for the issuing of medical diplomas, etc." This seems to have discouraged St. Luke's as a diploma mill. About the time the new law went into effect, a personal tragedy overtook Dr. Granville, St. Luke's president, when, as the Board of Health put it, "one of his numerous wives found him out and, after being put under $500 bond, he left for parts unknown."

What with facing the difficulties of a new law, and with the hospital's president fleeing the chance of penal difficulty with an older statute against plural wives, Doc Probert apparently gave up St. Luke's. He did not, however, abandon the magnificent idea that had prompted St. Luke's.

Of Doc Probert, Dr. Fred Belknap, a member of the Michigan Board of Health, observed that he had previously "held positions of honor, influence and trust, in business, politics and religion. He is a nice appearing man and a particularly dangerous one."

Just what Doc Probert was up to, during 1900, with his partner gone and St. Luke's in decay, is not certain, but trouble was catching up with *him*, too. Within a few months, so wrote Dr. Belknap, "proceedings for Probert's extradition from this state [Michigan] by the governor of Indiana, for defrauding the inhabitants of Bourbon, Ind., and vicinity, are in progress."

It is not now known specifically why the governor of Indiana and assorted Hoosiers of Bourbon and vicinity wanted to lay hands on Doc Probert. One may be sure it was for some kind of medical fraud, for when Probert turns up again in the case book of the American Medical Association's Department of Investigation he is a member of the Medical and Surgical Staff, and apparently second in command, of what the austere letterhead entitled the Christian Hospital, 617 La Salle Avenue, Chicago.

Not only the name of Doc Probert but also the circulars with which the new Christian Hospital began to burden the mails caused the AMA men to know that here, in all save name, was St. Luke's Hospital of Niles, Michigan. There were the same offers of staff positions, facsimiles of diplomas, and mention of the prestige and other advantages that almost automatically accompanied the handsome certificates. There were minor changes in the diplomas. The engrossing was now in Old English, instead of "old round hand style"; and the two pieces of ribbon were now of marine, rather than dark, blue.

A casual study of the staff roster shows that though many of Doc Probert's associates were new, at least two of them were sound, reliable old quacks: Doc Granville, who had fronted for St. Luke's until charged with polygamy, was now with the Christian Hospital; and its president and superintendent signed himself Dr. N. News Wood. The treasurer was N. E. Wood, A.M., M.D., LL.D., formerly a quack specialist and now none other than the hospital's president and superintendent using a slightly revised moniker.

Doc Wood was a con man who always looked ahead. It was he who had discovered possibilities in something which in 1893 had been incorporated under Illinois laws as The Boston Store, a general merchandise enterprise at 617 La Salle Street, Chicago. In 1901 he bought The Boston Store's charter, then changed its name and purpose to permit operating "a hospital and dispensary." Here in 1903 he and several associates opened the Christian Hospital, the authorized capital of which was $250,000.

It is most probable that the commercially pious Doc Probert composed the official statement of purpose of Christian Hospital:

"For the Care and Cure of the Afflicted (of any Creed or Nationality) according to the Ethics of the Golden Rule, using to that Noble end all the combined wisdom afforded by Modern Medical and Surgical Science, with an association of Expert Specialists, representing every school, branch and system of the healing art, all working harmoniously together for the Cure of the Sick, with the Golden Rule as their code of moral and professional ethics." It is good to know that the code of ethics was no hidebound thing, and amusing that Doc Wood, who in the Christian Hospital's literature had already used two different names, was pleased to use a third when he signed the beautiful diplomas. Here he became Dr. Nathan E. Wood.

About this new gathering of quacks under the banner of the Golden Rule, the *Journal* of the American Medical Association mentioned the similarity of the late St. Luke's and the new Christian Hospital, then spoke of "the boldness of these impostors in thus coming out under their real names." The *Journal* thought their timing was very good: "They probably have reckoned on a similar deficiency in Illinois statutes as that they first profited from in Michigan, and have, it would seem, cleverly timed this initiation of their work to coincide with the end of the legislative session, expecting, therefore, to have a free hand for the next two years."

In any case, the Christian Hospital could not have flourished very long. The record is none too clear, but the premises at 617 La Salle Street seem to have been soon taken over by a Chicago Medical and Surgical Institute, a walk-in and mail-order outfit, the president of which was Dr. E. N. Wood. Doc Wood was now using his portrait to display his wonderfully black beard in fine contrast to his gates-ajar collar, a string tie of purest white, and a snowy waistcoat. He, or at least the institute, was also offering a 160-page book "on all Chronic and Surgical Diseases and List of 130 Questions," which was sent free on request.

Doc Wood wanted all sufferers, no matter from what disease, to consult him; he was right in tone with the period which was the heyday of "Medical Institutes for Men Only," and his advertising copy stressed "Cases of Nervous Debility and the Secret Diseases resulting from abuses and indiscretions of Youth and Manhood." Like the highly successful Rinehardts of Milwaukee, St. Paul, and Chicago, Doc Wood made some effort to establish a chain of institutes;

and by 1909, billing himself as The Eminent Chicago Specialist, he was appearing for consultation every Saturday in Clinton, Iowa, where his offices were at 212 Fifth Avenue (Over Pool's China Store).

Other diploma mills had been finding it difficult to remain in profitable business very long. As early as 1897 the Illinois Health University's charter was revoked by the Illinois Supreme Court. Its founder was Doctor James Armstrong. Associated with him was a Thomas Armstrong, who signed himself Ph.D., and a Doctor John H. Randall. There was little pretense to being a place of learning and no pretense of having a hospital. From Illinois Health University anyone with the price could buy a medical diploma. The court's action laid it low in less than a year. But within two months more the Armstrongs and Randall were again in the diploma business, this time as the Independent Medical College of Chicago.

This time the crew of con workers came out with an immense faculty of twenty-three distinguished specialists in everything from the Principles and Practice of Surgery to Hypnotism, Psychology, and Magnetic Healing. The general setup still did not appeal to the State Supreme Court, which within a few months revoked the charter.

Illinois was getting tough. What had happened so suddenly to the brand-new Independent Medical College of Chicago was reported by the *Journal* of the AMA as follows: "Having obtained proof of the wholesale sale of diplomas by this institution, the attorney-general brought suit in the Circuit Court of Cook County to have the charter of the 'college' revoked. After hearing the evidence, the court on Feb. 15, 1899, entered a judgment of ouster. The 'faculty' made no defense but took an appeal to the Supreme Court, simply to gain time. The decree of the circuit court has not apparently interfered with the sale of diplomas."

Thus, with only a few months of grace, the Armstrong-Randall diploma factory worked overtime, to such effect that the scale of prices for the documents was notably lowered, especially in Michigan, Kansas, and Texas, where the demand for bogus medical degrees was unusually brisk. From the latter commonwealth it was reported that an agent for the state board of health purchased one for $20.

During this period, when the Illinois Supreme Court was mulling over the appeal, the alert Independent Medical College of Chicago was not only busy peddling degrees; its promoters were also preparing purposefully for the loss of their charter. (What a fine windfall for some printing house were these determined men of the Armstrong-Randall institutions of medical learning!) By the time the Supreme Court's ax fell, announcements were ready for mailing and advertising circulars, and facsimile samples of diplomas of a brand-new Metropolitan Medical College were prepared, described in resounding Latin as Collegium Medicinae Metropolitanium. (It is perhaps worth knowing that this was the first time, in any of the Armstrong-Randall colleges, that the faculty included an Instructor in Osteopathy.)

Late in October, 1899, when the ax fell and the Independent Medical College's charter was revoked, the Metropolitan went into gear. The Metropolitan's career was brief. Eight months later Chicago papers reported the arrest, on the charge of using the mails to defraud, of James Armstrong, Thomas Armstrong, and John H. Randall. In December, 1900, James Armstrong, described as the "leading spirit in this fraud," was sentenced to one year in jail and to pay a fine of $500. Thomas Armstrong was also convicted. John Randall, late president of the Metropolitan Medical College, pleaded guilty. The Post Office meanwhile issued fraud orders against James Armstrong "and all the institutions conducted by him."

It is not to be thought that the diploma-mill industry was laid in its grave, either in Chicago or elsewhere. But the life of diploma mills was becoming increasingly precarious. This was not true of the actual diplomas. For instance, the pioneer St. Luke's Hospital of Niles, Michigan, probably issued its last sheepskin in 1899 or 1900. As late as 1917, when a noted piece of quackery called Sargol was deep in trouble with the Post Office on fraud charges, evidence against it included a series of advertisements captioned "What Famous Doctors Say About Sargol." None of these eminent medical men spoke up better for Sargol than Dr. Hare Cuddy, who was proud to describe himself as "Formerly Hon. Physician, St. Luke's Hospital, Michigan."

2

The St. Louis and Kansas City Scandals

It is possible that since the founding of the Republic there have been more business concerns and cultural institutions using "national" or "American" in their titles than any other adjective. They might be as genuine as the National Geographic Society and the American Express Company, or as bogus as the American Cross Bearers of Birmingham, Alabama, and the National University of Arts and Sciences of St. Louis, Missouri.

Probably in all lines of endeavor con workers have favored "American" or "National" because the one implies patriotism and the other indicates vastness of scope. In the field of therapy not everyone was endowed with the fine imagination that inspired the gifted Doc Probert to invent St. Luke's Hospital of Niles, Michigan. Here, as already mentioned, was a bogus enterprise whose medical diplomas were the cherished wall decorations of successful quacks the country over. I wonder if some of them are not still doing duty, fifty-nine years after St. Luke's issued its last sheepskin.

One of the numerous diploma factories that sought to fill the void left by St. Luke's was the National Medical University, 1428 Wells Street, Chicago, founded by a Dr. L. D. Rogers, with which was affiliated the National Maternity Hospital and the Chicago Night University. All these institutions were to be found at the Wells Street address, characterized by Dr. George B. Young, Chicago's health commissioner during 1911-1915, as "the worst place in this city." Despite "powerful political pull," the National Medical University began to fall apart in 1912 when one of its graduates in medicine was involved in the death of a patient, and the *Chicago Tribune* gave Dr. Rogers's institutions an airing in its crusade against quacks.

Among other graduates of the National Medical University was one Henry Lindlahr who, though he signed himself M.D., was to become better known as the founder and president of the Progressive College of Chiropractic of Chicago. This was the school which, on March 1, 1923, was to make a Doctor of Chiropractic of "Harry Thompson," who turned out to be a reporter on the St. Louis *Star*, and who wrote one of the most sensational and far-reaching exposés in the medical field in many a year.

The St. Louis newspaper was after bigger game than an obscure chiropractic school in Chicago. It had reason to believe that the long defunct National University of Arts and Sciences, in St. Louis, was and had been doing a wholesale business selling medical degrees, and that a number of professional men in the field of medicine, both in St. Louis and in Kansas City, were involved.

Early in August, 1923, Reporter Harry Thompson Brundige was informed by his managing editor of the existence of a diploma mill with which a well known physician, Dr. Robert Adcox, was believed to be connected. He was told to leave the *Star*, get a job as a salesman that would permit him to circulate widely in the city, and to see what he could do about buying a degree as a doctor of medicine.

It was any ambitious reporter's dream of a perfect assignment, and young Brundige was just the man for it. He decided to operate under his first two names. As Harry Thompson he got a job as a coal salesman. Posing as a young fellow who had just come to the big city from Springfield, Missouri, he rented a room two doors west of Dr. Robert Adcox's home in a St. Louis residential district, and into his new lodging house he moved on August 13.

Next morning, sitting on the front porch, he watched the letter carrier coming up the street, and saw Dr. Adcox come out to get the mail. When the carrier came to the lodging house, Thompson got into conversation with the postman and asked if there was a doctor in the neighborhood. "I got a sore throat," he said. The postman pointed to Adcox, who was still on his porch.

Thompson went immediately to introduce himself to Adcox, who replied he had retired from practice, but with a little urging treated the personable young stranger and suggested he come back next day. Thompson did so. This time Thompson remarked that a doctor had a pretty good life. Adcox agreed, and also seemed to warm up. So did Thompson. On the following day, while Thompson's throat was being treated again, Adcox came right out and asked if the young fellow would like to be a doctor.

Thompson replied that he would, but added, with regret in his voice, that such a thing could never be; he was almost thirty years old. He could not hope to begin a medical course at his age. Furthermore, he had not even finished high school. Adcox took the bait eagerly. It was not necessary to go to school to get a medical diploma, he said. Then he asked, "How much money have you saved?"

"Oh, somewhere around a thousand dollars," replied Thompson. Dr. Adcox's face seemed to light up. "If you are willing to spend your thousand to become a doctor," he said, "you are as good as a doctor right now." After only a little more resistance from Thompson, which Adcox airily dismissed, the doctor told the young man to be ready to leave with him next day for Kansas City. The bait had gone down; the hook was in.

In Kansas City, Adcox took Thompson to the Minor Building, where Dr. Ralph A. Voight occupied a suite of nine rooms; and there, after Adcox and Voight had been closeted alone for about an hour, Thompson was called in and questioned by Voight. Thompson recalled that the interview went like this:

"So you want to be a doctor?" Voight asked me.

"That's what I came here for."

"Do you know anything about medicine?"

"Not a thing."

"Did you graduate from high school?"

"I did not."

"Well, let's see. The first thing to do is to get you a high school diploma. Then I think we'd better get you three years' credits from a medical school and let you do your senior year at Alex's."

"What do you mean by doing the senior year at Alex's?"

"I mean that Dr. D. R. Alexander, dean of the Kansas City College of Medicine and Surgery, will enroll you for your senior year after we get the credits for you. Then after eight months at school you'll get your diploma and be a full-fledged doctor."

"Can't I get by without going to school?"

"Well, inasmuch as you don't know anything about medicine

you ought to put in a few months of study before trying your wings. But we'll see."

Dr. Voight then began figuring on a bit of scratch paper.

"How much money have you?" he inquired.

"How much will I need?"

"Well, figuring roughly, about $1,000. But I'll let you know later. However, if you want me to get busy you will have to make a deposit. Can you let me have something down today?"

Thompson counted his money and asked Dr. Adcox, who had announced his intention of returning to St. Louis on the noon train, how much he would need to get back. He said it would take about $15, which sum Thompson gave him. Thompson then offered Dr. Voight a deposit of $50.

"It isn't much, but I'll take it," he said. "But you will have to send me $600 before I can start work. Can you get that much for me by Monday?"

Thompson promised to give him the money not later than Tuesday, August 21st.

"Send it by certified check," Voight instructed.

Thompson returned to St. Louis, where he opened a checking account with a St. Louis bank, depositing $800 in currency. He then made out a check, payable to Dr. Ralph A. Voight, signed it Harry Thompson, and had the check certified. The check was photographed in the office of the *Star*.

On Tuesday, August 21st, Thompson returned to Kansas City, met Voight in his office, and handed him the check. Voight protested he had asked Thompson to get a certified check. The following conversation ensued:

"Why give me this kind of check?" Voight demanded rather sharply.

"You told me to have it certified."

"I didn't mean this kind of certification—why didn't you get a cashier's check made out to bearer? Now I've got to endorse this darned thing. I don't like it."

Thompson apologized and offered to take the check back and get the kind he wanted, but Voight must have concluded that $600 in the hand was worth more than a promise for that sum, so he retained it.

Said Voight: "I've been very busy getting things lined up for you. I have taken steps to get a high-school certificate, which will arrive shortly, and I have written to a former official of the Baltimore College of Physicians and Surgeons, which is now closed, to place your name in the records as having attended classes in 1914, 1915, and 1916, and to send me a certified copy of your credits for those years. It will take about two weeks to get them. The Kansas City College of Medicine and Surgery will open two weeks from today and I have made arrangements with Dr. Alexander, the dean, to enroll you for your senior year."

Thompson returned to St. Louis. A day or so later a cryptic letter from Dr. Voight arrived:

DEAR THOMPSON: Your letter at hand and was glad to hear from you. I have not had a reply to your letter as yet, though I expect it at any time. I have taken the liberty to make a change in the arrangements and know that you will be better satisfied with my judgment. Instead of going to the east for the stock, consisting of three shares, I have gone to the west coast for completed stock, so you can have less trouble and be better off. I will send you a wire as soon as it arrives and you can get it here whenever you see fit to come. Unless you are at leisure at present I would not pass up your job at this time, as it is your best time, but hold on until I notify you and I am sure you will be better off.

Thompson replied at once:

Dear Doctor: Received your letter and was surely pleased to note that you are going to get a diploma for me instead of the three years' credits. The way you wrote about stock was very clever; but I caught on at once. I can hardly wait for that telegram telling me you have everything. Don't forget the high school diploma. How will the diploma thing work out? Will I have to go to school or will you get me the license to practice without going to school? I am very much interested and would like to know. I bought the book you told me about and am studying it religiously. Business is good and I will stick it out here until you wire me.

Days passed. On September 4th Thompson got a wire from Voight reading: "Change in plan makes it necessary for 300 more. Wire it at once Western Union." Later that day Dr. Adcox got in touch with Thompson. He, too, had received a wire from Voight, reading:

> Alex agrees to issue final paper on Pacific for honorable cause two fifty. Can arrange through personal friends sit in Arkansas and complete Thompson. Wire him today 300. Had no reply. Advise him Alex building addition and needs cash ready to go at once.

Thompson asked Adcox to explain Voight's wire. Adcox did: "By Alex, he means Dr. Alexander of Kansas City College of Medicine and Surgery. By final paper, he means a diploma. Voight means that Dr. Alexander has agreed to give you a diploma based on the credits obtained for you from a college on the Pacific Coast. Voight will go to Arkansas with the diploma and take the state medical board examinations in your name. He also means that Dr. Alexander is getting ready to build an addition to his college and needs cash. The reference to 'honorable cause' is just one of Voight's little jokes. Don't you understand, my boy? Voight means you are about to have the degree of doctor of medicine conferred on you."

Thompson indicated a proper amount of pleasure in contemplating his new status, then asked Adcox to give him the telegram so that he might answer Dr. Voight. After carefully clipping his own name and address from the message, Adcox did so. Thompson wired $300 to Dr. Voight. But the business was not quite done. Voight wrote to Thompson to say that the diploma had not yet come and that as far as the cost was concerned Thompson had paid all that was necessary for the diploma; getting a state license would, however, be an added expense.

On September 22nd a wire from Voight told Thompson to come to Kansas City; the "final document" could be had at any time now. But on arrival there next morning, Thompson found Dr. Voight stalling. The reporter recalled the discussion as follows:

> "Well, doctor, I see you arrived on schedule," said Voight, "and I am looking for your diploma in every mail. It hasn't come. That bird in California certainly works slow, but he's sure and the stuff he puts out is A-1. Dr. Alexander has promised to issue

another diploma to back up the California degree and as soon as I get them I'm going down to Arkansas to take the state board examination and get you a license. Meanwhile, I think you should go out to Dr. Alexander's college and take a few months so as to have a background for your work. You can hang out your shingle as a chiropractor or an electro-specialist and use one of my offices. You can catch enough suckers to pay your expenses while you are getting a couple of months' study. I think you ought to start in out there tomorrow."

"But," I protested, "how can I go to school until you get the diploma proving my previous medical study?"

"Dr. Alex don't care. He'll take my word for it that I'll produce your paper in the next week or two."

I told Voight that I didn't want to go to school. "It is too big a chance," I said. "The first time a professor asked me a question I'd betray my ignorance of all things pertaining to medicine."

"Why, you idiot," Voight replied, "they won't ask any questions. You'll be in the ringer class. The professors will put you on the list with the others who are there to listen and not to answer questions."

I then told Voight I would *not* go to school; that he had agreed to get me a diploma and a state license and to sell me a sucker machine, and electric apparatus used in "treating" sick men and women. Voight manufactured these machines, which are patterned after the ERA boxes, the Electronic Reactions of Abrams.

Voight sought to calm Thompson, declaring that he really didn't care whether or not Thompson went to school: it made little or no difference. But as the diploma had failed to materialize, Thompson began to put on the heat by making a persistent nuisance of himself. It worked. On October 3rd Voight gave the diploma to Thompson, and displayed a license to practice in the State of Tennessee, granted to Harry Thompson, M.D.

Thompson did not accept the license with the delight Voight might have expected. The young man gave it a long, bilious look, then pointed out that the document showed erasure marks where the name was written in. "It's a crude piece of work," he said, and passed the license back to Voight. Voight agreed that it was, indeed, a "rotten job." But never mind. Voight would see that he got another license and that it would be perfectly executed.

While waiting for the medical diploma and a state license to practice, Thompson went ahead with his plan to become a chiropractor. Adcox and Voight, between them, made all the arrangements. At first, Adcox told Thompson he would get his instruction from "a deputy sheriff assigned to duty in one of the circuit courts and who practiced chiropractic on the side." Because Thompson was afraid the deputy might recognize him as a newspaper reporter, he demurred. Adcox then phoned Dr. Florence F. Baars, a St. Louis chiropractor. "Florence," he said, "this is Doc Ad. I've got a friend here who wants to do chiropractics while he goes to school . . . No, he don't know anything about it. But I want you and Dr. Strecker to give him a course that will enable him to get by. You know, he don't care anything about the origin of nerves or the intervertebral foramina—all he wants to know is how to give the patients their thumps. And to get the money . . . Sure, he's all right . . . Yes, I'll send him over this afternoon."

Doc Florence Baars told Thompson the course would take him three or four days and would cost $25. That evening he was introduced to Doc Strecker and, after he had given Doc Baars a check for $25, the first lesson got under way. It lasted one hour and five minutes. Doc Strecker, on leaving, gave him a pamphlet, "The Science of Chiropractice Explained." Next evening Thompson got the second lesson. Time: fifty-five minutes. He then paid Strecker $2.50 for a booklet explaining all about adjustments. Another evening's lesson lasted only twenty-two minutes, and Thompson bought still another book. This cost $12. It also completed the course in the science of chiropractic. Total expired time: two hours and twenty-two minutes.

Now Thompson reported back to Dr. Adcox, who congratulated him on his graduation. Thompson then wrote to Dr. Voight and said he was ready to start chiropracticing in St. Louis just as soon as he received the promised diploma in that science. Voight replied that he would advise Thompson as soon as the document came.

The good news that Thompson was ready to go into business got around quickly. Within an hour or so after Thompson talked with Voight in Kansas City, the young man got a call from Doc Strecker

in St. Louis: How about an adjusting table? Strecker just happened
to have one. It had been used, but it was in good condition. Thompson could have it for $22.50. Come to think of it, Thompson would
need a spinal chart, and Doc Florence Baars had one she would sell
for $2.50. Musing, doubtless, on the mounting expense of becoming
a full-fledged master of chiropractic, Thompson purchased the table
and chart.

Meanwhile, the wheels had been turning, and Thompson got a
wire from Voight; the chiropractic diploma was ready. It was a fine-
looking job, too; and though it reached Thompson by way of the
office of Dr. Alexander, head of the Kansas City College of Medicine
and Surgery, it purported to have been issued by the Progressive
College of Chiropractic, Chicago, Illinois, whose founder and president, Doc Henry Lindlahr, was mentioned earlier in this chapter as
being himself a graduate of the notorious National Medical University, an institution also of Chicago, and exposed back in 1912 as "the
worst place in this city," by the *Chicago Tribune*.

Anyhow, "Doc" Harry Thompson now had a degree in Chiropractic, backed by more than two hours' instruction. He had a fine
adjustment table and a nice spinal chart. He toted up the over-all
cost: $64.50.

Other much desired events were coming to pass. One day soon
Harry Thompson received his Doctor of Medicine degree as attested
by a diploma from the Department of Medicine, National University
of Arts and Sciences, St. Louis, Missouri. And for good measure he
came into possession of a high school certificate signed by the State
Superintendent of Public Instruction of Missouri. The certificate
was dated 1914, and the diploma 1916, or two years before the
National University went out of business.

Harry Thompson Brundige had done his work well. On October
15, 1923, the *St. Louis Star* broke the story with the first of a series
of articles. The police were busy arresting Dr. Ralph A. Voight, of
Kansas City; Dr. Robert Adcox, St. Louis; Dr. D. R. Alexander,
dean of the Kansas City College of Medicine and Surgery; and
Professor W. P. Sachs, a former examiner of Missouri schools.

In one of his articles Reporter Brundige wrote that the total cost
of his medical degree, the chiropractic degree, together with equipment and books, transportation to and from Kansas City, and board

and lodging, came to approximately $3,000. It was a small sum to pay for the far-reaching results brought about by the exposé.

In another article of the series Brundige recalled that Dr. Voight, once he and Brundige had got chummy, proved to be quite a talker. He enjoyed relating the feats he had performed over many years to secure medical degrees and licenses to practice for persons who were in no way fit to have them.

Voight recalled, Brundige said, that though he had "accomplished the impossible on a number of occasions," by far the hardest job of his life was the time he "took forty-two boobs to New Haven to get licenses for them." He had paid $1,500 for an advance copy of the examination questions, and then, "assisted by a couple of other smart guys who knew their stuff," the three con workers sat up all night in the Hotel Garde writing answers. It was a tough job. "We prepared forty-two different sets of answers, one for each boob, and all they had to do was go into the examination room and copy the answers in their own handwriting. Only one failed to get his license —a dumb bird who could not copy his paper."

There were other methods for providing a man with necessary papers. "A cheap way," Voight went on, was "to purchase the credentials of a recently deceased physician. If you call on the widow before the insurance has been paid, you will find her in need of ready cash, and on some pretense or other you can usually induce her to part with the credentials of the late lamented. All you have to do, then, is have your boob change his name, move to some distant state, and obtain a license by reciprocity in the State to which he moves." This method sounded dangerous, but Voight assured the reporter, "I know dozens of men who have done that little trick and are now living in dead men's shoes."

Professor Sachs, he who had issued the bogus high-school certificate, made a long confession to the St. Louis prosecuting attorney. "My traffic in fraudulent educational credentials," he said, "began about eleven years ago when a ring was organized. I was then superintendent of schools in Washington county, Missouri. I started by issuing fraudulent certificates of examination and high school diplomas from the Potosi high school. My traffic continued after I became dean of the National University of Arts and Sciences of St. Louis, during which time I had access to the diplomas granting college and university degrees. I left National University to become the examiner of schools under State Superintendent Howard A. Cass, now deceased. I induced him to sign thousands of high school certificates, which are equivalent of high school diplomas, on the plea I needed them for immediate use.

"I attached the official seal, and throughout my tenure of office supplied them to other members of our ring. I took thousands of them with me when I resigned to become dean of Walther College of St. Louis. I sold approximately 5,000 of these certificates, directly or indirectly, to persons who could not have passed the examinations but later became doctors of medicine.

"I had access to the lithograph stone used to print the diplomas of the National University of Arts and Sciences, and had such diplomas printed as I needed them. I also trafficked in the papers of Walther College." Sachs added that "hundreds of county school superintendents and other officials issued high school certificates, for a price, without giving the required examinations. The practice is almost universal. Educators generally are underpaid, and the temptation for easy money is too strong to resist."

Sachs closed his confession with a crack at the smart guy Voight. "My last transaction," Sachs said, "was in October, 1923, when I supplied Dr. Voight with credentials for Harry Thompson who, I later learned, was Brundige the reporter. Just think—it was Dr. Voight who once called me a blundering idiot, yet it was Dr. Voight who led Brundige and the police to my door."

Following Sachs into the confessional was B. H. Jolley, county superintendent of schools in St. Charles County, Missouri, who added weight to Sachs' remark about underpaid educators. Poverty, said Jolley, was responsible for his own undoing. His salary was $1,100 a year. Dr. Adcox, he continued, had pointed the way to increased revenues by the issuance of high school certificates without examination. Adcox had paid him $5 for each certificate, and resold them for $200 each.

The resounding scandal was far from being a mere local affair. It echoed in legislative halls across the United States. The *Journal* of the American Medical Association hailed it as bringing to an end the eclectic school of medicine which "treats disease by the application of single remedies to known disturbances, without reference to any scientific classification but giving special attention to the

development of plant remedies." Eclecticism had flourished errati-
cally in the United States during the latter part of the nineteenth
century. In 1900 there were nine schools giving eclectic instructions.
Twenty years later there was one.

Over many years the proponents of this or that healing method
had prevailed on state legislatures to form separate licensing boards
for physicians until there were ninety-six separate and independent
boards created by as many independent medical-practice acts, representing many different standards of educational qualification. For
a number of years the AMA had been protesting specifically against
the low standards of the boards of *eclectic* examiners of Arkansas
and Connecticut. (It was to New Haven that Dr. Voight "took forty-
two boobs . . . to get licenses for them.") The *St. Louis Star* exposé was followed by the license revocation of 167 physicians who
had been certified by the Connecticut Eclectic Board.

The influence of Harry Thompson Brundige's career continued to
have effect in other states for many years. A decade later Dr. Morris
Fishbein, editor of the *Journal* of AMA, observed that the history of
medical cults like that of eclecticism would seem to indicate an
early relapse and a not far-distant end. "The patient," he wrote, "is
not moribund, but very weak."

Reporter Brundige was pleased with the continuing effects of his
series of articles, yet he seemed to doubt that the inherent gullibility
of a majority of human beings would change very much. "If I advertise in the newspapers," he wrote, "that at a certain time I will
bring to life the body of a man who has been pronounced dead, I
will draw a whopping big crowd. If I advertise that I will prove why
the dead cannot be restored to life, I will not get half a dozen lis-
teners. If I advertise that I will guarantee to cure any chronic disease
and unfurl the banner of No Money Until Cured, my office will be
crowded with patients."

Brundige thought that few if any of his imagined patients would
question his methods. They were not interested in methods; they
wanted relief from suffering. "Chronic sufferers," he wrote, "are ever
on the alert for news of a new healer. Quacks all know this, and therefore they specialize in chronic diseases."

At the time Brundige's skeptical observations got into print, Dr.
Albert Abrams had just died, leaving some two million dollars
to mark his success with the Abrams Electronic cure-all machines;

and Gaylord Wilshire, long a real-estate and gold-mine promoter, was moving into the field of therapy with his IONACO, which would fill any void of gullibility occasioned by the failure of the Abrams system of mechanical medicine.

Epilogue

Some Notes on Samuel Hopkins Adams and Fools in Their Folly

On Sunday November 16, 1958, Samuel Hopkins Adams died at his winter home in Beaufort, South Carolina. Had he lived till January he would have been eighty-eight years old.

In August, while on my way from Oregon to visit Mr. Adams at his summer place, Widewaters, on Lake Owasco, New York, a garbled message at the switchboard of a New York publisher had resulted in an erroneous report of his death. When I arrived a few days later, his greeting was characteristically lively. He was also grumbling at what he called "the inaccuracy of people."

During my stay the old gentleman occasionally referred again to the false report. When somebody present recalled that Mark Twain had undergone a similar experience, Mr. Adams replied that Mark had survived only one such report, while he, Adams, had survived two of them. Nobody present could recall a previous report on Mr. Adams's state of health. I asked what he was talking about. "In 1912," he said, "I was in England and engaged passage home on the great new *Titanic*, but at the last moment had to cancel it.

"You know what happened to the *Titanic*. Before I left England a cabled report from the United States had me among those who went down with the ship. The canard survived repeated denials over several years."

Someone present pointed out that Sam Adams had virtually doubled Mark Twain's experience. "That is true," he agreed, "but it doesn't do one's work any good, these reiterations."

My four-day visit in August was the last time I was to see the man I considered one of the finest reporters of all time. I had originally

283

planned my visit for late September, but a note from him in July urged me to come sooner. "Intimations of mortality," he wrote, "come thicker. You had best stop on your way East, rather than when you are returning to Oregon." He added that he had "dredged up some things" he wanted to tell me about quacks and quackery to "go into the book" he knew I was writing.

Mr. Adams had already read the first drafts of chapters in which he appeared, and by letter made a few suggestions. Now that I was there, he went on to tell me of incidents he thought might be of interest. Among them was "the most embarrassing incident" of his Great American Fraud campaign of 1906.

"One day after the series had been running in *Collier's* for several weeks," he remembered, "I received a note from Samuel Clemens, asking me to call to see him, and saying that he had information of a worse piece of quackery than anything I had so far exposed. I was elated to know that the great Mark Twain, whom I had seen but never met, was following my articles. Without delay I took a cab to his residence on lower Fifth Avenue, and without delay was shown to his bedroom which, as almost everybody in the United States had come to know, was where he wrote.

"He was sitting up in a bed that was pretty much covered with newspapers, magazines, and sheets of manuscript. He was smoking like a locomotive. He hailed me genially and declared the *Collier's* articles were just what the doctor ordered. Then he unfolded what he said was the worst fraud of all, and asserted that it was being perpetrated—naturally enough, he added—by a religious outfit.

"This should have put me sufficiently on guard. Mark Twain was known to be devoutly antagonistic to all religious groups. As he went on with his story, it became clear that the only religious aspect of the alleged fraud was that it was touted in testimonials by a bishop of a Protestant denomination. Its operators were a crew of professionals with no church affiliation. It was a so-called drink-and-drug cure.

"The bishop was giving to the treatment the warmest kind of public testimony because it was saving souls from the pit of ruin. This was all very well, Mark Twain went on as he lighted a fresh cigar, and for all he knew the treatment did cure addiction. But he knew it also accomplished something more. It left men as impotent as so many eunuchs. . . ."

Mr. Adams had already investigated at least two other drug-and-drink cures, the St. James Society and the St. Paul Association, which he said were as phony as the pseudoreligious flavor of their corporate titles; and he was quite ready to believe Mark Twain's charges against this new quackery. But he needed some evidence; and then and there, in the great man's room, he got from Mark Twain himself what he supposed was evidence enough to expose the fraud. Thanking Mr. Clemens, who seemed to be very happy he had interested the reporter, Mr. Adams went away to write the story.

Fifty-two years later Mr. Adams told how it came out. "I did some investigation after I left Mr. Clemens," he remembered, "but it turned out to be less than enough. I might say, less than half enough. I wrote the story, *Collier's* ran it, and then both magazine and writer were promptly threatened with libel suits by the eminent bishop. What is more, neither I nor a whole detail of attorneys and investigative agents could produce anything to substantiate in court the charge that the so-called treatment produced sexual impotency.

"Luckily for us, the maligned bishop turned out to be a Christian gentleman who demanded no blood money, but merely a correction and apology in *Collier's*. He got it, too, in the first possible issue.

"Although Mark Twain was responsible for getting me into the mess, and expressed himself as most penitent, I blamed myself because, in my great faith in him, I did not investigate in my usual, and if I may say so, rather thorough manner."

It was quite in keeping with Mr. Adams that he should have wanted me to know of his grievous mistake. Integrity was the supreme quality of his character.

On this my last visit to Widewaters I took occasion to ask the physically failing yet mentally alert old gentleman some questions to indicate his opinion of the status of nostrums today. Because it was a subject he had never lost interest in, he had kept up more than casually with medical legislation. He believed that although credulity learned little from experience, Americans were somewhat less easily fooled in the field of medicine than they were fifty years ago.

"They can be and still are buncoed into buying nostrums," he said, "but the nostrums are more likely to be worthless than actively harmful. The old-time con-talk will no longer fetch them. The Van-dyked slicker with a diamond shirt-stud and gates-ajar collar cannot sell his goods. But the TV-doc with the white coat and mirror strapped to his forehead is doing fine, even if his actual pitch is a weak and graceless thing of no artistry. He starts off with 'Doctors say that so-and-so' and drones reiteration. But he *looks* the way a doctor should. So does the stethoscope fellow in the magazine ads. All these con-men do is to parrot some scientific hog-wash, and close with the doctors-say reiteration. Basically, it is the same old Kickapoo pitch, but it has been given modern overtones to fit the pseudo-sophistication of the mass of people. And it *works*."

He spoke highly of the Food and Drug Administration people, but thought they should be given responsibility for the advertised claims of a nostrum as well as the claims on its label. The former is currently the responsibility of the Federal Trade Commission. It might be best, Mr. Adams thought, to remove the FTC from the nostrum field. He also remarked that the Post Office Department can curb sale of a product through the mails but can do nothing if the product is switched to over-the-counter distribution.

"Nothing is more certain," Mr. Adams said, "than that the success of a patent medicine relies today, as it did half a century ago, on its advertising. We should demand that the claims on the label be identical with the claims in the advertisement, whether it is print, or radio, or television."

I mentioned the fact that while researching and writing about patent medicines, I sometimes began to feel superior in intelligence, or at least in common sense, to those who in former times became addicted to somebody's sarsaparilla or celery compound, or had bought an Oxydonor or an I-ON-A-CO. Such quackeries were at best laughable, and I contemplated their addicts with condescension—that is, until it occurred to me that I had been taking vitamin pills off and on for several years. I know no more about vitamin pills than the customers used to know about Hostetter's Bitters or Swamp Root. It was a thought so sobering and corrective that my condescension disappeared.

Mr. Adams laughed. "Young feller," said he, using the flattering adjective he often applied to friends still under seventy, "Young feller, the foundation of the original Food and Drug Act, and of supplementary legislation, is based on the old admonition 'He that hath eyes to see, let him see.' The laws were passed to give the public a chance to know, not to save fools from their folly." He added: "I, too, sometimes give vitamins a run, but merely on the chance that even if they are no good, they are less deleterious than they are outright harmless frauds."

Acknowledgments

My interest in the subject of this book began more than fifteen years ago when, through the late Henry L. Mencken, I had the good fortune to meet Samuel Hopkins Adams. The meeting grew into a close friendship that lasted until Mr. Adams's death late in 1958. During the years I often got him to talk of his 1905 campaign against what he called "The Great American Fraud" and which had no little to do with the reforms generally known as the Pure Food and Drug Act.

Meanwhile Mr. Cecil Scott, my editor at The Macmillan Company, suggested the present book, and I began research. Though dropped when other things intervened, it was continued in a desultory manner until 1956, when Mr. Scott urged me to devote all my time to completing research and to write an account of American patent medicines and general quackery from the earliest times through their great and gaudy heyday.

Because of the good offices of Mr. Holt Seale, director of Macmillan's Medical Department, I was made welcome in the incomparable library of the American Medical Association, Chicago, by Mr. Oliver Field, head of the Association's Bureau of Investigation, and his secretary, Miss Julema Williams; and at the New York Academy of Medicine, New York City, by Dr. Howard Craig, Mrs. Alice Weaver, and Miss Florence Lyons, Reference Librarian. To these institutions and individuals I owe a good deal, as I do also to the University of Oregon Medical School Library, on my home grounds in Portland, and Miss Bertha Hallam, its Librarian.

At the New York Public Library, Dr. Gerald D. McDonald, Chief of the American History Division, together with Miss Louise Leak and Miss Marion Wiethorn, gave me every aid. At the Portland Public Library, Mr. Bernard Van Horne, Librarian, and Mr. James

Burghardt, Social Sciences Division, made me welcome; and friends who have been helping writers for many years, and who include Miss Louise Prichard, Miss Elizabeth Johnson, and Miss Ione Morgan, did everything possible.

Among the institutions and people which and who responded graciously to requests were the Historical and Philosophical Library of Ohio, Cincinnati, and its Mrs. Alice Hook; the Fletcher Free Library, Burlington, Vermont, and its Miss Fannie Rothman; the Buffalo and Erie County Public Library, and Mrs. Warren C. Sledd; the Chicago Public Library, and its then Chief Reference Librarian, Mr. Herbert H. Hewitt; the University of Oregon's Archivist, Mr. Martin Schmitt; the Minnesota Historical Society, and Mr. James Taylor Dunn; the Carnegie Library, Pittsburgh, and Miss H. Dorothy English; and the American Antiquarian Society, Worcester, and Mrs. Dorothea E. Spear.

To the Pacific Northwest Bibliographic Center at the University of Washington, and the wonderful system called Inter-Library Loan, I owe a great debt.

Over a considerable period Mr. Wallace F. Janssen of the Food and Drug Administration, United States Department of Health, Education, and Welfare, kept me well posted on events, past and present, in the affairs of various quacks, including their protean efforts to keep at least one alias between them and a day of reckoning. The Portland division of the Better Business Bureau, Mr. Lyle Janz, Director, made available its most interesting files on the activities of two old masters of the high-pressure medical pitch in the machine age of therapy.

Mr. H. A. Boucher and the late John Ankcorn managed, somehow or other, to find and present me with proprietary medicines in the veritable bottles and packages, their labels faded yet still legible and beautiful, of the Golden Age of the patents. Ranged along my writing table, they were a constant challenge to do them justice. Dr. and Mrs. Kenneth Williams, of Hamden, Connecticut, performed a notable feat in discovering and interviewing former employees of Healy and Bigelow, makers of immortal Kickapoo Indian Sagwa. Mr. Paul Reppeto, of Chehalis, Washington, went forth on a clear day in June to photograph a handsome great barn recently painted by the busy artisans of Dr. R. V. Pierce, thus putting to rest a canard that his

Favorite Prescription and Golden Medical Discovery had been retired from the rural circuit.

Mr. Lewis Gannett, editor and literary critic, of West Cornwall,
Connecticut, lent me books hard to come by and offered suggestions
for research that proved fruitful and entertaining. Mr. H. A. Holbrook, of Colebrook, New Hampshire, discovered a long-deserted
house whose owner, Mr. Sam Weeks, permitted us to plumb the
many layers of almanacs, hundreds of them, covering three decades,
and other magnificent examples of the therapy pitch during the era
of its greatest potency; and to come away with a staggering load of
illuminating literature. The Messrs. Henry Lang and Theodore Wilson, of Bath, New Hampshire, recalled the days when Lady Poor's
Ointment was made in that hamlet and shipped to all or at least
nearly all of the known world. Miss Mary Jean Simpson, of East
Craftsbury, Vermont, lent her rare copy of the superb Kickapoo
Cooking Book for Ladies. Mr. Ralph N. Hill, of Burlington, Vermont, supplied me generously of his knowledge of Paine's Celebrated Celery Compound, whose vast mixing vats were wonders of
his boyhood, as was also the splendid manner of living of the wealthy
families who manufactured a product even more widely known than
Vermont marble or maple syrup.

Mr. Luke Teasley, of Columbia, Georgia, helped me to understand the inherent goodness of *Southern* liniment, in former days,
as compared with the shoddy balms Yankee quacks were trying to
foist upon the South. Mr. John Newert, of Augusta, Maine; Mr.
James Anderson, of Lake Wales, Florida; and Mr. Lew Vermilyea,
of Boston, all deposed evidence concerning various cure-alls they remembered. Dr. Harry D. Piercy, of Cleveland, helped with the
Shakers and their remedies. Mr. Trafford Tallmage, of Columbus,
Ohio, and Mr. Hugh Allen, of St. Louis, supplied useful information about the times when Dr. Hartman's Peruna was virtually a
sovereign cure for all manner of the prevalent "catarrhs."

Mr. Bert Baker, of Minneapolis, and Mr. Bob Eddy, newspaper
editor of St. Paul, combined efforts to the end that I should report
with accuracy the life and times of a family of quacks who had few
if any peers in the chain Medical Institute and Free Anatomical
Museum business. Mr. George T. Springer, of Minneapolis, let me
use his research notes dealing with a noted back-country healer.

Mr. Click Relander, writer and newspaperman, of Yakima, Washington, made known to me a long-forgotten book purporting to contain the nigh magical formulas of many old-time proprietary nostrums.

Among the many Oregonians who aided and abetted research, I must name Mrs. Joseph Peaper, Dr. Virgil McMickle, Mr. Reg C. Brummer, Mr. Robert W. Sawyer, and Mr. E. B. Macnaughton.

Miss Esther Watson prepared the manuscript for the printer. My daughters, the Misses Sibyl Morningstar and Bonnie Stewart Holbrook, helped to prepare the index.

STEWART H. HOLBROOK

PORTLAND, OREGON
May, 1959

Bibliography

Adams, Samuel Hopkins, *The Great American Fraud*, 1906.
———, *Grandfather Stories*, 1955.
American Medical Association, *Nostrums and Quackery*, 3 vols., 1912-1936.
Burton, Jean, *Lydia Pinkham Is Her Name*, 1949.
Clark, Thomas D., *Pills, Petticoats and Plows*, 1944.
Cohn, David L., *The Good Old Days*, 1940.
Cook, James, *Remedies and Rackets*, 1958.
Davis, Perry, *The People's Pamphlet, An Account of the Origin, Name and Use of Perry Davis's Vegetable Pain Killer*, Providence, 1845.
Davis, Perry, & Son, *Around the World in 40 Years*, n.d., n.p.
De Ford, Miriam Allen, *They Were San Franciscans*, 1941.
Dictionary of American Biography, 22 vols., 1928-1958.
Edwards, Richard, *The Industries of Pittsburgh*, n.d.
Emmet, Boris, and John E. Jeuck, *Catalogues and Counters, A History of Sears, Roebuck and Company*, 1950.
Fishbein, Morris, *Fads and Quackery in Healing*, 1933.
———, *A History of the American Medical Association*, 1947.
Hill, Henry Wayland, *Municipality of Buffalo, New York, A History*, 4 vols., 1923.
Hill, Ralph Nading, *The Winooski*, 1949.
Holbrook, Stewart H., *Lost Men of American History*, 1946.
———, *The Yankee Exodus*, 1950.
———, *Dreamers of the American Dream*, 1957.
Irwin, Wallace, *At the Sign of the Dollar*, 1905.
La Wall, Charles H., *Four Thousand Years of Pharmacy*, 1927.
Kremers, Edward, and George Urdang, *History of Pharmacy*, 1951.
Mathison, Richard, *The Eternal Search*, 1958.

Medical Society of the City of New-York, *Reports of, on Nostrums or Secret Medicines*, Part 1, 1827.

McNeal, Violet, *Four White Horses and a Brass Band*, 1947.

O'Connor, Richard, *Bat Masterson*, 1957.

Oleson, Charles W., M.D., *Secret Nostrums*, 1890.

Pickard, Madge E., and R. Carlyle Buley, *The Midwest Pioneer*, 1945.

Pierce, R. V., M.D., *The People's Common Sense Medical Adviser in Plain English; or, Medicine Simplified*, 66th ed., Buffalo (circa 1905); 1st ed. 1875.

Piercy, Dr. Harry D., *Shaker Medicine*, 1957.

The Proprietary Association, *Facts Worth Knowing*, 1908.

Shafer, Henry Burnell, M.D., *The American Medical Profession*, 1936.

Sinclair, Upton, *American Outpost*, 1932.

Turner, E. S., *The Shocking History of Advertising*, 1953.

Washburn, Robert C., *The Life and Times of Lydia E. Pinkham*, 1931.

Zenger, Peter (printer), *An Abstract of the Patent Granted by His Majesty King George to Benj. Okell, the Inventor of a Medicine call'd Dr. Bateman's Pectoral Drops . . . that he shall enjoy the sole benefit of the Said Medicine . . .* London, 1731; reprinted 1731.

Zuver, Dudley, *The Lengthened Shadow of a Maine Man, A Biography of Guy P. Gannett*, 1956.

Articles in Magazines; Unpublished Material; Almanacs

The Bulletin-Index (Pittsburgh [?]), April 11, 1935, "Bitters Comeback."

Cramp, Arthur J., "I-On-A-Co, The Magic Horse Collar," in *Hygeia*, February, 1927.

Douglas, W. A. S., "Pitch Doctors," in *American Mercury*, February, 1927.

Dunn, James Taylor, "The Plaster Doctor of Somerset," in *Wisconsin Magazine of History*, Summer, 1956.

Johnson, Winifred, "Medicine Show," in *Southwest Review*, Summer, 1936.

Stout, Wesley, "Med Show," in *Saturday Evening Post*, September 14, 1929.

Young, James Harvey, "Patent Medicines: The Early Post-Frontier Phase," in *Illinois State Historical Journal*, Autumn, 1953.

Unpublished Letters: The William McKay Papers, Umatilla County Library, Pendleton, Oregon; microfilms in the University of Oregon Library, Eugene.

Almanacs, Cookbooks, and Pamphlets issued 1846-1910, in the interests of: Hostetter's Bitters, Jaynes Family Medicines, Peruna, Dr. O. Phelps Brown, Mrs. Pinkham's Vegetable Compound, Ayer's Remedies, Hood's Sarsaparilla, Clark's ABC, Dr. L. R. Herrick, Mrs. Winslow, Radway's Ready Relief, Healy and Bigelow, Pitcher's Castoria, Paine's Celery Compound, Graefenberg Family Medicines, Swamp Root, Walker's Vinegar Bitters, Boschee's German Syrup, Wright's Indian Vegetable Pills, Brandreth's Pills, St. Jacobs Oil.

Index

Abrams, Dr. Albert, 129 ff.
Adams, Samuel Hopkins, 4, 14 ff., 87, 283-287
Adcox, Dr. Robert, 270
Aldrich, Senator Nelson W., 27
Alexander, Dr. D. R., 273
Almena, Wis., 226
American Animal Therapy Company, 73
The American Dispensatory, 59
American Medical Association, 8, 26, 28, 49, 74, 101, 109, 127, 129, 140, 165
American Medical Botany, 59
Appliance Company, 251
Armour & Company, 72
Armstrong, Dr. James, 267
Arter, Bill, 98
Ashland, Me., 252
Atkins, Louen V., 74
Augusta, Me., 174
Ayer, Dr. James C., 11, 47 ff.
Ayer's Cherry Pectoral, 10, 47, 50
Ayer's Sarsaparilla, 47

Baars, Dr. Florence F., 276
Baptist Record, 8
Barton, Mrs. S. Louise, 159
Bateman's Pectoral Drops, 32
Bath, N.H., 50
Battle Creek Sanatorium, 98
Beardsley, Guy, 116
Beebe, William C., 137-138
Beecher, Henry Ward, 247, 256
Belknap, Dr. Fred, 264
Beloit, Wis., 235
Bernhardt, Sarah, 257
Better Business Bureau, 28, 139, 144

Bigelow, Charles H. (Texas Charlie), 208 ff.
Bigelow, Dr. Jacob, 59
Binghamton, N.Y., 24, 111
Binghamton Herald, 116
Binghamton Press, 115
Bishop Creek Gold Company, 143
Black-Draught, 103, 109
Blaine, Gov. John J., 229
Blakeslee, Mrs. Ethel R., 213-214
Blaydes, Dr. John A., 251
Blessed Handkerchiefs, 231, 234
Bloomington, Ill., 232
Blossom, Mrs. Violet, 187-195
Bok, Edward, 65, 97
Boschee's German Syrup, 11
Boston Almanac (1692), 31
Boston Globe, 159
Boston Herald, 61, 62
Brandreth's Pills, 41
Braun, Bonita Rose, 237
Braun, John Himself, 231-238
Braun, Kate Herself, 231-238
Brother Benjamin, 6
Brother John, 6
Brouillard, M., waxworks artist, 83
Brundige, Harry Thompson, reporter, 270-281
Bucklen & Company, 107
Buffalo, N.Y., 89, 127, 167
Bull's Cough Syrup, 23
Burlington, Vt., 52
Butter Color, Improved, 55

California Medical Society, 129
Canandaigua, N.Y., 88
Carboline, 257
Cassab, E. K., 142
Castoria, 32, 61, 247